**SOLUTIONS MANUAL**
*to accompany*

# MODERN
# PHYSICS

## Second Edition

**Kenneth S. Krane**
*Department of Physics*
*Oregon State University*

**John Wiley & Sons, Inc.**
New York   Chichester   Brisbane   Toronto   Singapore

ISBN 0-471-10815-4

Printed in the United States of America

10  9  8  7  6  5  4  3  2  1

Printed and bound by Malloy Lithographing, Inc.

# Preface

This manual contains the solutions to the end-of-chapter problems from the textbook *Modern Physics*, 2nd edition (1996). It is intended for use by instructors who assign homework problems from the text and wish to make solutions to selected problems available to students. This manual is *not* intended as a programmed workbook for student use.

Generally I have tried to prepare these solutions from the point of view of the student, and thus I have adopted the approach that students are most likely to choose. This is frequently not the most concise or elegant method, but it is direct and easily understood. Each solution is self-contained, and nearly all intermediate steps are included. I have given special attention to the number of significant figures in the solutions and answers.

I am pleased to acknowledge the help of Jon Symmes and Emily Townsend in preparing these solutions.

I welcome correspondence from users of the manual regarding errors or suggestions for improving the solutions.

Kenneth S. Krane
e-mail: kranek@physics.orst.edu

Corvallis, Oregon
March 1996

# Table of Contents

# Chapter 1

1.  Let $m_1 = m$ and $m_2 = 3m$. Before the collision, the speeds are $v_1 = v$ and $v_2 = 0$. After the collision, the speeds are $v_1'$ (in the $y$ direction) and $v_2'$ (at an angle $\theta$ with the $x$ axis.

Conservation of energy gives

$$\tfrac{1}{2}m_1v_1^2 = \tfrac{1}{2}m_1v_1'^2 + \tfrac{1}{2}m_2v_2'^2 \qquad \text{or} \qquad \tfrac{1}{2}v^2 = \tfrac{1}{2}v_1'^2 + \tfrac{1}{2}3v_2'^2 \tag{1}$$

Conservation of $p_x$:

$$m_1v_1 = m_2v_2'\cos\theta \qquad \text{or} \qquad v = 3v_2'\cos\theta \tag{2}$$

Conservation of $p_y$:

$$0 = m_1v_1' - m_2v_2'\sin\theta \qquad \text{or} \qquad v_1' = 3v_2'\sin\theta \tag{3}$$

Squaring (2) and (3) and adding gives

$$v_2'^2 = \tfrac{1}{9}(v^2 + v_1'^2)$$

Substituting into (1) gives

$$v^2 = v_1'^2 + \tfrac{1}{3}(v^2 + v_1'^2)$$

Solving, we obtain

$$v_1' = \frac{v}{\sqrt{2}} \qquad \text{and} \qquad v_2' = \frac{v}{\sqrt{6}}$$

and then (2) gives

$$\cos\theta = \sqrt{\frac{2}{3}} \qquad \text{or} \qquad \theta = 35.3°$$

2.    Let $m_1 = m$ and $m_2 = 2m$. The combination $m' = 3m$ moves with speed $v'$ at an angle $\theta$ with respect to the $x$ axis.

Conservation of $p_x$:

$$m_1 v_1 = m'v'\cos\theta \qquad \text{or} \qquad v = 3v'\cos\theta \qquad (1)$$

Conservation of $p_y$:

$$m_2 v_2 = m'v'\sin\theta \qquad \text{or} \qquad \tfrac{4}{3}v = 3v'\sin\theta \qquad (2)$$

Dividing (1) and (2), we obtain

$$\tan\theta = \frac{4}{3} \qquad \text{or} \qquad \theta = 53.1°$$

Using (1) with $\cos\theta = 3/5$, we obtain

$$v' = 5v/9$$

$$\Delta K = K_i - K_f = \tfrac{1}{2}mv^2 + \tfrac{1}{2}(2m)(\tfrac{2}{3}v)^2 - \tfrac{1}{2}(3m)(\tfrac{5}{9}v)^2 = \tfrac{26}{27}(\tfrac{1}{2}mv^2)$$

3.    Let the two helium atoms move in opposite directions along the $x$ axis with speeds $v_1'$ and $v_2'$.

Conservation of $p_x$:

$$0 = m_1 v_1' - m_2 v_2' \qquad \text{or} \qquad v_1' = v_2'$$

Conservation of energy:

$$92 \text{ keV} = K_1' + K_2'$$

Since $v_1' = v_2'$, it follows that $K_1' = K_2' = 46.0$ keV, so

$$v_1' = \sqrt{\frac{2K_1'}{m_1}} = \sqrt{\frac{2(0.0460 \text{ MeV})}{(4.00 \text{ u})(931.5 \text{ MeV}/c^2)/\text{u}}} = 4.969 \times 10^{-3}c$$

$$v_1' = v_2' = 1.49 \times 10^6 \text{ m/s}$$

$$p_1' = m_1 v_1' = (4.00 \text{ u})(1.660540 \times 10^{-27} \text{ kg/u})(1.49 \times 10^6 \text{ m/s})$$

$$p_1' = p_2' = 9.90 \times 10^{-21} \text{ kg·m/s}$$

4.  (a) $\quad \dfrac{v}{c} = \dfrac{100 \; \dfrac{\text{km}}{\text{h}} \cdot \dfrac{1 \text{ h}}{3600 \text{ s}}}{3 \times 10^5 \text{ km/s}} \cong 10^{-7}$

(b) $\quad \dfrac{v}{c} = \dfrac{330 \text{ m/s}}{3 \times 10^8 \text{ m/s}} \cong 10^{-6}$

(c) $\quad \dfrac{v}{c} = \dfrac{11 \text{ km/s}}{3 \times 10^5 \text{ km/s}} \cong 4 \times 10^{-5}$

(d) $\quad v = \dfrac{2\pi R}{T} \cong \dfrac{2\pi (1.5 \times 10^8 \text{ km})}{\pi \times 10^7 \text{ s}} = 30 \text{ km/s}$

$$\dfrac{v}{c} = \dfrac{30 \text{ km/s}}{3 \times 10^5 \text{ km/s}} \cong 10^{-4}$$

5.  $$\text{joule} \cdot \text{second} = \frac{\text{kilogram} \cdot \text{meter}^2}{\text{second}^2} \cdot \text{second}$$

$$= \frac{\text{kilogram} \cdot \text{meter}}{\text{second}} \cdot \text{meter}$$

$$= \text{linear momentum} \times \text{displacement}$$

6.  $$F = \frac{1}{4\pi\epsilon_0} \frac{e^2}{r^2} = \frac{e^2}{4\pi\epsilon_0} \frac{1}{r^2}$$

Thus $e^2/4\pi\epsilon_0$ has the same dimensions as $Fr^2$, or

force $\times$ distance$^2$ = (force $\cdot$ distance) $\times$ distance = energy $\times$ distance

7.  (a)   $$F = G \frac{m^2}{r^2}$$

$Gm^2$ has the same dimensions as $Fr^2$, or energy $\times$ distance as in Problem 6.

(b)   $Gm^2 = (6.6726 \times 10^{-11} \text{ N} \cdot \text{m}^2/\text{kg}^2)(1.6726231 \times 10^{-27} \text{ kg})^2$

$$= (1.8668 \times 10^{-64} \text{ J} \cdot \text{m}) \frac{10^9 \text{ nm/m}}{1.6022 \times 10^{-19} \text{ J/eV}}$$

$$= 1.1651 \times 10^{-36} \text{ eV} \cdot \text{nm}$$

(c)   $$\frac{Gm^2}{e^2/4\pi\epsilon_0} = \frac{1.1651 \times 10^{-36} \text{ eV} \cdot \text{nm}}{1.439965 \text{ eV} \cdot \text{nm}} = 8.0912 \times 10^{-37}$$

8. $$N_A = 6.022137 \times 10^{23} \text{ mole}^{-1}$$

An atom of carbon has a mass of 12 u and a mole of carbon has a mass of 12 g, so

$$12 \text{ g} = (6.022137 \times 10^{23} \text{ atoms/mole})(12 \text{ u/atom})$$

$$1 \text{ u} = \frac{1}{6.022137 \times 10^{23}} \text{ g} = 1.660540 \times 10^{-27} \text{ kg}$$

9. $$L = m_e v r$$

$$v = \frac{L}{m_e r} = \frac{h/2\pi}{m_e h^2 \epsilon_0 / \pi m_e e^2} = \frac{e^2}{2h\epsilon_0} = \frac{e^2}{2hc\epsilon_0} c$$

Using Equation 1.16, we obtain

$$v = \alpha c$$

10. (a) $$K = \frac{3}{2} kT$$

$$\Delta K = \frac{3}{2} k \Delta T = \frac{3}{2}(1.38 \times 10^{-23} \text{ J/K})(80 \text{ K})$$

$$= 1.66 \times 10^{-21} \text{ J} = 0.0104 \text{ eV}$$

(b) $$U = mgh$$

$$h = \frac{U}{mg} = \frac{1.66 \times 10^{-21} \text{ J}}{(40.0 \text{ u})(1.66 \times 10^{-27} \text{ kg/u})(9.80 \text{ m/s}^2)} = 2550 \text{ m}$$

11. (a) $$\mu_B = \frac{eh}{4\pi m_e}$$

The dimensions of $\mu_B$ are

$$\frac{\text{charge} \cdot (\text{energy} \cdot \text{time})}{\text{mass}} = \frac{\text{charge} \cdot \text{length}^2}{\text{time}}$$

A tesla is

$$\text{tesla} = \frac{N}{A \cdot m} = \frac{J}{A \cdot m^2}$$

and so

$$\frac{\text{joule}}{\text{tesla}} = A \cdot m^2 = \frac{\text{charge}}{\text{time}} \cdot \text{length}^2$$

Thus the dimensions of $\mu_B$ are identical with joule/tesla.

(b)     $\dfrac{\text{charge} \cdot \text{length}^2}{\text{time}} = \dfrac{\text{charge}}{\text{time}} \cdot (\text{length})^2 = \text{current} \cdot \text{area}$

12.     (a)     $r = \dfrac{h^2 \epsilon_0}{\pi m_e e^2} = \dfrac{h^2}{m_e} \dfrac{\epsilon_0}{\pi e^2}$

Since $h$ has dimension energy $\times$ time and $e^2/\epsilon_0$ has dimension energy $\times$ length, $r$ has dimension

$$\frac{(\text{energy} \times \text{time})^2}{\text{mass}} \frac{1}{\text{energy} \times \text{length}} = \frac{\text{energy} \cdot \text{time}^2}{\text{mass} \cdot \text{length}}$$

Since energy has dimension mass $\times$ length$^2$/time$^2$, this reduces directly to the dimension of length.

(b)     $r = \dfrac{h^2 \epsilon_0}{\pi m_e e^2} = \dfrac{h^2 c^2 4\pi \epsilon_0}{4\pi^2 (m_e c^2) e^2}$

$$= \frac{(1239.8424 \ \text{eV} \cdot \text{nm})^2}{4\pi^2 (510999.1 \ \text{eV})(1.439965 \ \text{eV} \cdot \text{nm})} = 0.05292 \ \text{nm}$$

13.  (a)  $\lambda_C = \dfrac{h}{m_e c}$

This has dimensions of

$$\frac{\text{energy·time}}{\text{mass·length/time}} = \frac{(\text{mass·length}^2/\text{time}^2)\cdot\text{time}}{\text{mass·length/time}} = \text{length}$$

(b)  $\dfrac{h}{m_e c} = \dfrac{hc}{m_e c^2} = \dfrac{1239.842\ \text{eV·nm}}{510999\ \text{eV}} = 2.426 \times 10^{-3}\ \text{nm}$

14.  $2m_p + 2m_n = 2(1.007276470\ \text{u}) + 2(1.008664924\ \text{u}) = 4.031882788\ \text{u}$

$\Delta m = 4.031882788\ \text{u} - 4.001506\ \text{u} = 0.030377\ \text{u}$

$= (0.030377\ \text{u})(931.502\ \text{MeV}/c^2)/\text{u} = 28.296\ \text{MeV}/c^2$

15.  (a) Let $v_1'$ represent the helium atom that moves in the $+x$ direction, and let $v_2'$ represent the other helium atom (which must move in the positive or negative $x$ direction).

Conservation of $p_x$:

$$mv = m_1 v_1' - m_2 v_2' \qquad \text{or} \qquad 2v = v_1' - v_2'$$

Conservation of energy:

$$92\ \text{keV} + K = \tfrac{1}{2}m_1 v_1'^2 + \tfrac{1}{2}m_2 v_2'^2 = \tfrac{1}{2}m_1 v_1'^2 + \tfrac{1}{2}m_2(v_1' - 2v)^2$$

Since $v$ and $K$ are known, this quadratic equation can be solved for $v_1'$:

$$v_1' = 2.47 \times 10^6\ \text{m/s}, \quad -0.508 \times 10^6\ \text{m/s}$$

The masses are identical, and so it doesn't matter which is called $m_1$ and which is called $m_2$. One of the roots is therefore $v_1'$ (which we originally assumed to be positive) and the other must be $v_2'$.

$$v_1' = 2.47 \times 10^6\ \text{m/s} \qquad\qquad v_2' = -0.508 \times 10^6\ \text{m/s}$$

(b)     The original speed of $m$ is

$$v = \sqrt{\frac{2K}{m}} = \sqrt{\frac{2(0.040 \ \text{MeV})}{(8.00 \ \text{u})(931.5 \ \text{MeV}/c^2)/\text{u}}} = 9.82 \times 10^5 \ \text{m/s}$$

If we were to travel at this speed, then the original Be would appear to be at rest and the two fragments would move at the identical speeds found in Problem 3.  Transforming back to the original frame, we find

$$v_1' = 1.49 \times 10^6 \ \text{m/s} + 0.982 \times 10^6 \ \text{m/s} = 2.47 \times 10^6 \ \text{m/s}$$

$$v_2' = -1.49 \times 10^6 \ \text{m/s} + 0.982 \times 10^6 \ \text{m/s} = -0.508 \times 10^6 \ \text{m/s}$$

16.     (a)  Let the second helium atom move at an angle $\theta$ with the $x$ axis.

Conservation of $p_x$:

$$mv = m_1 v_1' \cos 30° + m_2 v_2' \cos\theta \quad \text{or} \quad 2v - \frac{\sqrt{3}}{2} v_1' = v_2' \cos\theta \qquad (1)$$

Conservation of $p_y$:

$$0 = m_1 v_1' \sin 30° - m_2 v_2' \sin\theta \quad \text{or} \quad \frac{1}{2} v_1' = v_2' \sin\theta \qquad (2)$$

Conservation of energy:

$$92 \ \text{keV} + \frac{1}{2} mv^2 = \frac{1}{2} m_1 v_1'^2 + \frac{1}{2} m_2 v_2'^2 \qquad (3)$$

Eliminating $\theta$ by squaring (1) and (2), we obtain

$$v_2'^2 = 4v^2 + v_1^2 - 2\sqrt{3} \, v_1 v_1' \qquad (4)$$

and substituting this result into (3) gives a quadratic expression in $v_1'$ that can be solved to give

$$v_1' = 2.405 \times 10^6 \ \text{m/s}, \quad -0.321 \times 10^6 \ \text{m/s}$$

Only the positive root is consistent with the directions assumed in the initial problem.  Using (4) to find $v_2'$ gives

$$v_1' = 2.41 \times 10^6 \text{ m/s}, \qquad v_2' = 1.25 \times 10^6 \text{ m/s}$$

The angle $\theta$ can be found from (2):

$$\theta = \sin^{-1}\left(\frac{v_1'/2}{v_2'}\right) = 74.9°$$

(b)  The original speed of $m$ is

$$v = \sqrt{\frac{2K}{m}} = 1.203 \times 10^6 \text{ m/s}$$

Suppose we travel at this speed and observe the split of the Be, which appears to be at rest.  The two fragments travel in opposite directions, as in Problem 3, each at a speed of $v' = 1.49 \times 10^6$ m/s in this reference frame, but now along a line that makes an angle $\phi$ with respect to the $x$ direction. Transforming back to the original frame gives

$$v_{1x}' = v'\cos\phi + v \qquad \text{and} \qquad v_{1y}' = v'\sin\phi$$

$$\frac{v_{1x}'}{v_{1y}'} = \cot 30° = \frac{v'\cos\phi + v}{v'\sin\phi}$$

Using the known values of $v$ and $v'$, we solve for $\phi$ and find $\phi = 53.8°$.  Then

$$v_{1x}' = 2.08 \times 10^6 \text{ m/s}$$

$$v_{1y}' = 1.20 \times 10^6 \text{ m/s}$$

$$v_1 = \sqrt{v_{1x}'^2 + v_{1y}'^2} = 2.41 \times 10^6 \text{ m/s}$$

$$v_{2x}' = -v'\cos\phi + v = 0.322 \times 10^6 \text{ m/s}$$

$$v_{2y}' = -v'\sin\phi = -1.20 \times 10^6 \text{ m/s}$$

$$v_2 = \sqrt{v_{2x}'^2 + v_{2y}'^2} = 1.25 \times 10^6 \text{ m/s}$$

$$\theta = \tan^{-1}\left(v_{2y}'/v_{2x}'\right) = 74.9°$$

17.

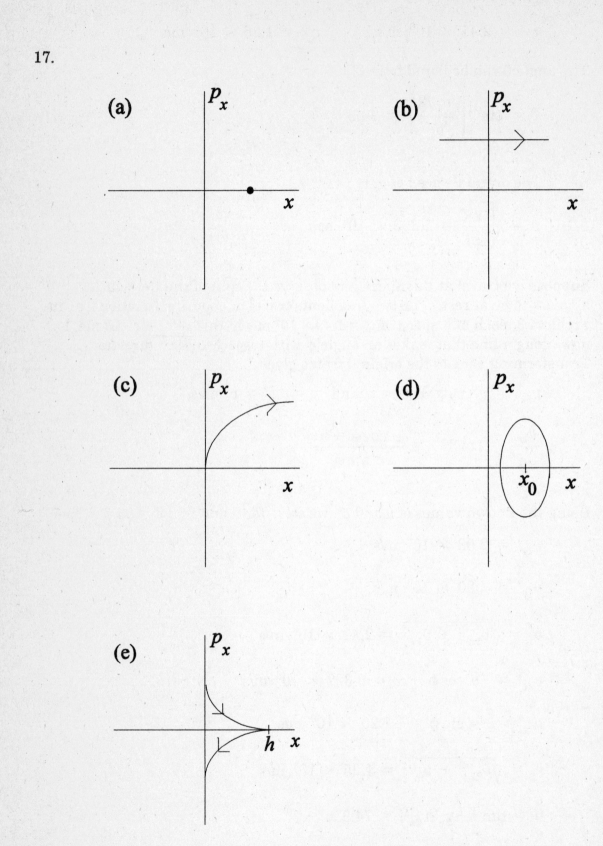

# Chapter 2

1. $$\Delta t = t_{up} + t_{down} - 2t_{across} = \frac{2L}{c}\left[\frac{1}{1 - u^2/c^2} - \frac{1}{(1 - u^2/c^2)^{1/2}}\right]$$

Assuming $u \ll c$,

$$\frac{1}{1 - u^2/c^2} \cong 1 + \frac{u^2}{c^2} \quad \text{and} \quad \frac{1}{(1 - u^2/c^2)^{1/2}} \cong 1 + \frac{1}{2}\frac{u^2}{c^2}$$

$$\Delta t \cong \frac{2L}{c}\left[1 + \frac{u^2}{c^2} - (1 + \frac{1}{2}\frac{u^2}{c^2})\right] = \frac{Lu^2}{c^3}$$

$$u = \sqrt{\frac{c^3\Delta t}{L}} = \sqrt{\frac{(3 \times 10^8 \text{ m/s})^3(2 \times 10^{-15} \text{ s})}{11 \text{ m}}} = 7 \times 10^4 \text{ m/s}$$

2. (a) $u = 100 \text{ km/h} = 28 \text{ m/s} \ll c$

$$\sqrt{1 - u^2/c^2} \cong 1 - \frac{1}{2}\frac{u^2}{c^2} = 1 - \frac{1}{2}\frac{(28 \text{ m/s})^2}{(3 \times 10^8 \text{ m/s})^2}$$

$$= 1 - 4.3 \times 10^{-15}$$

$$L = L_0(1 - 4.3 \times 10^{-15})$$

$$L_0 - L = (4.3 \times 10^{-15})L_0 = (4.3 \times 10^{-15})(5 \times 10^6 \text{ m})$$

$$= 2.1 \times 10^{-8} \text{ m} \quad \text{(less than one wavelength of light)}$$

(b) $$\Delta t = \frac{\Delta t_0}{1 - 4.3 \times 10^{-15}} \cong \Delta t_0(1 + 4.3 \times 10^{-15})$$

$$\Delta t - \Delta t_0 = (4.3 \times 10^{-15})(50 \text{ h})(3600 \text{ s/h}) = 7.7 \times 10^{-10} \text{ s}$$

3.        $\frac{1}{2}L_0 = L_0 \sqrt{1 - u^2/c^2}$

          $u = \sqrt{3/4}\ c = 2.6 \times 10^8$ m/s

4.    The astronaut must travel 400 light-years at a speed close to the speed of
      light and must age only 10 years.  To an Earth-bound observer, the trip takes
      about $\Delta t = 400$ years, but this is a dilated time interval; in the astronaut's
      frame of reference, the elapsed time is the proper time interval $\Delta t_0$ of 10
      years.  Thus

$$400 \text{ years} = \frac{10 \text{ years}}{\sqrt{1 - u^2/c^2}} \qquad \text{or} \qquad 1 - u^2/c^2 = \left(\frac{1}{40}\right)^2$$

          $u = 0.9997c$

5.    (a)   $\Delta t = \dfrac{\Delta t_0}{\sqrt{1 - u^2/c^2}} = \dfrac{100.0 \text{ ns}}{\sqrt{1 - (0.960)^2}} = 357.1$ ns

      (b)   $d = v\,\Delta t = 0.960\,(3.00 \times 10^8 \text{ m/s})(357.1 \times 10^{-9} \text{ s}) = 103$ m

      (c)   $d_0 = v\,\Delta t_0 = 0.960(3.00 \times 10^8 \text{ m/s})(100.0 \times 10^{-9} \text{ s}) = 28.8$ m

6.    In the laboratory reference frame, the lifetime is

$$\Delta t = \frac{1.25 \text{ mm}}{0.995c} = 0.418 \times 10^{-11} \text{ s}$$

$$\Delta t_0 = \Delta t \sqrt{1 - u^2/c^2} = (0.418 \times 10^{-11} \text{ s})\sqrt{1 - (0.995)^2} = 4.17 \times 10^{-13} \text{ s}$$

7. From Equation 2.15, $\Delta t_1 = L/(v - u)$, and from Equation 2.16, $\Delta t_2 = L/(c + u)$.

$$\Delta t = \Delta t_1 + \Delta t_2 = \frac{L}{v - u} + \frac{L}{c + u} = \frac{\Delta t_0}{\sqrt{1 - u^2/c^2}}$$

$$\frac{L}{v - u} + \frac{L}{c + u} = \frac{1}{\sqrt{1 - u^2/c^2}} \left[ \frac{L_0}{v'} + \frac{L_0}{c} \right]$$

Using $L = L_0 \sqrt{1 - u^2/c^2}$, we obtain

$$\frac{1}{v - u} + \frac{1}{c + u} = \frac{1}{1 - u^2/c^2} \left[ \frac{1}{v'} + \frac{1}{c} \right]$$

Solving for $v$, we obtain

$$v = \frac{v' + u}{1 + v'u/c^2}$$

8. Let ship $A$ represent observer $O$, and let observer $O'$ be on Earth. Then $v' = 0.826c$ and $u = -0.753c$.

$$v = \frac{v' + u}{1 + v'u/c^2} = \frac{0.851c + 0.753c}{1 + (0.851)(0.753)} = 0.978c$$

If now ship $B$ represents observer $O$, then $v' = -0.753c$ and $u = -0.851c$.

$$v = \frac{-0.753c - 0.851c}{1 + (-0.753)(-0.851)} = -0.978c$$

9.  Let $O'$ be the observer on Earth, and let $O$ be the observer on ship $B$. Then $v' = 0.826c$ and $u = -0.635c$.

$$v = \frac{v' + u}{1 + v'u/c^2} = \frac{0.826c - 0.635c}{1 + (0.826)(-0.635)} = 0.402c$$

10. (a)
$$\lambda' = \lambda \sqrt{\frac{1 + u/c}{1 - u/c}}$$

$$366 \text{ nm} = 122 \text{ nm} \sqrt{\frac{1 + u/c}{1 - u/c}}$$

$$u/c = 0.800 \qquad \text{or} \qquad u = 2.40 \times 10^8 \text{ m/s}$$

(b)
$$\lambda' = 122 \text{ nm} \sqrt{\frac{1 + 0.8}{1 - 0.8}} = 40.7 \text{ nm}$$

11.
$$\lambda' = \lambda \sqrt{\frac{1 + u/c}{1 - u/c}}$$

$$\frac{1 + u/c}{1 - u/c} = \left(\frac{\lambda'}{\lambda}\right)^2 = \left(\frac{550 \text{ nm}}{650 \text{ nm}}\right)^2 = 0.716$$

$$u/c = 0.166 \qquad \text{or} \qquad u = 5.0 \times 10^7 \text{ m/s}$$

12.
$$t_1' = \frac{t_1 - \frac{u}{c^2}x_1}{\sqrt{1 - u^2/c^2}} \qquad \text{and} \qquad t_2' = \frac{t_2 - \frac{u}{c^2}x_2}{\sqrt{1 - u^2/c^2}}$$

$$t_2' - t_1' = \frac{t_2 - t_1}{\sqrt{1 - u^2/c^2}} - \frac{\frac{u}{c^2}(x_2 - x_1)}{\sqrt{1 - u^2/c^2}}$$

In the $O$ frame of reference, the "cause" can travel to the effect with a speed of at most $c$.

$$\frac{x_2 - x_1}{t_2 - t_1} \leq c$$

$$t_2' - t_1' \geq \frac{t_2 - t_1}{\sqrt{1 - u^2/c^2}} - \frac{\frac{u}{c^2}(t_2 - t_1)c}{\sqrt{1 - u^2/c^2}} = (t_2 - t_1)\frac{1 - \frac{u}{c}}{\sqrt{1 - u^2/c^2}} \geq 0$$

13.
$$dx' = \frac{dx - u\,dt}{\sqrt{1 - u^2/c^2}} \qquad \text{and} \qquad dt' = \frac{dt - \frac{u}{c^2}dx}{\sqrt{1 - u^2/c^2}}$$

$$\frac{dx'}{dt'} = \frac{dx - u\,dt}{dt - \frac{u}{c^2}dx} = \frac{\frac{dx}{dt} - u}{1 - \frac{u}{c^2}\frac{dx}{dt}}$$

$$v_x' = \frac{v_x - u}{1 - uv_x/c^2}$$

$$dz' = dz$$

$$\frac{dz'}{dt'} = \frac{dz\sqrt{1 - u^2/c^2}}{dt - \dfrac{u}{c^2}\,dx} = \frac{\dfrac{dz}{dt}\sqrt{1 - u^2/c^2}}{1 - uv_x/c^2}$$

$$v_z' = \frac{v_z\sqrt{1 - u^2/c^2}}{1 - uv_x/c^2}$$

14.   $O$ measures $v_x = 0,\quad v_y = c$

$$v_x' = \frac{0 - u}{1 - 0u/c^2} = -u$$

$$v_y' = \frac{c\sqrt{1 - u^2/c^2}}{1 - 0u/c^2} = c\sqrt{1 - u^2/c^2}$$

According to $O'$, the speed of the light beam is

$$v' = \sqrt{(v_x')^2 + (v_y')^2} = \sqrt{u^2 + c^2(1 - u^2/c^2)} = c$$

15.   $x_1 = 0$ at $t_1 = 0$, $x_2 = 3.26$ km at $t_2 = 7.63$ μs, and $x_1' = 0$ at $t_1' = 0$.

$$x_2' = \frac{x_2 - ut_2}{\sqrt{1 - u^2/c^2}} = \frac{3.26\text{ km} - (0.625c)(7.63\text{ μs})}{\sqrt{1 - (0.625)^2}} = 2.34\text{ km}$$

$$t_2' = \frac{t_2 - (u/c^2)x_2}{\sqrt{1 - u^2/c^2}} = \frac{7.63\text{ μs} - (0.625)(3.26\text{ km})/(0.3\text{ km/μs})}{\sqrt{1 - (0.625)^2}} = 1.07\text{ μs}$$

16.  $O$ measures $t_1$ and $t_2$, and $O'$ measures $t_1'$ and $t_2'$.  Using Equation 2.23d,

$$t_1' = \frac{t_1 - \frac{u}{c^2}x}{\sqrt{1 - u^2/c^2}} \quad \text{and} \quad t_2' = \frac{t_2 - \frac{u}{c^2}x}{\sqrt{1 - u^2/c^2}}$$

The same coordinate $x$ appears in both expressions, because the bulb is at rest according to $O$.  Subtracting, we obtain

$$t_2' - t_1' = \frac{t_2 - t_1}{\sqrt{1 - u^2/c^2}} \quad \text{or} \quad \Delta t' = \frac{\Delta t}{\sqrt{1 - u^2/c^2}}$$

17.  Let $O'$ be the observer on ship $A$, traveling at $u = 0.60c$.  Observer $O$ measures $v_{Bx} = 0$, $v_{By} = 0.50c$ for ship $B$.  According to $O'$,

$$v_{Bx}' = \frac{0 - 0.60c}{1 - 0} = -0.60c$$

$$v_{By}' = \frac{0.50c\sqrt{1 - (0.60)^2}}{1 - 0} = 0.40c$$

$$v_B' = \sqrt{(v_{Bx}')^2 + (v_{By}')^2} = 0.72c$$

$$\theta_B = \tan^{-1}\frac{v_{By}'}{v_{Bx}'} = \tan^{-1}\frac{0.40c}{-0.60c} = 146°$$

For $C$, $O$ measures $v_{Cx} = -0.50c$, $v_{Cy} = 0$.

$$v_{Cx}' = \frac{-0.50c - 0.60c}{1 - (-0.50)(0.60)} = -0.85c$$

$$v_{Cy}' = 0$$

$$v_C' = 0.85c \qquad \text{at} \qquad \theta_C = 180° \qquad \text{(negative } x \text{ direction)}$$

For $D$, $O$ measures $v_{Dx} = -0.50c \sin 45° = -0.35c$, $v_{Dy} = 0.35c$.

$$v_{Dx}' = \frac{-0.35c - 0.60c}{1 - (-0.35)(0.60)} = -0.79c$$

$$v_{Dy}' = \frac{0.35c\sqrt{1 - (0.60)^2}}{1 - (-0.35)(0.60)} = 0.23c$$

$$v_D' = \sqrt{(v_{Dx}')^2 + (v_{Dy}')^2} = 0.82c \qquad \text{at} \qquad \theta_D = \tan^{-1}\frac{v_{Dy}'}{v_{Dx}'} = 164°$$

18.  (a)   On the outward journey at $0.6c$, the rate at which the signals are received is

$$v' = v\sqrt{\frac{1 - u/c}{1 + u/c}} = (1/\text{year})\sqrt{\frac{0.4}{1.6}} = 0.5/\text{year}$$

(b)   During the return journey,

$$v' = v\sqrt{\frac{1 + u/c}{1 - u/c}} = (1/\text{year})\sqrt{\frac{1.6}{0.4}} = 2/\text{year}$$

(c)    According to Casper, Amelia's outward journey lasts 32 years (it is 32 years before he sees her arrive at the planet), and during that time he receives 16 signals (0.5/year × 32 years). Since her total journey lasts 40 Earth years, the return journey lasts 8 Earth years, during which 16 signals are received (2/year × 8 years). Thus Casper receives 32 signals and correctly concludes that his sister has aged 32 years.

19.    $$K_i' = \tfrac{1}{2}m(v_1')^2 + \tfrac{1}{2}m(v_2')^2 = \frac{1}{2}m\left(\frac{2v}{1 + v^2/c^2}\right)^2 + 0 = \frac{2mv^2}{(1 + v^2/c^2)^2}$$

$$K_f' = \tfrac{1}{2}m(v_1')^2 + \tfrac{1}{2}m(v_2')^2 = \frac{1}{2}mv^2\left(2 - \frac{v^2}{c^2}\right) + \frac{1}{2}mv^2\left(2 - \frac{v^2}{c^2}\right)$$

$$= mv^2\left(2 - \frac{v^2}{c^2}\right)$$

20.    $$K_i' = \frac{mc^2}{\sqrt{1 - (v_1')^2/c^2}} - mc^2 + 0 = \frac{mc^2}{\sqrt{1 - \dfrac{4v^2}{c^2(1 + v^2/c^2)^2}}} - mc^2$$

$$= \frac{mc^2(c^2 + v^2)}{c^2 - v^2} - mc^2 = \frac{2mc^2v^2}{c^2 - v^2}$$

$$K_f' = \frac{2mc^2}{\sqrt{1 - v^2(2 - v^2/c^2)/c^2}} - 2mc^2 = \frac{2mc^4}{c^2 - v^2} - 2mc^2 = \frac{2mc^2v^2}{c^2 - v^2}$$

21.
$$W = \int F \, dx = \int \frac{dp}{dt} \, dx = \int dp \, \frac{dx}{dt} = \int v \, dp$$

$$K = \int_0^v v \, dp = pv - \int_0^v p \, dv = \frac{mv^2}{\sqrt{1 - v^2/c^2}} - \int_0^v \frac{mv}{\sqrt{1 - v^2/c^2}} \, dv$$

$$= \frac{mv^2}{\sqrt{1 - v^2/c^2}} + mc^2\sqrt{1 - v^2/c^2} - mc^2 = \frac{mc^2}{\sqrt{1 - v^2/c^2}} - mc^2$$

22.  For what range of velocities is $K - \frac{1}{2}mv^2 \le 0.01K$? At the upper limit of this range,

$$K - \frac{1}{2}mv^2 = 0.01K$$

$$0.99K = 0.99\left[\frac{mc^2}{\sqrt{1 - v^2/c^2}} - mc^2\right] = \frac{1}{2}mv^2$$

With $x = v^2/c^2$,

$$0.99\left[\frac{1}{\sqrt{1 - x}} - 1\right] = \frac{1}{2}x$$

$$\frac{1}{1 - x} = \left(1 + \frac{0.5}{0.99}x\right)^2$$

$$1 = (1 - x)(1 + 1.0101x + 0.2551x^2)$$

$$0.2551x^2 + 0.7550x - 0.0101 = 0$$

Solving using the quadratic formula, we find $x = 0.0133$ or $-2.97$. Only the positive root is physically meaningful, and so

$$v = \sqrt{0.0133}\,c = 0.115c$$

That is, for speeds smaller than $0.115c$, the classical kinetic energy is accurate within 1%. For a different approach to this same type of calculation, see Problem 27.

23. As in Problem 22, let us find the *lower* limit on the momentum such that

$$\sqrt{(pc)^2 + (mc^2)^2} - pc \leq 0.01 \sqrt{(pc)^2 + (mc^2)^2}$$

Evaluating the momentum at the lower limit, we find

$$0.99\sqrt{(pc)^2 + (mc^2)^2} = pc$$

$$(pc)^2 = \frac{m^2c^4}{\dfrac{1}{(0.99)^2} - 1} \qquad \text{or} \qquad pc = 7.02mc^2$$

Using the relativistic momentum, we obtain

$$\frac{v/c}{\sqrt{1 - v^2/c^2}} = 7.02$$

$$\frac{v^2}{c^2} = 49.25\left(1 - \frac{v^2}{c^2}\right) \qquad \text{or} \qquad v/c = 0.990$$

Whenever $v/c \geq 0.990$, the expression $E = pc$ will be accurate to within 1%.

24. $$E^2 = \frac{(mc^2)^2}{1 - v^2/c^2} = (mc^2)^2\left(\frac{1 - v^2/c^2 + v^2/c^2}{1 - v^2/c^2}\right)$$

$$= (mc^2)^2 + \frac{m^2c^2v^2}{1 - v^2/c^2} = (mc^2)^2 + (cp)^2$$

$$E = \sqrt{(mc^2)^2 + (cp)^2}$$

25.     (a)   $O'$ measures $v' = (v - u)/(1 - uv/c^2)$, and according to $O'$ the energy is

$$E' = \frac{mc^2}{\sqrt{1 - v'^2/c^2}} = \frac{mc^2}{\sqrt{1 - \left[\dfrac{(v - u)/c}{1 - uv/c^2}\right]^2}}$$

and the momentum is

$$p' = \frac{mv'}{\sqrt{1 - v'^2/c^2}} = \frac{m\left[\dfrac{(v - u)}{1 - uv/c^2}\right]}{\sqrt{1 - \left[\dfrac{(v - u)/c}{1 - uv/c^2}\right]^2}}$$

(b)       $$E'^2 - p'^2c^2 = \frac{m^2c^4 - m^2\left[\dfrac{(v - u)}{1 - uv/c^2}\right]^2}{1 - \left[\dfrac{(v - u)/c}{1 - uv/c^2}\right]^2} = m^2c^4$$

The quantity $E'^2 - p'^2c^2$ is an *invariant* -- it has the same value no matter what frame of reference is chosen.

26. (a) $O'$ measures $v_x' = -u$, $v_y' = v\sqrt{1 - u^2/c^2}$

$$v' = \sqrt{(v_x')^2 + (v_y')^2} = \sqrt{u^2 + v^2 - u^2v^2/c^2}$$

$$E' = \frac{mc^2}{\sqrt{1 - v'^2/c^2}} = \frac{mc^2}{\sqrt{1 - \dfrac{u^2}{c^2} - \dfrac{v^2}{c^2} + \dfrac{u^2v^2}{c^4}}}$$

$$p' = \frac{m\sqrt{u^2 + v^2 - u^2v^2/c^2}}{\sqrt{1 - \dfrac{u^2}{c^2} - \dfrac{v^2}{c^2} + \dfrac{u^2v^2}{c^4}}}$$

(b) $$E'^2 - c^2p'^2 = \frac{(mc^2)^2 - m^2(u^2 + v^2 - u^2v^2/c^2)}{1 - \dfrac{u^2}{c^2} - \dfrac{v^2}{c^2} + \dfrac{u^2v^2}{c^4}} = m^2c^4$$

27. $$K = mc^2\left[\frac{1}{\sqrt{1 - v^2/c^2}} - 1\right]$$

$$(1 - v^2/c^2)^{-1/2} = 1 + \frac{1}{2}\frac{v^2}{c^2} + \frac{(-1/2)(-3/2)}{2}\left[\frac{v^2}{c^2}\right]^2 + \dots$$

$$K = mc^2\left[1 + \frac{1}{2}\frac{v^2}{c^2} + \frac{3}{8}\frac{v^4}{c^4} + \dots - 1\right] = \tfrac{1}{2}mv^2\left[1 + \frac{3}{4}\frac{v^2}{c^2} + \dots\right]$$

The correction term is $3v^2/4c^2$, which has the value 0.01% when $3v^2/4c^2 = 0.0001$, or

$$v = \sqrt{0.0001(4/3)}\,c = 0.0115c$$

28.        $\Delta E = mc\Delta T = (1 \text{ g})(0.40 \text{ J/g·K})(100 \text{ K}) = 40 \text{ J}$

$$\Delta m = \frac{\Delta E}{c^2} = \frac{40 \text{ J}}{9 \times 10^{16} \text{ m}^2/\text{s}^2} = 4.4 \times 10^{-16} \text{ kg}$$

29.    (a)    At such low speed, the classical approximation is valid.

$$K = \tfrac{1}{2}mv^2 = \tfrac{1}{2}mc^2\frac{v^2}{c^2}$$

$$= \tfrac{1}{2}(0.511 \text{ MeV}/c^2)c^2(1.00 \times 10^{-4})^2 = 2.56 \times 10^{-3} \text{ eV}$$

(b)    We will try both the classical and relativistic expressions. The classical expression gives

$$K = \tfrac{1}{2}mc^2\frac{v^2}{c^2} = \tfrac{1}{2}(0.511 \text{ MeV}/c^2)c^2(1.00 \times 10^{-2})^2 = 25.6 \text{ eV}$$

The relativistic expression gives

$$K = mc^2\left[\frac{1}{\sqrt{1 - v^2/c^2}} - 1\right] = 0.511 \text{ MeV}\left[\frac{1}{\sqrt{1 - (0.01)^2}} - 1\right] = 25.6 \text{ eV}$$

To three significant figures, the classical and relativistic expressions give identical results.

(c)

$$K = mc^2\left[\frac{1}{\sqrt{1 - v^2/c^2}} - 1\right] = 0.511 \text{ MeV}\left[\frac{1}{\sqrt{1 - (0.3)^2}} - 1\right] = 24.7 \text{ keV}$$

Here the classical expression gives

$$K = \tfrac{1}{2}mc^2\frac{v^2}{c^2} = \tfrac{1}{2}(0.511\ \text{MeV})(0.300)^2 = 23.0\ \text{keV}$$

which is incorrect by about 7%.

(d)  $K = 0.511\ \text{MeV}\left[\dfrac{1}{\sqrt{1 - (0.999)^2}} - 1\right] = 10.9\ \text{MeV}$

30.  (a)  To about 10 significant figures, $v \cong c$

$$\Delta t = \frac{L_0}{v} = \frac{3\ \text{km}}{3 \times 10^8\ \text{m/s}} = 1 \times 10^{-5}\ \text{s}$$

(b)  $L = L_0\sqrt{1 - v^2/c^2} = L_0\sqrt{\dfrac{(c + v)(c - v)}{c^2}} \cong L_0\sqrt{\dfrac{2(c - v)}{c}}$

$$= 3\ \text{km}\sqrt{\frac{2(0.016\ \text{m/s})}{3 \times 10^8\ \text{m/s}}} = 3\ \text{cm}$$

To the moving electron the accelerator appears to be 3 cm long!

(c)  $\Delta t_0 = \dfrac{0.03\ \text{m}}{3 \times 10^8\ \text{m/s}} = 1 \times 10^{-10}\ \text{s}$

31.    (a)    Before the first acceleration, $E_0 = 0.511$ MeV.  The energy after the acceleration is

$$E_1 = \frac{mc^2}{\sqrt{1 - v^2/c^2}} = \frac{0.511 \text{ MeV}}{\sqrt{1 - (0.99)^2}} = 3.6 \text{ MeV}$$

$$\Delta E = E_1 - E_0 = 3.1 \text{ MeV}$$

The first stage therefore adds 3.1 MeV to the energy of the electron.

(b)    $$E_2 = \frac{mc^2}{\sqrt{1 - v^2/c^2}} = \frac{0.511 \text{ MeV}}{\sqrt{1 - (0.999)^2}} = 11.4 \text{ MeV}$$

$$\Delta E = E_2 - E_1 = 7.8 \text{ MeV}$$

The second stage adds about 2.5 times the energy of the first stage, but increases the velocity by only 0.9%.

32.    Since the electric charges of the proton and electron are equal in magnitude, after acceleration through 10 million volts, they will each have a kinetic energy of 10 MeV.  For the electron

$$E = K + mc^2 = 10.5 \text{ MeV}$$

$$p = \frac{1}{c}\sqrt{E^2 - (mc^2)^2} = \frac{1}{c}\sqrt{(10.5 \text{ MeV})^2 - (0.5 \text{ MeV})^2} = 10.5 \text{ MeV}/c$$

If we had used the classical relation $K = p^2/2m$, we would have obtained

$$p = \sqrt{2mK} = \sqrt{2(0.511 \text{ MeV}/c^2)(10 \text{ MeV})} = 3.20 \text{ MeV}/c$$

which is far from the correct result.

For the proton

$$E = K + mc^2 = 10.0 \text{ MeV} + 938.3 \text{ MeV} = 948.3 \text{ MeV}$$

$$p = \frac{1}{c}\sqrt{E^2 - (mc^2)^2} = \frac{1}{c}\sqrt{(948.3 \text{ MeV})^2 - (938.3 \text{ MeV})^2} = 137 \text{ MeV}/c$$

The classical formula gives

$$p = \sqrt{2mK} = \sqrt{2(938.3 \text{ MeV}/c^2)(10.0 \text{ MeV})} = 137 \text{ MeV}/c$$

Because of its large mass, the proton is moving non-relativistically at an energy of 10.0 MeV.

33.  The molar mass of uranium is about 238 g, so one kilogram of uranium is

$$\frac{1000 \text{ g}}{238 \text{ g/mole}} = 4.2 \text{ moles}$$

and contains

$$(4.2 \text{ moles})(6.02 \times 10^{23} \text{ atoms/mole}) = 2.5 \times 10^{24} \text{ atoms}$$

The total energy released is

$$\Delta E = 200 \text{ MeV/atom} \times 2.5 \times 10^{24} \text{ atoms} = 5.0 \times 10^{26} \text{ MeV}$$

$$\Delta m = \frac{\Delta E}{c^2} = \frac{(5.0 \times 10^{26} \text{ MeV})(1.6 \times 10^{-13} \text{ J/MeV})}{9.0 \times 10^{16} \text{ m}^2/\text{s}^2} = 8.9 \times 10^{-4} \text{ kg}$$

34.    Before the collision, the energy of each electron is

$$E_2 = \frac{mc^2}{\sqrt{1 - v^2/c^2}} = \frac{0.511 \text{ MeV}}{\sqrt{1 - (0.99999)^2}} = 114.3 \text{ MeV}$$

The total collision energy is therefore 228.6 MeV. After the collision, the muons must move with equal momenta and thus with equal energies, so each muon has an energy of 114.3 MeV, and a kinetic energy of

$$K = 114.3 \text{ MeV} - 105.7 \text{ MeV} = 8.6 \text{ MeV}$$

35.        $$E_1 + E_2 = 9700 \text{ MeV}$$

$$E_1 = E_2 = \frac{mc^2}{\sqrt{1 - v^2/c^2}} \qquad \text{where} \qquad mc^2 = 938 \text{ MeV}$$

$$\frac{2mc^2}{\sqrt{1 - v^2/c^2}} = 9700 \text{ MeV}$$

$$1 - \frac{v^2}{c^2} = \left[ \frac{2(938 \text{ MeV})}{9700 \text{ MeV}} \right]^2 = 0.0374 \qquad \text{so} \qquad v = 0.981c$$

36.    The initial energy is

$$E_\pi = \frac{mc^2}{\sqrt{1 - v^2/c^2}} = \frac{135 \text{ MeV}}{\sqrt{1 - (0.98)^2}} = 678 \text{ MeV}$$

and the momentum is

$$p_\pi = \frac{1}{c}\sqrt{E_\pi^2 - (mc^2)^2} = \frac{1}{c}\sqrt{(678 \text{ MeV})^2 - (135 \text{ MeV})^2} = 664 \text{ MeV}/c$$

Since the gamma-ray energies are equal, each gamma has an energy of 0.5(678 MeV), so $E_\gamma = 339$ MeV. Each gamma ray has a momentum $p_\gamma = E_\gamma/c$ which has component $p_\gamma \cos\theta$ along the direction of the initial pi-meson. Thus conservation of momentum gives

$$p_\pi = 2p_\gamma \cos\theta$$

$$\cos\theta = \frac{p_\pi}{2p_\gamma} = \frac{cp_\pi}{2E_\gamma} = \frac{664 \text{ MeV}}{678 \text{ MeV}} \qquad \text{or} \qquad \theta = 11.7°$$

37.  As in Example 2.16, the total energy of the kaon is 823 MeV. The speed of the kaon is the same as the transformation speed $u$ between the lab frame and the kaon's rest frame:

$$823 \text{ MeV} = \frac{m_K c^2}{\sqrt{1 - u^2/c^2}}$$

Solving, we find $u/c = 0.796$.

When a kaon at rest decays into two pions,

$$E_{\pi_1} = E_{\pi_2} = \tfrac{1}{2}m_K c^2 = 249 \text{ MeV} = \frac{m_\pi c^2}{\sqrt{1 - v^2/c^2}}$$

Solving, we find the speed of each pions is $v/c = 0.827$.

Now transform these speeds back to the lab frame at $u = 0.796c$:

$$v_1 = \frac{v_1' + u}{1 + uv_1'/c^2} = \frac{0.827c + 0.796c}{1 + (0.796)(0.827)} = 0.9787c$$

$$v_2 = \frac{-0.827c + 0.796c}{1 + (0.796)(-0.827)} = -0.0907c$$

$$K_1 = \frac{mc^2}{\sqrt{1 - v_1^2/c^2}} - mc^2 = \frac{140 \text{ MeV}}{\sqrt{1 - (0.9787)^2}} - 140 \text{ MeV} = 542 \text{ MeV}$$

$$K_2 = \frac{140 \text{ MeV}}{\sqrt{1 - (0.0907)^2}} - 140 \text{ MeV} = 0.6 \text{ MeV}$$

38.
$$p = 3094 \text{ MeV}/c = \frac{mv}{\sqrt{1 - v^2/c^2}} = \frac{mc^2 \left(\dfrac{v}{c}\right) \dfrac{1}{c}}{\sqrt{1 - v^2/c^2}}$$

$$3094 \text{ MeV}/c = \frac{v/c}{\sqrt{1 - v^2/c^2}} (105.7 \text{ MeV}/c)$$

$$v/c = 0.99942$$

$$\Delta t = \frac{\Delta t_0}{\sqrt{1 - v^2/c^2}} = \frac{2.198 \text{ } \mu s}{\sqrt{1 - (0.99942)^2}} = 64.38 \text{ } \mu s$$

39.
$$c^2 p^2 = E^2 - (mc^2)^2 = (K + mc^2)^2 - (mc^2)^2 = K^2 + 2Kmc^2$$

$$\frac{p^2}{2K} = m + \frac{K}{2c^2}$$

# Chapter 3

1.  $$\Delta y = y_{n+1} - y_n = \frac{\lambda D}{d} = \frac{(589.0 \text{ nm})(2.357 \text{ m})}{1.05 \text{ mm}} = 1.32 \text{ mm}$$

2.  $$\sin \theta = \frac{n\lambda}{2d} = \frac{2(0.250 \text{ nm})}{2(0.282 \text{ nm})} = 0.8865$$

    $$\theta = \sin^{-1} 0.8865 = 62.4°$$

3.  (a) $$\lambda = \frac{2d \sin \theta}{n} = \frac{2(0.347 \text{ nm})(\sin 34.0°)}{1} = 0.388 \text{ nm}$$

    (b) The spacing between planes is

    $$d \sin 45° = (0.347 \text{ nm})\frac{\sqrt{2}}{2} = 0.245 \text{ nm}$$

    $$\sin \theta = \frac{\lambda}{2d} = \frac{0.388 \text{ nm}}{2(0.245 \text{ nm})} = 0.791 \qquad \text{or} \qquad \theta = 52.2°$$

    This angle is measured with respect to the crystal planes. The angle of incidence measured from the crystal surface is $\theta - 45° = 7.2°$. The emerging beam makes an angle of $\theta + 45° = 97.2°$ with the surface (measured from the opposite side of the surface).

4.  (a) $E = 10.0 \text{ MeV} = 1.60 \times 10^{-12} \text{ J}$

    $$p = \frac{E}{c} = \frac{10.0 \text{ MeV}}{c} = 1.00 \times 10^7 \text{ eV}/c$$

    $$p = \frac{1.60 \times 10^{-12} \text{ J}}{3.00 \times 10^8 \text{ m/s}} = 5.33 \times 10^{-21} \text{ kg·m/s}$$

(b)     $E = 25 \text{ keV} = 4.0 \times 10^{-15} \text{ J}$

$$p = \frac{25 \text{ keV}}{c} = 2.5 \times 10^4 \text{ eV}/c$$

$$p = \frac{4.0 \times 10^{-15} \text{ J}}{3.00 \times 10^8 \text{ m/s}} = 1.3 \times 10^{-23} \text{ kg·m/s}$$

(c)     $\lambda = 1.0 \text{ μm} = 1.0 \times 10^3 \text{ nm}$

$$p = \frac{h}{\lambda} = \frac{1}{c}\frac{hc}{\lambda} = \frac{1}{c}\frac{1240 \text{ eV·nm}}{1.0 \times 10^3 \text{ nm}} = 1.2 \text{ eV}/c$$

$$p = \frac{6.6 \times 10^{-34} \text{ J·s}}{1.0 \times 10^{-6} \text{ m}} = 6.6 \times 10^{-28} \text{ kg·m/s}$$

(d)     $\nu = 150 \times 10^6 \text{ Hz}$

$E = h\nu = (4.14 \times 10^{-15} \text{ eV·s})(150 \times 10^6 \text{ Hz}) = 6.2 \times 10^{-7} \text{ eV}$

$= 9.9 \times 10^{-26} \text{ J}$

$$p = \frac{E}{c} = \frac{6.2 \times 10^{-7} \text{ eV}}{c} = 6.2 \times 10^{-7} \text{ eV}/c$$

$$p = \frac{9.9 \times 10^{-26} \text{ J}}{3.00 \times 10^8 \text{ m/s}} = 3.3 \times 10^{-34} \text{ kg·m/s}$$

5.     At 1 Mhz $= 10^6$ Hz, $E = h\nu \cong 4 \times 10^{-9}$ eV.

At 100 Mhz, $E = h\nu \cong 4 \times 10^{-7}$ eV.

The range is approximately $4 \times 10^{-9}$ eV to $4 \times 10^{-7}$ eV.

6.     (a)     $\lambda = \dfrac{hc}{E} = \dfrac{1240 \text{ eV·nm}}{1.00 \times 10^4 \text{ eV}} = 0.124 \text{ nm}$

(b)    $\lambda = \dfrac{1240 \text{ eV·nm}}{1.00 \times 10^6 \text{ eV}} = 1.24 \times 10^{-3} \text{ nm}$

(c)    350 nm:   $E = \dfrac{1240 \text{ eV·nm}}{350 \text{ nm}} = 3.5 \text{ eV}$

700 nm:   $E = \dfrac{1240 \text{ eV·nm}}{700 \text{ nm}} = 1.8 \text{ eV}$

The range is 1.8 eV to 3.5 eV.

7.    At $\lambda = 550$ nm,

$$E = \frac{hc}{\lambda} = \frac{1240 \text{ eV·nm}}{550 \text{ nm}} = 2.25 \text{ eV}$$

The rate at which 2.25-eV photons are emitted is found from

$$100 \text{ W} = 100 \frac{\text{J}}{\text{s}} = 6.25 \times 10^{20} \frac{\text{eV}}{\text{s}} = 2.8 \times 10^{20} \frac{\text{photons}}{\text{s}}$$

Assume the photons are distributed uniformly over a sphere of radius 1 m.

Area of sphere  $= 4\pi r^2 = 4\pi \text{ m}^2$

Area of paper  $= 20 \text{ cm} \times 30 \text{ cm} = 0.06 \text{ m}^2$

The number of photons striking the paper is thus

$$2.8 \times 10^{20} \frac{\text{photons}}{\text{s}} \frac{0.06 \text{ m}^2}{4\pi \text{ m}^2} = 1.3 \times 10^{20} \frac{\text{photons}}{\text{s}}$$

8.    With $\phi = 4.08$ eV for aluminum,

$$\lambda_c = \frac{hc}{\phi} = \frac{1240 \text{ eV·nm}}{4.08 \text{ eV}} = 304 \text{ nm}$$

9.  $$eV_s = \frac{hc}{\lambda} - \phi$$

$$0.65 \text{ eV} = \frac{hc}{420 \text{ nm}} - \phi \qquad \text{and} \qquad 1.69 \text{ eV} = \frac{hc}{310 \text{ nm}} - \phi$$

Subtracting, we find

$$1.04 \text{ eV} = hc\left(\frac{1}{310 \text{ nm}} - \frac{1}{420 \text{ nm}}\right)$$

$$hc = \frac{1.04 \text{ eV}}{\dfrac{1}{310 \text{ nm}} - \dfrac{1}{420 \text{ nm}}} = 1.23 \times 10^3 \text{ eV·nm}$$

$$h = 4.10 \times 10^{-15} \text{ eV·s} = 6.57 \times 10^{-34} \text{ J·s}$$

$$\phi = \frac{hc}{420 \text{ nm}} - 0.65 \text{ eV} = \frac{1.23 \times 10^3 \text{eV·nm}}{420 \text{ nm}} - 0.65 \text{ eV} = 2.28 \text{ eV}$$

10.  $$\phi = \frac{hc}{\lambda_c} = \frac{1239.853 \text{ eV·nm}}{325.6 \text{ nm}} = 3.808 \text{ eV}$$

$$eV_s = \frac{hc}{\lambda} - \phi = \frac{1239.853 \text{ eV·nm}}{259.8 \text{ nm}} - 3.808 \text{ eV} = 0.964 \text{ eV}$$

$$V_s = 0.964 \text{ volts}$$

11.  $$eV_{s_{Cu}} = \frac{hc}{\lambda} - \phi_{Cu} \qquad \text{and} \qquad eV_{s_{Na}} = \frac{hc}{\lambda} - \phi_{Na}$$

Subtracting, we obtain

$$eV_{s_{Cu}} - eV_{s_{Na}} = \phi_{Na} - \phi_{Cu} = 2.28 \text{ eV} - 4.70 \text{ eV} = -2.42 \text{ eV}$$

$$V_{s_{Na}} = V_{s_{Cu}} + 2.42 = V + 2.42 \text{ volts}$$

12.  (a)  $\phi = \dfrac{hc}{\lambda_c} = \dfrac{1240 \text{ eV·nm}}{254 \text{ nm}} = 4.88 \text{ eV}$

(b)  $\lambda < 254 \text{ nm}$

13.  (a)  $\phi = 4.31 \text{ eV}$

$$\lambda_c = \dfrac{hc}{\phi} = \dfrac{1240 \text{ eV·nm}}{4.31 \text{ eV}} = 288 \text{ nm}$$

(b)  $eV_s = \dfrac{hc}{\lambda} - \phi = \dfrac{1240 \text{ eV·nm}}{220.0 \text{ nm}} - 4.31 \text{ eV} = 1.33 \text{ eV}$

$$V_s = 1.33 \text{ volts}$$

14.  Assume the photons are of near ultraviolet light ($\lambda = 300$ nm).

$$p = \frac{h}{\lambda} = \frac{1}{c}\frac{hc}{\lambda} = \frac{1}{c}\frac{1240 \text{ eV·nm}}{300 \text{ nm}} = 4.1 \text{ eV}/c$$

Suppose the work function is 2 eV, so the photoelectrons are emitted with a maximum kinetic energy of 2.1 eV. The momentum of an electron is

$$p = \sqrt{2mK} = \frac{1}{c}\sqrt{2mc^2K} = \frac{1}{c}\sqrt{2(0.511 \text{ MeV})(2.1 \text{ eV})} = 1465 \text{ eV}/c$$

To conserve momentum, an atom on the surface must recoil with a momentum of 1465 eV/$c$ – 4.1 eV/$c$ = 1461 eV/$c$. For a medium weight atom, the recoil energy is

$$E = \frac{p^2}{2M} = \frac{p^2 c^2}{2Mc^2} = \frac{(1461\ \text{eV})^2}{2(100\ \text{u})(931.5\ \text{MeV/u})} = 1.15 \times 10^{-5}\ \text{eV}$$

Because of its large mass, the atom can supply the recoil momentum at very little cost in energy.

15.    (a)    $(4\ \text{W/m}^2)(1\ \text{cm})^2 = 4 \times 10^{-4}\ \text{W} = 4 \times 10^{-4}\ \text{J/s} = 2.5 \times 10^{15}\ \text{eV/}c$

Suppose each photon has an energy of 2.5 eV, and let each photon release one photoelectron. Then we have

$$(1.0 \times 10^{15}\ \text{electrons/s})(1.6 \times 10^{-19}\ \text{C/electron}) = 0.16\ \text{mA}$$

(b)    Assume that all electrons in the metal will flow to the surface to replace the emitted electrons. The volume of the metal sample is $(0.01\ \text{cm})(1\ \text{cm})^2 = 10^{-2}\ \text{cm}^3$. Let the density be 9 g/cm$^3$, so $m = 9 \times 10^{-2}$ g. If we take 1 mole = 50 g, then

$$\frac{9 \times 10^{-2}\ \text{g}}{50\ \text{g/mole}}\ 6.02 \times 10^{23}\ \frac{\text{atoms}}{\text{mole}} = 10^{21}\ \text{atoms}$$

At $10^{15}$ electrons/s and 1 electron/atom,

$$t = \frac{10^{21}\ \text{electrons}}{10^{15}\ \text{electrons/s}} = 10^6\ \text{s} \approx 10\ \text{days}$$

16.    $$R(\lambda) = \frac{c}{4}\ \frac{8\pi}{\lambda^4}\ \frac{hc}{\lambda}\ \frac{1}{e^{hc/\lambda kT} - 1}$$

$$\frac{dR}{d\lambda} = \frac{8\pi hc^2}{4}\left[\left(\frac{-5}{\lambda^6}\right)\frac{1}{e^{hc/\lambda kT} - 1} + \left(\frac{1}{\lambda^5}\right)\frac{(-e^{hc/\lambda kT})(-hc/\lambda^2 kT)}{(e^{hc/\lambda kT} - 1)^2}\right]$$

Setting $dR/d\lambda$ equal to zero gives

$$-\frac{5}{\lambda} + \frac{(e^{hc/\lambda kT})(hc/\lambda^2 kT)}{e^{hc/\lambda kT} - 1} = 0$$

Letting $x = hc/\lambda kT$, we obtain

$$(x - 5)e^x + 5 = 0$$

This equation does not have an exact solution, but an approximate solution may be found by trial and error:

$$x = 4.9651 = \frac{hc}{\lambda kT}$$

$$\lambda T = \frac{hc}{4.9651k} = \frac{1239.853 \text{ eV·nm}}{4.9651(8.6174 \times 10^{-5} \text{ eV/K})} = 2.8978 \times 10^{-3} \text{ m·K}$$

17. 
$$R(\lambda) = \frac{8\pi hc^2}{4} \frac{1}{\lambda^5} \frac{1}{e^{hc/\lambda kT} - 1}$$

$$\int_0^\infty R(\lambda) \; d\lambda = \frac{8\pi hc^2}{4} \int_0^\infty \left(\frac{1}{\lambda^5}\right) \frac{d\lambda}{e^{hc/\lambda kT} - 1}$$

With $x = \frac{hc}{\lambda kT}$, then $dx = \left(\frac{-hc}{\lambda^2 kT}\right) d\lambda$

$$\int_0^\infty R(\lambda) \; d\lambda = \left(\frac{8\pi hc^2}{4}\right) \left(\frac{kT}{hc}\right)^3 \left(\frac{-kT}{hc}\right) \int_\infty^0 \frac{x^3 \; dx}{e^x - 1}$$

$$= 2\pi hc^2 \left(\frac{k}{hc}\right)^4 T^4 \int_0^\infty \frac{x^3 \; dx}{e^x - 1} = \frac{2\pi^5 k^4}{15h^3 c^2} T^4 = \sigma T^4$$

with $\sigma = \frac{2\pi^5 k^4}{15h^3 c^2}$

18.  $h^3 = \dfrac{2\pi^5 k^4}{15\sigma c^2}$

$$h = \left[\frac{2\pi^5(1.38066 \times 10^{-23} \text{ J/K})^4}{15(5.67 \times 10^{-8} \text{ W/m}^2\cdot\text{K}^4)(2.9979 \times 10^8 \text{ m/s})}\right]^{1/3} = 6.626 \times 10^{-34} \text{ J}\cdot\text{s}$$

19.  $\lambda T = 2.898 \times 10^{-3} \text{ m}\cdot\text{K}$

$\lambda = \dfrac{2.898 \times 10^{-3} \text{ m}\cdot\text{K}}{6000 \text{ K}} = 483 \text{ nm}$   (middle of the visible spectrum)

20.  $\lambda = \dfrac{2.898 \times 10^{-3} \text{ m}\cdot\text{K}}{2.7 \text{ K}} = 1.1 \text{ mm}$   (microwave region)

$E = \dfrac{hc}{\lambda} = \dfrac{1240 \text{ eV}\cdot\text{nm}}{1.1 \text{ mm}} = 1.1 \times 10^{-3} \text{ eV}$

21.  (a)   At $T = 1150$ K,

$\lambda_{max} = \dfrac{2.898 \times 10^{-3} \text{ m}\cdot\text{K}}{1150 \text{ K}} = 2.52 \text{ }\mu\text{m}$

(b)   $\dfrac{hc}{\lambda_{max}kT} = \dfrac{1240 \text{ eV}\cdot\text{nm}}{(2.898 \times 10^{-3} \text{ m}\cdot\text{K})(8.617 \times 10^{-5} \text{ eV/K})} = 4.9655$

$\dfrac{R}{R_{max}} = \dfrac{\lambda_{max}^5}{\lambda^5}\left[\dfrac{e^{hc/\lambda_{max}kT} - 1}{e^{hc/\lambda kT} - 1}\right] = \dfrac{\lambda_{max}^5}{(2\lambda_{max})^5}\left[\dfrac{e^{4.9655} - 1}{e^{4.9655/2} - 1}\right] = 0.405$

22. Let the body be represented by a cylinder of height $h = 1.8$ m and diameter $d = 0.3$ m.

$$\text{Surface area} = \pi dh = 1.7 \text{ m}^2$$

$$T = 37°C = 310 \text{ K}$$

$$I = \sigma T^4 = (5.67 \times 10^{-8} \text{ W/m}^2 \cdot \text{K}^4)(310 \text{ K})^4 = 524 \text{ W/m}^2$$

$$P = IA = (524 \text{ W/m}^2)(1.7 \text{ m}^2) = 890 \text{ W}$$

23. $$I = \sigma T^4 = (5.67 \times 10^{-8} \text{ W/m}^2 \cdot \text{K}^4)(1650 \text{ K})^4 = 4.20 \times 10^5 \text{ W/m}^2$$

$$P = IA = (4.20 \times 10^5 \text{ W/m}^2)\pi(0.0005 \text{ m})^2 = 0.33 \text{ W}$$

24. $$(E + m_e c^2 - E')^2 = c^2(p^2 - 2pp'\cos\theta + p'^2) + m_e^2 c^4$$

$$E^2 + E'^2 + m_e^2 c^4 + 2Em_e c^2 - 2EE' - 2E'm_e c^2 =$$

$$c^2 p^2 - 2c^2 pp'\cos\theta + c^2 p'^2 + m_e^2 c^4$$

Using $E = pc$ and $E' = p'c$ allows common terms to be cancelled, so

$$Em_e c^2 - EE' - E'm_e c^2 = -EE'\cos\theta$$

$$m_e c^2(E - E') = EE'(1 - \cos\theta)$$

$$\frac{1}{E'} - \frac{1}{E} = \frac{1}{m_e c^2}(1 - \cos\theta)$$

25.    (a)
$$\frac{1}{E'} = \frac{1}{E} + \frac{1}{m_e c^2}(1 - \cos\theta)$$

$$= \frac{1}{10.39 \text{ keV}} + \frac{1}{510.999 \text{ keV}}\left(1 - \frac{\sqrt{2}}{2}\right) = 0.09682 \text{ keV}^{-1}$$

$$E' = 10.33 \text{ keV}$$

(b)
$$K_e = E_e - m_e c^2 = E - E' = 10.39 \text{ keV} - 10.33 \text{ keV} = 0.06 \text{ keV}$$

26.    (a)
$$\lambda' - \lambda = (0.002426 \text{ nm})(1 - \cos\theta)$$

At 90°, for $\lambda = 0.02480$ nm,

$$\lambda' = 0.02480 \text{ nm} + 0.002426 \text{ nm} = 0.02723 \text{ nm}$$

(b)    The incident photon has momentum in the $x$ direction of

$$p = \frac{h}{\lambda} = \frac{1}{c}\frac{hc}{\lambda} = \frac{1}{c}\frac{1240 \text{ eV·nm}}{0.02480 \text{ nm}} = 4.999 \times 10^4 \text{ eV}/c$$

The scattered photon has momentum in the $y$ direction of

$$p' = \frac{h}{\lambda} = \frac{1}{c}\frac{hc}{\lambda} = \frac{1}{c}\frac{1240 \text{ eV·nm}}{0.02723 \text{ nm}} = 4.553 \times 10^4 \text{ eV}/c$$

(c)
$$K_e = E_e - m_e c^2 = E - E' = cp - cp'$$

$$= 4.999 \times 10^4 \text{ eV} - 4.553 \times 10^4 \text{ eV} = 4.46 \times 10^3 \text{ eV}$$

(d)    Since momentum must be conserved, the $x$ component of the electron's momentum must equal $p$, and the $y$ component must equal $-p'$:

$$p_{ex} = p \qquad \text{and} \qquad p_{ey} = -p'$$

$$p_e = \sqrt{(p_{ex})^2 + (p_{ey})^2} = \sqrt{p^2 + p'^2} = 6.762 \times 10^4 \text{ eV}/c$$

in the direction given by

$$\theta = \tan^{-1} \frac{p_{ey}}{p_{ex}} = \tan^{-1}(-0.9108) = -42.3°$$

27.  $K_e$ is largest when $E'$ is smallest (since $K_e = E - E'$) or when $1/E'$ is largest, which occurs when $\cos \theta = -1$ ($\theta = 180°$).

$$\frac{1}{E'} = \frac{1}{E} + \frac{2}{m_e c^2}$$

$$E' = \frac{E m_e c^2}{2E + m_e c^2}$$

$$K_e = E - \frac{E m_e c^2}{2E + m_e c^2} = \frac{2E^2}{2E + m_e c^2}$$

28.  When $\theta \cong 180°$, $\cos \theta \cong -1$ and

$$\frac{1}{E'} \cong \frac{1}{E} + \frac{2}{m_e c^2}$$

$$E' \cong \frac{E m_e c^2}{2E + m_e c^2} \cong \frac{m_e c^2}{2} = 0.25 \text{ MeV} \quad \text{when} \quad E \gg m_e c^2$$

29.    (a)    $\dfrac{1}{E'} = \dfrac{1}{E} + \dfrac{1}{m_e c^2}(1 - \cos\theta)$

$$= \dfrac{1}{0.662 \text{ MeV}} + \dfrac{1}{0.511 \text{ MeV}}(1 - \cos 60°) = 2.489 \text{ MeV}^{-1}$$

$E' = 0.402 \text{ MeV}$

(b)    $K_e = E - E' = 0.662 \text{ MeV} - 0.402 \text{ MeV} = 0.260 \text{ MeV}$

30.    Suppose the electron moves with velocity $v$ in the $x$ direction, and let the photon be emitted at an angle $\theta$ with momentum $p$ and energy $E$. After emission, the electron moves with velocity $v'$ at an angle $\phi$. Then conservation of momentum gives

$$\dfrac{m_e v}{\sqrt{1 - v^2/c^2}} = \dfrac{m_e v' \cos\phi}{\sqrt{1 - v'^2/c^2}} + p\cos\theta$$

and

$$0 = \dfrac{m_e v' \sin\phi}{\sqrt{1 - v'^2/c^2}} - p\sin\theta$$

Squaring and adding these two equations, we obtain,

$$\dfrac{m_e^2 v^2}{1 - v^2/c^2} = \dfrac{m_e^2 v'^2}{1 - v'^2/c^2} + p^2 - \dfrac{2m_e v' p}{\sqrt{1 - v'^2/c^2}}\cos(\theta + \phi)$$

Conservation of energy gives $E_e = E_e' + pc$, or

$$\dfrac{m_e c^2}{\sqrt{1 - v^2/c^2}} = \dfrac{m_e c^2}{\sqrt{1 - v'^2/c^2}} + pc$$

$$\frac{m_e^2 c^2}{1 - v^2/c^2} = \frac{m_e^2 c^2}{1 - v'^2/c^2} + p^2 + \frac{2p m_e c}{\sqrt{1 - v'^2/c^2}}$$

Subtracting the momentum conservation equation from this one, we find

$$\frac{m_e^2(c^2 - v^2)}{1 - v^2/c^2} = \frac{m_e^2(c^2 - v'^2)}{1 - v'^2/c^2} + \frac{2m_e p}{\sqrt{1 - v'^2/c^2}}\left[c + v'\cos(\theta + \phi)\right]$$

$$0 = \frac{2m_e p}{\sqrt{1 - v'^2/c^2}}\left[c + v'\cos(\theta + \phi)\right]$$

The last factor in this expression can never be zero, and so this can be true only if $p = 0$ -- no photon at all is emitted! We can analyze this problem more easily if we switch to a frame of reference in which the electron is at rest, so that its total energy is $m_e c^2$. After the emission, the total energy will be $m_e c^2 + K_e + E$, but since $K_e$ and $E$ can never be negative, energy is conserved only if $K_e = E = 0$. Again, no photon is emitted.

31. The recoil energy will certainly be smaller than 6.4 keV and thus far smaller than the atom's rest energy (about 50,000 MeV). We are therefore safe in using nonrelativistic expressions for the momentum and kinetic energy of the atom. The momentum of the photon is

$$p = \frac{E}{c} = \frac{6.4 \text{ keV}}{c} = 6.4 \times 10^3 \text{ eV}/c$$

Conservation of momentum requires that the recoil momentum of the atom must be equal to the momentum of the photon (since the atom was initially at rest). Assuming the mass of the iron atom to be 56 u,

$$K = \frac{p^2}{2m} = \frac{p^2 c^2}{2mc^2} = \frac{(6.4 \times 10^3 \text{ eV})^2}{2(56 \text{ u})(931.5 \text{ MeV/u})} = 3.9 \times 10^{-4} \text{ eV}$$

32.     From Equation 3.48,

$$\lambda_{min} = \frac{hc}{K} = \frac{1240 \text{ eV·nm}}{2.50 \times 10^4 \text{ eV}} = 0.0496 \text{ nm}$$

33.     Let $p_e$ and $E_e$ be the momentum and energy of each electron after the encounter.  Then momentum conservation gives

$$\frac{E}{c} = 3p_e$$

and energy conservation gives

$$E + m_e c^2 = 3E_e = 3\sqrt{(p_e c)^2 + (m_e c^2)^2}$$

Squaring this expression, we obtain

$$E^2 + 2Em_e c^2 + m_e^2 c^4 = 9(p_e c)^2 + 9(m_e^2 c^4)$$

Combining this with the momentum conservation result gives

$$2Em_e c^2 + m_e^2 c^4 = 9(m_e^2 c^4) \qquad \text{or} \qquad E = 4m_e c^2$$

The initial energy is therefore $E + m_e c^2 = 5m_e c^2$.  The final energy is $3(m_e c^2 + K_e)$.  Equating the initial and final energies, we obtain

$$5m_e c^2 = 3(m_e c^2 + K_e)$$

$$K_e = \tfrac{2}{3} m_e c^2$$

# Chapter 4

1.    (a)    $K = \dfrac{p^2}{2m} = \dfrac{3}{2}kT$

$$p = \sqrt{3mkT} = \frac{1}{c}\sqrt{3mc^2kT}$$

$$= \frac{1}{c}\sqrt{3(28 \text{ u})(931.5 \text{ MeV/u})(8.6174 \times 10^{-5} \text{ eV/K})(293 \text{ K})}$$

$$= 4.45 \times 10^4 \text{ eV}/c$$

$$\lambda = \frac{h}{p} = \frac{hc}{pc} = \frac{1240 \text{ eV·nm}}{4.45 \times 10^4 \text{ eV}} = 0.0279 \text{ nm}$$

   (b)    At 5 MeV, $K \ll mc^2$, so we use nonrelativistic kinetic energy.

$$p = \sqrt{2mK} = \frac{1}{c}\sqrt{2mc^2K}$$

$$= \frac{1}{c}\sqrt{2(938.3 \text{ MeV})(5 \text{ MeV})} = 96.9 \text{ MeV}/c$$

$$\lambda = \frac{hc}{pc} = \frac{1240 \text{ MeV·fm}}{96.9 \text{ MeV}} = 13 \text{ fm}$$

   (c)    Since $K \gg mc^2$, the extreme relativistic approximation, $E = pc$, is appropriate.

$$\lambda = \frac{hc}{pc} = \frac{hc}{E} = \frac{1240 \text{ MeV·fm}}{50 \times 10^3 \text{ MeV}} = 0.025 \text{ fm}$$

   (d)    The speed is small compared with $c$, so nonrelativistic formulas will be applicable.

$$\lambda = \frac{h}{p} = \frac{h}{mv} = \frac{6.63 \times 10^{-34} \text{ J·s}}{(9.11 \times 10^{-31} \text{ kg})(1.0 \times 10^6 \text{ m/s})} = 0.73 \text{ nm}$$

2.    (a)    $K = \frac{3}{2}kT = \frac{3}{2}(8.6174 \times 10^{-5}\ \text{eV/K})(293\ \text{K}) = 0.0379\ \text{eV}$

      (b)    $K \ll mc^2$, so

$$p = \sqrt{2mK} = \frac{1}{c}\sqrt{2mc^2K}$$

$$p = \frac{1}{c}\sqrt{2(939.6 \times 10^6\ \text{eV})(0.0379\ \text{eV})} = 8.44 \times 10^3\ \text{eV/}c$$

$$\lambda = \frac{hc}{pc} = \frac{1240\ \text{eV·nm}}{8.44 \times 10^3\ \text{eV}} = 0.15\ \text{nm}$$

3.    For $\lambda = 12$ nm,

$$p = \frac{h}{\lambda} = \frac{1}{c}\frac{hc}{\lambda} = \frac{1}{c}\frac{1240\ \text{eV·nm}}{12\ \text{nm}} = 100\ \text{eV/}c$$

Since $cp \ll mc^2$,

$$K = \frac{p^2}{2m} = \frac{p^2c^2}{2mc^2} = \frac{(100\ \text{eV})^2}{2(0.511\ \text{MeV})} = 0.010\ \text{eV}$$

$$V = 0.010\ \text{volts}$$

For $\lambda = 0.12$ nm,

$$p = \frac{1}{c}\frac{hc}{\lambda} = \frac{1}{c}\frac{1240\ \text{eV·nm}}{0.12\ \text{nm}} = 1.0 \times 10^4\ \text{eV/}c$$

$$K = \frac{p^2c^2}{2mc^2} = \frac{(1.0 \times 10^4\ \text{eV})^2}{2(0.511\ \text{MeV})} = 100\ \text{eV}$$

$$V = 100\ \text{volts}$$

For $\lambda = 1.2$ fm,

$$p = \frac{1}{c}\frac{hc}{\lambda} = \frac{1}{c}\frac{1240 \text{ MeV·fm}}{1.2 \text{ fm}} = 1000 \text{ MeV}/c$$

Here $cp \gg mc^2$, so we use the extreme relativistic approximation:

$$E \cong pc = 1.0 \times 10^9 \text{ eV} = 1.0 \text{ GeV}$$

$$V = 1.0 \times 10^9 \text{ volts}$$

(Although it is possible to accelerate electrons to such high energies, it is not done by a single acceleration through a large potential difference.)

4.   (a)   The wavelength should be roughly the size of (or smaller than) the object we want to study; thus

$$\lambda \le 0.10 \text{ μm}$$

(b)   Corresponding to $\lambda \le 0.10$ μm,

$$p = \frac{1}{c}\frac{hc}{\lambda} = \frac{1}{c}\frac{1240 \text{ eV·nm}}{100 \text{ nm}} = 12.4 \text{ eV}/c$$

$$K = \frac{p^2}{2m} = \frac{p^2c^2}{2mc^2} = \frac{(12.4 \text{ eV})^2}{2(0.511 \times 10^6 \text{ eV})} = 1.5 \times 10^{-4} \text{ eV}$$

$$V = 1.5 \times 10^{-4} \text{ volts}$$

This is a lower limit on the accelerating voltage. If $V$ is smaller than this value, the wavelength is too large and details of the particles could not be seen because of diffraction effects. As $V$ is increased above this value, finer details would be observed.

5.    (a)    $p = \dfrac{1}{c}\dfrac{hc}{\lambda} = \dfrac{1}{c}\dfrac{1240 \text{ MeV·fm}}{14 \text{ fm}} = 88.6 \text{ MeV}/c$

For electrons, $cp \gg mc^2$, so we use the extreme relativistic approximation.

$E = pc = 88.6 \text{ MeV}$

$K = E - mc^2 = 88.6 \text{ MeV} - 0.5 \text{ MeV} = 88 \text{ MeV}$

(b)    For neutrons, $cp \ll mc^2$, so

$$K = \frac{p^2}{2m} = \frac{p^2c^2}{2mc^2} = \frac{(88.6 \text{ MeV})^2}{2(939.6 \text{ MeV})} = 4.2 \text{ MeV}$$

(c)    $K = \dfrac{p^2c^2}{2mc^2} = \dfrac{(88.6 \text{ MeV})^2}{2(3727.4 \text{ MeV})} = 1.1 \text{ MeV}$

6.    (a)

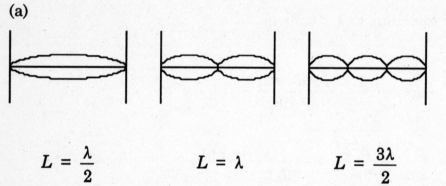

$L = \dfrac{\lambda}{2}$              $L = \lambda$              $L = \dfrac{3\lambda}{2}$

In each case there is an integral number of half-wavelengths between the walls:

$L = n\dfrac{\lambda}{2}$          $n = 1, 2, 3, \cdots$

$\lambda_n = \dfrac{2L}{n}$

(b) $\quad p_n = \dfrac{h}{\lambda_n} = n\dfrac{h}{2L}$

Here $cp$ is of the order of keV, so nonrelativistic kinetic energy is applicable.

$$K_n = \frac{p^2c^2}{2mc^2} = \frac{n^2h^2c^2}{2mc^2L^2}$$

$$K_n = n^2\frac{(1240 \text{ eV·nm})^2}{2(0.511 \times 10^6 \text{ eV})(0.50 \text{ nm})^2} = n^2(1.50 \text{ eV})$$

$$K_1 = 1.50 \text{ eV}, \quad K_2 = 6.00 \text{ eV}, \quad K_3 = 13.5 \text{ eV}$$

7.　(a) $\quad p = \sqrt{2mK} = \dfrac{1}{c}\sqrt{2mc^2K}$

$$= \frac{1}{c}\sqrt{2(3727 \times 10^6 \text{ eV})(0.020 \text{ eV})} = 1.22 \times 10^4 \text{ eV}/c$$

$$\lambda = \frac{hc}{pc} = \frac{1240 \text{ eV·nm}}{1.22 \times 10^4 \text{ eV}} = 0.10 \text{ nm}$$

　　(b)　The fringes are separated by about 9 μm.

$$\lambda = \frac{d\Delta y}{D} = \frac{(8 \times 10^{-6} \text{ m})(9 \times 10^{-6} \text{ m})}{0.64 \text{ m}} = 0.11 \text{ nm}$$

8.　　$\quad p = 1.0 \text{ atm} = 1.0 \times 10^5 \text{ Pa}$

$\quad T = 20°\text{C} = 293 \text{ K}$

$\quad K = \dfrac{3}{2}kT = \dfrac{3}{2}(8.617 \times 10^{-5} \text{ eV/K})(293 \text{ K}) = 0.0379 \text{ eV}$

$$cp = \sqrt{2mc^2K} = \sqrt{2(3727 \times 10^6 \text{ eV})(0.0379 \text{ eV})} = 1.68 \times 10^4 \text{ eV}$$

$$\lambda = \frac{hc}{pc} = \frac{1240 \text{ eV·nm}}{1.68 \times 10^4 \text{ eV}} = 0.0738 \text{ nm}$$

$$\rho = \frac{nM}{V} = \frac{Mp}{RT} = \frac{(0.004 \text{ kg/mole})(1.01 \times 10^5 \text{ Pa})}{(8.31 \text{ J/mole·K})(293 \text{ K})}$$

$$= \left(0.164 \frac{\text{kg}}{\text{m}^3}\right) \frac{1 \text{ atom}}{6.64 \times 10^{-27} \text{ kg}} = 2.47 \times 10^{25} \frac{\text{atom}}{\text{m}^3}$$

The average spacing is of order $\rho^{-1/3} = 3.4$ nm, which is much greater than $\lambda$. To get a spacing of $\sim 0.074$ nm would require a pressure of

$$1 \text{ atm} \left(\frac{3.4 \text{ nm}}{0.074 \text{ nm}}\right)^3 = 10^5 \text{ atm}$$

To get a de Broglie wavelength of 3.4 nm would require a temperature of

$$(293 \text{ K}) \left(\frac{0.074 \text{ nm}}{3.4 \text{ nm}}\right)^2 = 0.14 \text{ K}$$

9.    For $m = 10^{-9}$ g and taking the density to be 2 g/cm$^3$, the volume of a particle is

$$V = \frac{10^{-9} \text{ g}}{2 \text{ g/cm}^3} = 5 \times 10^{-10} \text{ cm}^3$$

which corresponds to a diameter of about 0.001 cm = $10^{-5}$ m.

$$\Delta y = \frac{\lambda D}{d} = \frac{(6.6 \times 10^{-20} \text{ m})(5 \times 10^6 \text{ m})}{10^{-5} \text{ m}}$$

$$= 3.3 \times 10^{-8} \text{ m} = 33 \text{ nm (about the size of an atom!)}$$

10.
$$\lambda = \frac{d\sin\phi}{2} = \frac{(0.215 \text{ nm})(\sin 55°)}{2} = 0.0881 \text{ nm}$$

$$cp = \frac{hc}{\lambda} = \frac{1240 \text{ eV·nm}}{0.0881 \text{ nm}} = 1.408 \times 10^4 \text{ eV}$$

$$K = \frac{(pc)^2}{2mc^2} = \frac{(1.408 \times 10^4 \text{ eV})^2}{2(0.511 \times 10^6 \text{ eV})} = 194 \text{ eV}$$

$$V = 194 \text{ volts}$$

11.
$$p = \frac{1}{c}\sqrt{2mc^2K} = \frac{1}{c}\sqrt{2(0.511 \times 10^6 \text{ eV})(175 \text{ eV})} = 1.337 \times 10^4 \text{ eV}/c$$

$$\lambda = \frac{hc}{pc} = \frac{1240 \text{ eV·nm}}{1.337 \times 10^4 \text{ eV}} = 0.0927 \text{ nm}$$

For $n = 1$: $\quad \phi = \sin^{-1}\dfrac{\lambda}{d} = \sin^{-1}\dfrac{0.0927 \text{ nm}}{0.352 \text{ nm}} = 15°$

For $n = 2$: $\quad \phi = \sin^{-1}\dfrac{2\lambda}{d} = 32°$

For $n = 3$: $\quad \phi = \sin^{-1}\dfrac{3\lambda}{d} = 52°$

There is no diffracted beam for $n = 4$.

12. $\quad K = 0.0105 \text{ eV}$

$$\lambda = \frac{h}{\sqrt{2mK}} = \frac{hc}{\sqrt{2mc^2K}}$$

$$= \frac{1240 \text{ eV·nm}}{\sqrt{2(940 \times 10^6 \text{ eV})(0.0105 \text{ eV})}} = 0.279 \text{ nm}$$

$$\sin \theta = \frac{m\lambda}{2d} = \frac{0.279 \text{ nm}}{2(0.247 \text{ nm})} \qquad \text{or} \qquad \theta = 34.4°$$

Other energies present at this location might be the second-order diffraction:

$$\lambda = \frac{2d \sin \theta}{m} = \frac{2(0.247 \text{ nm})(\sin 34.4°)}{2} = 0.140 \text{ nm}$$

The wavelength is reduced by half, so the kinetic energy is increased by $\sqrt{2}$:

$$\sqrt{2}K = 0.0148 \text{ eV}$$

Also present is the third-order diffraction of a wave with 1/3 the original wavelength, which has an energy of

$$\sqrt{3}K = 0.0182 \text{ eV}$$

The other energies that appear at this angle are $\sqrt{m}K$, where $m = 2, 3, 4, ...$

13.  The number of wave crests passing the observation point in time $\Delta t$ is $N = \nu \, \Delta t$. The uncertainty in this number is

$$\Delta N = \Delta \nu \, \Delta t$$

Since $\nu = v/\lambda$,

$$d\nu = -\frac{v}{\lambda^2} d\lambda \qquad \text{or} \qquad \Delta \nu = \frac{v}{\lambda^2} \Delta \lambda$$

And using $\Delta t = \Delta x/v$ ($\Delta x$ is the distance traveled by the wave in the time $\Delta t$),

$$\Delta N = \left( \frac{v}{\lambda^2} \Delta \lambda \right) \left( \frac{\Delta x}{v} \right) = \frac{\Delta x \Delta \lambda}{\lambda^2}$$

If the uncertainty in counting is of order one ($\Delta N \sim 1$), then these results are consistent with $\Delta x \, \Delta \lambda \sim \lambda^2$ and $\Delta \omega \, \Delta t \sim 1$.

14.        $\Delta v = 2.0 \times 10^4$ m/s

$$\Delta x \sim \frac{\hbar}{\Delta p} = \frac{\hbar}{m \, \Delta v} = \frac{1.05 \times 10^{-34} \text{ J·s}}{(9.11 \times 10^{-31} \text{ kg})(2.0 \times 10^4 \text{ m/s})} = 5.8 \text{ nm}$$

15.    (a)    $$\Delta p \sim \frac{\hbar}{\Delta x} = \frac{h}{2\pi \, \Delta x} = \frac{1}{c} \frac{hc}{2\pi \, \Delta x} = \frac{1}{c} \frac{1240 \text{ eV·nm}}{2\pi (0.1 \text{ nm})} = 2000 \text{ eV}/c$$

(b)    $$K = \frac{(\Delta p)^2}{2m} = \frac{(c \, \Delta p)^2}{2mc^2} = \frac{(2000 \text{ eV})^2}{2(0.511 \times 10^6 \text{ eV})} = 4 \text{ eV}$$

16.        $$\Delta E \sim \frac{\hbar}{\Delta t} = \frac{6.58 \times 10^{-16} \text{ eV·s}}{2.0 \times 10^{-23} \text{ s}} = 33 \text{ MeV}$$

Measurements of the $\Sigma^+$ rest energy are likely to fall in the range 1385 MeV ± 33 MeV, or from 1352 MeV to 1418 MeV.

17.        $$\Delta t \sim \frac{\hbar}{\Delta E} = \frac{6.58 \times 10^{-16} \text{ eV·s}}{120 \times 10^6 \text{ eV}} = 5.5 \times 10^{-24} \text{ s}$$

18.    (a)    $$\Delta E \sim \frac{\hbar}{\Delta t} = \frac{6.58 \times 10^{-16} \text{ eV·s}}{1.2 \times 10^{-9} \text{ s}} = 5.5 \times 10^{-7} \text{ eV}$$

19.  Since the initial nucleus is at rest, the momenta of the final products must be equal (and opposite):

$$p_n = p_{He}$$

The total kinetic energy is equal to the energy liberated in the break-up.

$$K_n + K_{He} = 0.89 \text{ MeV}$$

We use nonrelativistic kinetic energies, so

$$\frac{p_n^2}{2m_n} + \frac{p_{He}^2}{2m_{He}} = \frac{p_n^2}{2m_n} + \frac{p_n^2}{2m_{He}} = \frac{p_n^2}{2m_n}\left(1 + \frac{m_n}{m_{He}}\right) = 0.89 \text{ MeV}$$

$$K_n = \frac{0.89 \text{ MeV}}{1 + \dfrac{m_n}{m_{He}}} = \frac{0.89 \text{ MeV}}{1 + \dfrac{1}{4}} = 0.71 \text{ MeV}$$

(b)     $$\Delta E \sim \frac{\hbar}{\Delta t} = \frac{6.58 \times 10^{-16} \text{ eV·s}}{1.0 \times 10^{-21} \text{ s}} = 0.66 \text{ MeV}$$

We are likely to observe neutrons in the energy range 0.71 MeV ± 0.66 MeV; thus the neutron energy is not at all well-defined in this experiment.

20.  For an alpha particle of momentum 19.7 MeV/*c*, the kinetic energy is

$$K = \frac{p^2}{2m} = \frac{p^2c^2}{2mc^2} = \frac{(19.7 \text{ MeV})^2}{2(3727 \text{ MeV})} = 0.052 \text{ MeV}$$

This is negligible compared with typical energies of alpha particles emitted in radioactive decays. Therefore, the uncertainty principle does not limit the existence inside the nucleus of alpha particles of the kind normally observed in nuclear decays.

21.    (a)     $\Delta p_x \sim \dfrac{\hbar}{\Delta x} = \dfrac{1}{c}\dfrac{hc}{2\pi\,\Delta x} = \dfrac{1}{c}\dfrac{1240\ \text{eV·nm}}{2\pi(1\ \text{cm})} = 2 \times 10^{-5}\ \text{eV}/c$

     (b)     $\Delta p = \sqrt{(\Delta p_x)^2 + (\Delta p_y)^2 + (\Delta p_z)^2} = \sqrt{3}\,\Delta p_x$

since all components of the momentum have the same uncertainty.

$$K = \frac{(\Delta p)^2}{2m} = \frac{(c\,\Delta p)^2}{2mc^2} = \frac{3(2 \times 10^{-5}\ \text{eV})^2}{2(0.511 \times 10^6\ \text{eV})} = 1.2 \times 10^{-15}\ \text{eV}$$

     (c)     The 1 cm³ piece of copper has a mass of (1 cm³)(8.95 g/cm³) = 8.95 g. Copper has a molar mass of 63.5 g, so the piece is 8.95 g/(63.5 g/mole) = 0.141 mole. Let us suppose we heat the copper from $T = 0$ K to $T = 300$ K (room temperature) and that its heat capacity remains constant in the process. (This is in fact not correct, since the heat capacity falls to zero as $T \to 0$, but it should be good enough for an order-of-magnitude estimate.) We would then estimate the internal energy $U$ as

$$U \sim \mu C\,\Delta T = (0.141\ \text{mole})(24.5\ \frac{\text{J}}{\text{mole·K}})(300\ \text{K}) \sim 1000\ \text{J}$$

Assuming one free electron per atom, the total energy of the electrons is

$$(0.141\ \text{mole})(6.02 \times 10^{23}\ \frac{\text{atoms}}{\text{mole}})(1\ \frac{\text{electron}}{\text{atom}})(1.2 \times 10^{-15}\ \frac{\text{eV}}{\text{electron}})$$

$$= 1.0 \times 10^8\ \text{eV} = 1.6 \times 10^{-11}\ \text{J}$$

This rough estimate suggests that, to within 14 orders of magnitude, the thermal energy of a room-temperature solid is not affected by the motion of the electrons.

22.    (a)     $\Delta E = m_\pi c^2 = 135\ \text{MeV}$

     (b)     $\Delta t \sim \dfrac{\hbar}{\Delta E} = \dfrac{6.58 \times 10^{-16}\ \text{eV·s}}{135 \times 10^6\ \text{eV}} = 4.87 \times 10^{-24}\ \text{s}$

     (c)     $\Delta x = c\,\Delta t = (3.00 \times 10^8\ \text{m/s})(4.87 \times 10^{-24}\ \text{s}) = 1.46\ \text{fm}$

23.    (a)        $\Delta p_x \sim \dfrac{\hbar}{\Delta x} = \dfrac{1}{c} \dfrac{hc}{2\pi \Delta x} = \dfrac{1}{c} \dfrac{1240 \text{ eV·nm}}{2\pi (0.20 \text{ nm})} = 990 \text{ eV}/c$

(b)     As in Problem 21 we estimate $p \sim \Delta p \sim \sqrt{3}\,\Delta p_x$.

$$K = \frac{p^2}{2m} = \frac{c^2 p^2}{2mc^2} = \frac{3(990 \text{ eV})^2}{2(65 \text{ u})(931.5 \text{ MeV/u})} = 2.4 \times 10^{-5} \text{ eV}$$

(c)     As in Problem 21 consider a 1 cm³ piece of copper (0.141 mole).  The motion of the atoms would correspond to an energy of

$$(0.141 \text{ mole})(6.02 \times 10^{23} \frac{\text{atoms}}{\text{mole}})(2.4 \times 10^{-5} \frac{\text{eV}}{\text{atom}})$$

$$= 2.04 \times 10^{18} \text{ eV} = 0.33 \text{ J}$$

This energy is small compared with the internal energy of order 1000 J, but it is not quite so negligibly small as the energy of the electronic motion.  This energy of 0.33 J is independent of temperature, and would therefore become relatively more significant as the temperature is reduced so that the internal energy is reduced.  This is one example of the phenomenon of "zero-point energy," a certain minimum energy that a confined quantum system must have.  There is no counterpart to this zero-point energy in classical physics.

24.    When the beam passes through a hole of width $\Delta x = d$, there is a resulting uncertainty in the transverse momentum of order

$$\Delta p_x \sim \frac{\hbar}{d}$$

and in the corresponding transverse velocity

$$\Delta v_x \sim \frac{\hbar}{md}$$

The diameter of the beam grows larger than its original diameter by an amount $\Delta d = t\,\Delta v_x$, where $t$ is the time the beam has been traveling. If the oven temperature is $T$, the particle leaves the hole with kinetic energy $K$, where

$$K = \tfrac{1}{2}mv^2 = \tfrac{3}{2}kT$$

$$v = \sqrt{\frac{3kT}{m}}$$

The beam travels the distance $L$ at speed $v$ in a time $t = L/v$, so

$$\Delta d = t\,\Delta v_x \sim \frac{L}{v}\frac{\hbar}{md} = \frac{L\hbar}{md\sqrt{3kT/m}} = \frac{L\hbar}{d\sqrt{3mkT}}$$

$$\Delta d = \frac{(2\ \text{m})(1.05 \times 10^{-34}\ \text{J·s})}{(0.003\ \text{m})\sqrt{3(7\ \text{u})(1.66 \times 10^{-27}\ \text{kg/u})(1.38 \times 10^{-23}\ \text{J/K})(1500\ \text{K})}}$$

$$= 3 \times 10^{-9}\ \text{m}$$

Thus the spreading is for most cases a negligibly small effect.

25. 
$$y(x) = A\cos k_1 x + A\cos k_2 x = A(\cos k_1 x + \cos k_2 x)$$

Using the identity

$$\cos x + \cos y = 2\cos\frac{(x + y)}{2}\cos\frac{(x - y)}{2}$$

we get directly

$$y(x) = 2A\cos\frac{(k_1 + k_2)x}{2}\cos\frac{(k_1 - k_2)x}{2}$$

26.    (a)    $\Delta x = v \Delta t = (330 \text{ m/s})(2.0 \text{ s}) = 660 \text{ m}$

       (b)    $\lambda = \dfrac{v}{\nu} = \dfrac{330 \text{ m/s}}{1.0 \times 10^3 \text{ Hz}} = 0.33 \text{ m}$

       (c)    $\Delta \lambda \sim \dfrac{\lambda^2}{2\pi \Delta x} = \dfrac{(0.33 \text{ m})^2}{4150 \text{ m}} = 0.026 \text{ mm}$

       (d)    $\Delta \omega \sim \dfrac{1}{\Delta t}$

              $\Delta \nu \sim \dfrac{1}{2\pi \Delta t} = \dfrac{1}{2\pi (2.0 \text{ s})} = 0.080 \text{ Hz}$

27.    (a)    $\Delta x = v \Delta t = (25 \text{ cm/s})(4.0 \text{ s}) = 1.0 \times 10^2 \text{ cm}$

       (b)    $\lambda = \dfrac{1.0 \times 10^2 \text{ cm}}{12} = 8.3 \text{ cm}$

              $\Delta \lambda \sim \dfrac{\lambda^2}{2\pi \Delta x} = \dfrac{(8.3 \text{ cm})^2}{6.3 \times 10^2 \text{ cm}} = 0.11 \text{ cm}$

28.           $\omega_1 = 2\pi \nu_1 = 2\pi \dfrac{v_1}{\lambda_1} = 2\pi \dfrac{3}{1} = 6\pi$

              $\omega_2 = 2\pi \nu_2 = 2\pi \dfrac{v_2}{\lambda_2} = 2\pi \dfrac{2.5}{10/9} = 4.5\pi$

              $k_1 = \dfrac{2\pi}{\lambda_1} = \dfrac{2\pi}{1} = 2\pi$

              $k_2 = \dfrac{2\pi}{\lambda_2} = \dfrac{2\pi}{10/9} = 1.8\pi$

              $v_{\text{group}} = \dfrac{\Delta \omega}{\Delta k} = \dfrac{\omega_1 - \omega_2}{k_1 - k_2} = \dfrac{6\pi - 4.5\pi}{2\pi - 1.8\pi} = 7.5$

29.   (a)   $y(x) = \int A(k)\cos kx \, dk = A \int_{k_0-\Delta k/2}^{k_0+\Delta k/2} \cos kx \, dk = A \left. \frac{\sin kx}{x} \right|_{k_0-\Delta k/2}^{k_0+\Delta k/2}$

$$= \frac{A}{x}\left[\sin x(k_0 + \frac{\Delta k}{2}) - \sin x(k_0 - \frac{\Delta k}{2})\right]$$

$$= \frac{A}{x}\left[\sin k_0 x \cos\frac{x\Delta k}{2} + \cos k_0 x \sin\frac{x\Delta k}{2}\right.$$

$$\left. - (\sin k_0 x \cos\frac{x\Delta k}{2} - \cos k_0 x \sin\frac{x\Delta k}{2})\right]$$

$$y(x) = \frac{2A}{x}\cos k_0 x \sin\frac{x\Delta k}{2}$$

We arbitrarily define the width $\Delta x$ of the wave packet to be the distance between the points where the envelope $\sin x\Delta k/2$ vanishes; that is, where $x\Delta k/2 = \pm\pi$.

$$\Delta x = \frac{2\pi}{\Delta k} - (-\frac{2\pi}{\Delta k}) = \frac{4\pi}{\Delta k} \qquad \text{or} \qquad \Delta x\Delta k = 4\pi$$

30.   $y(x) = \int_{-\infty}^{\infty} A(k)\cos kx \, dk = \int_{-\infty}^{\infty} e^{-(k-k_0)^2/2(\Delta k)^2}\cos kx \, dk$

Let $k' = k - k_0$.

$$y(x) = \int_{-\infty}^{\infty} e^{-k'^2/2(\Delta k)^2}[\cos k'x \cos k_0 x - \sin k'x \sin k_0 x] \, dk'$$

The second integral vanishes because $\sin k'x$ is an odd function of $k'$ (the contribution of the integral from $-\infty$ to 0 cancels the part from 0 to $+\infty$).

$$y(x) = 2\int\limits_0^\infty e^{-k'^2/2(\Delta k)^2} \cos k'x \, \cos k_0 x \, dk'$$

The integral is a standard form found in integral tables.

$$y(x) = 2\cos k_0 x \, \sqrt{\pi} \, \frac{e^{-x^2(\Delta k)^2/2}}{2\dfrac{1}{\sqrt{2}\Delta k}} = \sqrt{2\pi}\,\Delta k \, \cos k_0 x \, e^{-x^2(\Delta k)^2/2}$$

31.    (a)    $v_{\text{phase}} = \dfrac{\omega}{k}$

$$v_{\text{group}} = \frac{d\omega}{dk} = \frac{d}{dk}(kv_{\text{phase}}) = v_{\text{phase}} + k\frac{dv_{\text{phase}}}{dk}$$

$$\frac{dv_{\text{phase}}}{dk} = \frac{dv_{\text{phase}}}{d\lambda}\frac{d\lambda}{dk} = \frac{dv_{\text{phase}}}{d\lambda}\left(-\frac{2\pi}{k^2}\right) = \left(-\frac{\lambda}{k}\right)\frac{dv_{\text{phase}}}{d\lambda}$$

$$v_{\text{group}} = v_{\text{phase}} - \lambda\frac{dv_{\text{phase}}}{d\lambda}$$

(b)    The index of refraction of light in glass decreases as $\lambda$ increases (shorter wavelengths are refracted more than longer wavelengths). Since $n = c/v_{\text{phase}}$, $dn/d\lambda$ and $dv_{\text{phase}}/d\lambda$ have opposite signs, so that $dv_{\text{phase}}/d\lambda > 0$, since $dn/d\lambda < 0$. Thus $v_{\text{group}} > v_{\text{phase}}$.

32.
$$v_{\text{phase}} = \sqrt{\frac{b}{\lambda}} = \sqrt{\frac{bk}{2\pi}} = \frac{\omega}{k}$$

$$\omega = \sqrt{\frac{b}{2\pi}} k^{3/2}$$

$$v_{\text{group}} = \frac{d\omega}{dk} = \sqrt{\frac{b}{2\pi}} \frac{3}{2} k^{1/2} = \frac{3}{2}\sqrt{\frac{bk}{2\pi}} = \frac{3}{2} v_{\text{phase}}$$

33.
$$K = \sqrt{p^2 c^2 + m^2 c^4} - mc^2 = E - mc^2$$

$$\frac{dK}{dp} = \frac{dE}{dp} = \frac{1}{2}(p^2 c^2 + m^2 c^4)^{-1/2} \, 2pc^2 = \frac{pc^2}{E}$$

For a relativistic particle

$$\frac{p}{E} = \frac{mv \big/ \sqrt{1 - v^2/c^2}}{mc^2 \big/ \sqrt{1 - v^2/c^2}} = \frac{v}{c^2}$$

$$\frac{dE}{dp} = \frac{v}{c^2} c^2 = v$$

# Chapter 5

1.

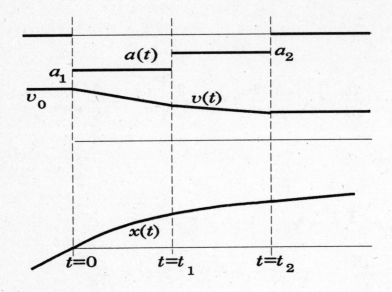

2.

$$y_1 = -A \, \cos\left(\frac{2\pi x}{\lambda} + \frac{\pi}{6}\right) \qquad x < 0$$

$$y_2 = A' \, \cos\left(\frac{2\pi x}{\lambda'} + \phi\right) \qquad x > 0$$

or

$$y_2 = A' \, \cos\left(\frac{4\pi x}{\lambda} + \phi\right) \qquad \text{with} \quad \lambda' = \frac{\lambda}{2}$$

at $x = 0 \quad y_1 = y_2 \qquad$ so $\qquad -A \, \cos\frac{\pi}{6} = A' \, \cos\phi$

at $x = 0 \qquad \dfrac{dy_1}{dx} = \dfrac{dy_2}{dx} \qquad$ so $\qquad A \, \dfrac{2\pi}{\lambda} \, \sin\dfrac{\pi}{6} = -A' \dfrac{4\pi}{\lambda} \, \sin\phi$

Dividing the second of these equations by the first, we obtain

$$\tan\frac{\pi}{6} = 2 \, \tan\phi \qquad \text{or} \qquad \phi = \tan^{-1}\left(\frac{1}{2}\tan\frac{\pi}{6}\right) = 16.1°$$

$$A' = -A \, \frac{\cos \pi/6}{\cos\phi} = -0.901A$$

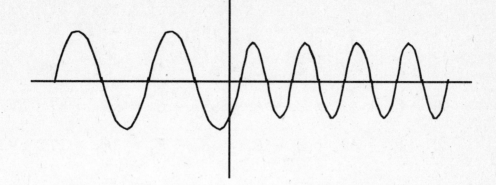

3.  $$E_1 = 4.4 \text{ eV} = \frac{\hbar^2 \pi^2}{2mL^2}$$

With $L' = 2L$,

$$E_1' = \frac{\hbar^2 \pi^2}{2mL'^2} = \frac{\hbar^2 \pi^2}{2m(4L^2)} = \frac{1}{4} \frac{\hbar^2 \pi^2}{2mL^2} = 1.1 \text{ eV}$$

4.  $$E_n = n^2 E_1 \qquad E_1 = 1.26 \text{ eV}$$

$$\Delta E_3 = E_3 - E_1 = 9E_1 - E_1 = 8E_1 = 8(1.26 \text{ eV}) = 10.1 \text{ eV}$$

$$\Delta E_4 = E_4 - E_1 = 16E_1 - E_1 = 15E_1 = 15(1.26 \text{ eV}) = 18.9 \text{ eV}$$

5.  (a)  $$E_1 = \frac{\hbar^2 \pi^2}{2mL^2} = \frac{h^2}{8mL^2} = \frac{(hc)^2}{8mc^2 L^2}$$

$$= \frac{(1240 \text{ eV·nm})^2}{8(0.511 \times 10^6 \text{ eV})(0.251 \text{ nm})^2} = 5.97 \text{ eV}$$

$4 \rightarrow 1$:  $\quad \Delta E = E_4 - E_1 = 16E_1 - E_1 = 15E_1 = 89.6 \text{ eV}$

(b)      $4 \rightarrow 3$:      $\Delta E = E_4 - E_3 = 16E_1 - 9E_1 = 7E_1 = 41.8$ eV

$4 \rightarrow 2$:      $\Delta E = E_4 - E_2 = 16E_1 - 4E_1 = 12E_1 = 71.6$ eV

$3 \rightarrow 2$:      $\Delta E = E_3 - E_2 = 9E_1 - 4E_1 = 5E_1 = 29.9$ eV

$3 \rightarrow 1$:      $\Delta E = E_3 - E_1 = 9E_1 - E_1 = 8E_1 = 47.8$ eV

$2 \rightarrow 1$:      $\Delta E = E_2 - E_1 = 4E_1 - E_1 = 3E_1 = 17.9$ eV

6.
$$\int_0^L A^2 \sin^2 \frac{n\pi x}{L} \, dx = A^2 \frac{L}{n\pi} \int_0^{n\pi} \sin^2 u \, du$$

with $u = n\pi x/L$. The integral is a standard form that is found in tables:

$$A^2 \frac{L}{n\pi} \int_0^{n\pi} \sin^2 u \, du = A^2 \frac{L}{n\pi} \left[ \frac{u}{2} - \frac{1}{4} \sin 2u \right]_0^{n\pi} = A^2 \frac{L}{2}$$

Setting the integral equal to 1 for normalization, we obtain

$$A^2 \frac{L}{2} = 1 \qquad \text{or} \qquad A = \sqrt{\frac{2}{L}}$$

7.
$$\psi_1 = \sqrt{\frac{2}{L}} \sin \frac{\pi x}{L}$$

(a)      $$P = \int_0^{L/3} \psi^2 \, dx = \int_0^{L/3} \frac{2}{L} \sin^2 \frac{\pi x}{L} \, dx = \frac{2}{L} \frac{L}{\pi} \int_0^{\pi/3} \sin^2 u \, du$$

$$= \frac{2}{\pi} \left[ \frac{u}{2} - \frac{1}{4} \sin 2u \right]_0^{\pi/3} = \frac{2}{\pi} \left( \frac{\pi}{6} - \frac{1}{4} \frac{\sqrt{3}}{2} \right) = 0.1955$$

(b) $\quad P = \int_{L/3}^{2L/3} \psi^2 \, dx = \frac{2}{\pi} \left[ \frac{1}{2} u - \frac{1}{4} \sin 2u \right]_{\pi/3}^{2\pi/3}$

$\quad\quad = \frac{2}{\pi} \left[ \frac{\pi}{3} - \frac{1}{4} \left( -\frac{\sqrt{3}}{2} \right) - \frac{\pi}{6} + \frac{1}{4} \frac{\sqrt{3}}{2} \right] = 0.6090$

(c) $\quad P = \frac{2}{\pi} \left[ \frac{1}{2} u - \frac{1}{4} \sin 2u \right]_{2\pi/3}^{\pi} = 0.1955$

8. $\quad P dx = \psi^2 dx = \frac{2}{L} \sin^2 \frac{3\pi x}{L} \, dx \quad\quad \text{with} \quad\quad \psi_1 = \sqrt{\frac{2}{L}} \sin \frac{3\pi x}{L}$

(a) $\quad P dx = \frac{2}{0.189 \text{ nm}} \sin^2 \frac{3\pi (0.188 \text{ nm})}{0.189 \text{ nm}} (10^{-3} \text{ nm}) = 2.63 \times 10^{-5}$

(b) $\quad P dx = \frac{2}{0.189 \text{ nm}} \sin^2 \frac{3\pi (0.031 \text{ nm})}{0.189 \text{ nm}} (10^{-3} \text{ nm}) = 0.0106$

(c) $\quad P dx = \frac{2}{0.189 \text{ nm}} \sin^2 \frac{3\pi (0.079 \text{ nm})}{0.189 \text{ nm}} (10^{-3} \text{ nm}) = 5.42 \times 10^{-3}$

For a classical particle, the probability is constant through the interval.

$\quad\quad P dx = \frac{1}{0.189 \text{ nm}} (10^{-3} \text{ nm}) = 5.29 \times 10^{-3}$

9.    (a)    $E = n^2 E_1 = 10^2 \dfrac{h^2}{8mL^2} = 10^2 \dfrac{(hc)^2}{8mc^2L^2}$

$$= 100 \frac{(1240 \ eV \cdot nm)^2}{8(0.511 \times 10^6 \ eV)(0.132 \ nm)^2} = 2160 \ eV$$

(b)    $\Delta p = \sqrt{p^2} = \sqrt{2mE} = \dfrac{1}{c}\sqrt{2mc^2E}$

$$= \frac{1}{c}\sqrt{2(0.511 \times 10^6 \ eV)(2160 \ eV)} = 4.70 \times 10^4 \ eV/c$$

(c)    $\Delta x = \dfrac{\hbar}{\Delta p} = \dfrac{1}{2\pi}\dfrac{hc}{c\Delta p} = \dfrac{1}{2\pi}\dfrac{(1240 \ eV \cdot nm)}{4.70 \times 10^4 \ eV} = 4.20 \times 10^{-3} \ nm$

10.    Take $L = 1.0 \times 10^{-14}$ m = 10 fm.  Then the wavelength in the ground state is $2L$ and the momentum is

$$p = \frac{1}{c}\frac{hc}{\lambda} = \frac{1}{c}\frac{1240 \ eV \cdot nm}{2.0 \times 10^{-14} \ m} = 62 \ MeV/c$$

Because $pc \gg mc^2$, it is incorrect to use Equation 5.25 to find the energy, since that equation was derived based on nonrelativistic kinematics.  In this case we can use the extreme relativistic approximation:

$$E \cong pc = 62 \ MeV$$

11.        Take $L = 1.0 \times 10^{-14}$ m = 10 fm.

$$E_0 = \frac{\hbar^2\pi^2}{2mL^2} = \frac{(hc)^2}{8mc^2L^2} = \frac{(1240 \ MeV \cdot fm)^2}{8(940 \ MeV)(10 \ fm)^2} = 2.0 \ MeV$$

Note that $E_0 \ll mc^2$, so that nonrelativistic formulas are valid, contrary to the result of Problem 10.

12.
$$(x^2)_{av} = \int_0^L \psi^2(x)\, x^2\, dx = \frac{2}{L} \int_0^L x^2 \sin^2 \frac{n\pi x}{L}\, dx$$

$$= \frac{2}{L} \left( \frac{L}{n\pi} \right)^3 \int_0^{n\pi} u^2 \sin^2 u\ du \qquad \text{with} \quad u = \frac{n\pi x}{L}$$

The integral is a standard form that is found in tables:

$$(x^2)_{av} = \frac{2}{L} \left( \frac{L}{n\pi} \right)^3 \left[ \frac{u^3}{6} - \left( \frac{u^2}{4} - \frac{1}{8} \right) \sin 2u - \frac{u \cos 2u}{4} \right]_0^{n\pi}$$

$$= \frac{2}{L} \left( \frac{L}{n\pi} \right)^3 \left[ \frac{(n\pi)^3}{6} - \frac{n\pi}{4} \right] = L^2 \left( \frac{1}{3} - \frac{1}{2n^2\pi^2} \right)$$

13. Using the result of Example 5.3, $x_{av} = L/2$, we find

$$\Delta x = \sqrt{(x^2)_{av} - (x_{av})^2} = \sqrt{L^2 \left( \frac{1}{3} - \frac{1}{2n^2\pi^2} \right) - \left( \frac{L}{2} \right)^2} = L \sqrt{\frac{1}{12} - \frac{1}{2n^2\pi^2}}$$

14. (a) Because the particle has no preferred direction of motion, it is found moving to the left as often as moving to the right, and thus we expect $p_{av} = 0$.

(b) Because the potential energy is zero inside the well, the kinetic energy is equal to the total energy. The total energy has a constant value, and thus

$$\frac{p^2}{2m} = K = E = \frac{\hbar^2\pi^2 n^2}{2mL^2}$$

Thus $p^2$ is a constant and always has the same value.

$$(p^2)_{av} = \frac{\hbar^2 \pi^2 n^2}{L^2}$$

(c)     $$\Delta p = \sqrt{(p^2)_{av} - (p_{av})^2} = \sqrt{\frac{\hbar^2 \pi^2 n^2}{L^2} - 0} = \frac{\hbar \pi n}{L}$$

$$\Delta x \Delta p = L \sqrt{\frac{1}{12} - \frac{1}{2n^2 \pi^2}} \left( \frac{\hbar \pi n}{L} \right) = \hbar \sqrt{\frac{n^2 \pi^2}{12} - \frac{1}{2}}$$

The product has its smallest value for $n = 1$, so

$$\Delta x \Delta p \geq \hbar \sqrt{\frac{\pi^2}{12} - \frac{1}{2}} = 0.57 \hbar$$

This is consistent with the uncertainty relationship, $\Delta x \, \Delta p \sim \hbar$.

15.     (a)     In region I, $E < U_0$ so the
                solution is given by
                Equation 5.54:

$$\psi_{I}(x) = A e^{kx} + B e^{-kx}$$

where

$$k = \sqrt{\frac{2m}{\hbar^2} (U_0 - E)}$$

In region II, $E > U_0$ and the solution is given by Equation 5.52:

$$\psi_{II}(x) = C \sin k_1 x + D \cos k_1 x \qquad \text{where} \qquad k_1 = \sqrt{\frac{2mE}{\hbar^2}}$$

In region III, $E < U_0$ again, so

$$\psi_{III}(x) = F e^{kx} + G e^{-kx}$$

(b) In region I, $x \to \infty$, so that $\psi_{\mathrm{I}}$ would become infinite because of the $e^{-kx}$ term. To prevent this we set $B = 0$. For the same reason, we set $F = 0$ in $\psi_{\mathrm{III}}$.

(c) In the infinite well $n$ gave the number of "bumps" in the probability density $\psi^2$ inside the well. Since the solutions for the finite well must gradually approach those for the infinite well for $U_0 \to \infty$, we guess at the same general property for the solutions to the finite well. The only difference is that, instead of having $\psi(x = 0)$ and $\psi(x = L)$ equal to 0 at the boundaries, the solutions within the well and beyond the well must match smoothly.

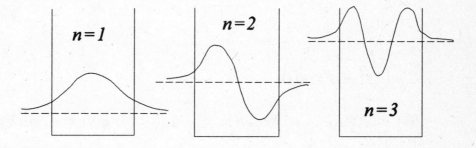

16.
$$E = E_0 (n_x^2 + n_y^2)$$

| $n_x$ | $n_y$ | $E$ | $n_x$ | $n_y$ | $E$ |
|---|---|---|---|---|---|
| 7 | 1 | $50E_0$ | 7 | 3 | $58E_0$ |
| 1 | 7 | $50E_0$ | 3 | 7 | $58E_0$ |
| 5 | 5 | $50E_0$ | 6 | 5 | $61E_0$ |
| 6 | 4 | $52E_0$ | 5 | 6 | $61E_0$ |
| 4 | 6 | $52E_0$ | 7 | 4 | $65E_0$ |
| 7 | 2 | $53E_0$ | 4 | 7 | $65E_0$ |
| 2 | 7 | $53E_0$ | 8 | 1 | $65E_0$ |
| | | | 1 | 8 | $65E_0$ |

The level at $E = 65E_0$ is 4-fold degenerate.

17.
$$E = E_0\left(n_x^2 + \frac{n_y^2}{4}\right)$$

| $n_x$ | $n_y$ | $E$ | $n_x$ | $n_y$ | $E$ |
|-------|-------|-----|-------|-------|-----|
| 1 | 1 | $1.25E_0$ | 2 | 3 | $6.25E_0$ |
| 1 | 2 | $2.00E_0$ | 1 | 5 | $7.25E_0$ |
| 2 | 1 | $2.25E_0$ | 2 | 4 | $8.00E_0$ |
| 1 | 3 | $3.25E_0$ | 3 | 1 | $9.25E_0$ |
| 2 | 2 | $5.00E_0$ * | 1 | 6 | $10.00E_0$ ** |
| 1 | 4 | $5.00E_0$ * | 3 | 2 | $10.00E_0$ ** |

* Lowest 2-fold degenerate level          **Second 2-fold degenerate level

18.
$$\psi(x,y) = f(x)g(y)$$

$$f(x) = A\sin k_x x + B\cos k_x x \qquad \text{and} \qquad g(y) = C\sin k_y y + D\cos k_y y$$

$$\frac{\partial \psi}{\partial x} = g(y)\frac{df}{dx} = g(y)(k_x A\cos k_x x - k_x B\sin k_x x)$$

$$\frac{\partial^2 \psi}{\partial x^2} = g(y)\frac{d^2 f}{dx^2} = g(y)(-k_x^2 A\sin k_x x - k_x^2 B\cos k_x x) = -k_x^2 g(y)f(x)$$

$$\frac{\partial \psi}{\partial y} = f(x)\frac{dg}{dy} = f(x)(k_y C\cos k_y y - k_y D\sin k_y y)$$

$$\frac{\partial^2 \psi}{\partial y^2} = f(x)\frac{d^2 g}{dy^2} = f(x)(-k_y^2 C\sin k_y y - k_y^2 D\cos k_y y) = -k_y^2 f(x)g(y)$$

With $U(x,y) = 0$ inside the well, Equation 5.28 gives

$$\frac{-\hbar^2}{2m}\left[-k_x^2 f(x)g(y) - k_y^2 f(x)g(y)\right] = Ef(x)g(y)$$

Thus

$$E = \frac{\hbar^2}{2m}(k_x^2 + k_y^2)$$

19.      $$E = E_0(n_x^2 + n_y^2 + n_z^2)$$

| $n_x$ | $n_y$ | $n_z$ | $E$ | degeneracy | $n_x$ | $n_y$ | $n_z$ | $E$ | degeneracy |
|---|---|---|---|---|---|---|---|---|---|
| 1 | 1 | 1 | $3E_0$ | 1 | 2 | 2 | 3 | $17E_0$ | 3 |
| | | | | | 2 | 3 | 2 | $17E_0$ | 3 |
| 1 | 1 | 2 | $6E_0$ | 3 | 3 | 2 | 2 | $17E_0$ | 3 |
| 1 | 2 | 1 | $6E_0$ | 3 | | | | | |
| 2 | 1 | 1 | $6E_0$ | 3 | 1 | 1 | 4 | $18E_0$ | 3 |
| | | | | | 1 | 4 | 1 | $18E_0$ | 3 |
| 1 | 2 | 2 | $9E_0$ | 3 | 4 | 1 | 1 | $18E_0$ | 3 |
| 2 | 1 | 2 | $9E_0$ | 3 | | | | | |
| 2 | 2 | 1 | $9E_0$ | 3 | 3 | 3 | 1 | $19E_0$ | 3 |
| | | | | | 3 | 1 | 3 | $19E_0$ | 3 |
| 1 | 1 | 3 | $11E_0$ | 3 | 1 | 3 | 3 | $19E_0$ | 3 |
| 1 | 3 | 1 | $11E_0$ | 3 | | | | | |
| 3 | 1 | 1 | $11E_0$ | 3 | 1 | 2 | 4 | $21E_0$ | 6 |
| | | | | | 1 | 4 | 2 | $21E_0$ | 6 |
| 2 | 2 | 2 | $12E_0$ | 1 | 2 | 1 | 4 | $21E_0$ | 6 |
| | | | | | 2 | 4 | 1 | $21E_0$ | 6 |
| 1 | 2 | 3 | $14E_0$ | 6 | 4 | 2 | 1 | $21E_0$ | 6 |
| 1 | 3 | 2 | $14E_0$ | 6 | 4 | 1 | 2 | $21E_0$ | 6 |
| 2 | 1 | 3 | $14E_0$ | 6 | | | | | |
| 2 | 3 | 1 | $14E_0$ | 6 | | | | | |
| 3 | 1 | 2 | $14E_0$ | 6 | | | | | |
| 3 | 2 | 1 | $14E_0$ | 6 | | | | | |

20.                    $\psi(x) = A e^{-ax^2}$

$$\int_{-\infty}^{\infty} \psi^2(x)\ dx = A^2 \int_{-\infty}^{\infty} e^{-2ax^2}\ dx = 2A^2 \int_0^{\infty} e^{-2ax^2}\ dx = \frac{2A^2 \sqrt{\pi}}{2\sqrt{2a}}$$

where we have used the standard form to evaluate the definite integral. This expression must be equal to 1 for the normalization condition

$$A^2 \sqrt{\frac{\pi}{2a}} = 1$$

With  $a = \dfrac{\sqrt{km}}{2\hbar} = \dfrac{\omega_0 m}{2\hbar}$ ,

$$A^2 = \sqrt{\frac{2a}{\pi}} = \sqrt{\frac{\omega_0 m}{\pi\hbar}} \qquad \text{so} \qquad A = \left( \frac{\omega_0 m}{\pi\hbar} \right)^{\frac{1}{4}}$$

21.  (a)  $E_0 = \dfrac{1}{2}\hbar\omega_0 = \dfrac{1}{2}kA_0^2$ \qquad so \qquad $A_0 = \sqrt{\dfrac{\hbar\omega_0}{k}}$

(b)  $E_1 = \dfrac{3}{2}\hbar\omega_0 = \dfrac{1}{2}kA_0^2$ \qquad so \qquad $A_0 = \sqrt{\dfrac{3\hbar\omega_0}{k}}$

$E_2 = \dfrac{5}{2}\hbar\omega_0 = \dfrac{1}{2}kA_0^2$ \qquad so \qquad $A_0 = \sqrt{\dfrac{5\hbar\omega_0}{k}}$

22.
$$x_{av} = \int_{-\infty}^{\infty} \psi^2(x) \, x \, dx = A^2 \int_{-\infty}^{\infty} e^{-2ax^2} \, x \, dx$$

$$= A^2 \left[ \int_{-\infty}^{0} e^{-2ax^2} \, x \, dx + \int_{0}^{\infty} e^{-2ax^2} \, x \, dx \right]$$

$$= A^2 \left[ -\int_{0}^{\infty} e^{-2ax^2} \, x \, dx + \int_{0}^{\infty} e^{-2ax^2} \, x \, dx \right] = 0$$

(We could have guessed at this result, since the motion of the oscillator is symmetric about $x = 0$.)

$$(x^2)_{av} = \int_{-\infty}^{\infty} \psi^2(x) \, x^2 \, dx = A^2 \int_{-\infty}^{\infty} e^{-2ax^2} \, x^2 \, dx = 2A^2 \int_{0}^{\infty} e^{-2ax^2} \, x^2 \, dx$$

$$= \frac{2A^2}{\sqrt{8a^3}} \int_{0}^{\infty} e^{-u^2} \, u^2 \, du = \frac{2A^2}{\sqrt{8a^3}} \frac{1}{4} \sqrt{\pi}$$

where we have used the substitution $u = \sqrt{2a} \, x$ to evaluate the integral.

With $A = \left( \dfrac{\omega_0 m}{\pi \hbar} \right)^{1/4}$ and $a = \dfrac{\omega_0 m}{2\hbar}$, we obtain

$$(x^2)_{av} = 2 \left( \frac{\omega_0 m}{\pi \hbar} \right)^{1/2} \frac{1}{2\sqrt{2}} \left( \frac{2\hbar}{\omega_0 m} \right)^{3/2} \frac{1}{4} \sqrt{\pi} = \frac{\hbar}{2\omega_0 m}$$

$$\Delta x = \sqrt{(x^2)_{av} - (x_{av})^2} = \sqrt{\frac{\hbar}{2m\omega_0}}$$

23.  (a)   The oscillator can move to the right or to the left with equal probability.  Thus we expect $p_{av} = 0$.

(b)   $E = K + U = \dfrac{p^2}{2m} + \dfrac{1}{2}kx^2$

With $E = \frac{1}{2}\hbar\omega_0$, this gives $p^2 = \hbar\omega_0 m - mkx^2$, or

$(p^2)_{av} = (\hbar\omega_0 m - mkx^2)_{av} = \hbar\omega_0 m - mk(x^2)_{av} = \hbar\omega_0 m - mk\left(\dfrac{\hbar}{2m\omega_0}\right)$

Using  $k = m\omega_0^2$ , we obtain

$(p^2)_{av} = \dfrac{\hbar\omega_0 m}{2}$

(c)   $\Delta p = \sqrt{(p^2)_{av} - (p_{av})^2} = \sqrt{\dfrac{\hbar\omega_0 m}{2}}$

24.        $\Delta x \Delta p = \sqrt{\dfrac{\hbar}{2\omega_0 m}}\ \sqrt{\dfrac{\hbar\omega_0 m}{2}} = \dfrac{\hbar}{2}$

This is the minimum possible value of $\Delta x \Delta p$ allowed by the uncertainty principle.  In this sense the wave packet of the harmonic oscillator ground state, which is also known as a Gaussian wave packet, is the most "compact" wave packet that can be constructed.

25.        $\psi(x) = Axe^{-ax^2}$

$\dfrac{d\psi}{dx} = Ae^{-ax^2} - 2Aax^2 e^{-ax^2} = A(1 - 2ax^2)e^{-ax^2}$

$\dfrac{d^2\psi}{dx^2} = A(-4ax)e^{-ax^2} - A(1 - 2ax^2)(-2ax)e^{-ax^2} = A(-6ax + 4a^2 x^3)e^{-ax^2}$

Substituting this result into the Schrödinger equation, we obtain

$$\frac{-\hbar^2}{2m}Ae^{-ax^2}(-6ax + 4a^2x^3) + \frac{1}{2}kx^2Axe^{-ax^2} = EAe^{-ax^2}$$

$$\left[6a\frac{\hbar^2}{2m} - E\right] + x^2\left[\frac{-2\hbar^2a^2}{m} + \frac{1}{2}k\right] = 0$$

For this to be valid for all $x$, both terms must vanish.

$$\frac{1}{2}k = \frac{2\hbar^2a^2}{m} \qquad \text{or} \qquad a = \frac{\omega_0 m}{2\hbar}$$

$$E = \frac{3a\hbar^2}{m} = \frac{3\hbar^2}{m}\frac{m\omega_0}{2\hbar} = \frac{3}{2}\hbar\omega_0$$

The normalization integral is

$$\int_{-\infty}^{\infty} \psi^2(x)\,dx = A^2\int_{-\infty}^{\infty} e^{-2ax^2}x^2\,dx = 2A^2\int_{0}^{\infty} e^{-2ax^2}x^2\,dx$$

$$= \frac{2A^2}{\sqrt{8a^3}}\int_{0}^{\infty} e^{-u^2}u^2\,du = \frac{2A^2}{\sqrt{8a^3}}\frac{1}{4}\sqrt{\pi}$$

where we have used the substitution $u = \sqrt{2a}\,x$ to evaluate the integral. Setting this result equal to 1 for normalization, we obtain

$$A^2 = \frac{2\sqrt{8a^3}}{\sqrt{\pi}} = \frac{4\sqrt{2}}{\sqrt{\pi}}\left(\frac{m\omega_0}{2\hbar}\right)^{3/2} \qquad \text{or} \qquad A = \frac{\sqrt{2}}{\pi^{1/4}}\left(\frac{m\omega_0}{\hbar}\right)^{3/4}$$

26.
$$\psi(x) = \left(\frac{m\omega_0}{\hbar\pi}\right)^{1/4} e^{-ax^2}$$

$$P = 2\int_{+A_0}^{\infty} \psi^2 \, dx = 2\int_{+A_0}^{\infty} \left(\frac{m\omega_0}{\hbar\pi}\right)^{1/2} e^{-2ax^2} \, dx$$

$$= 2\sqrt{\frac{m\omega_0}{\hbar\pi}} \, \frac{1}{\sqrt{2a}} \int_1^{\infty} e^{-u^2} \, du = \frac{2}{\sqrt{\pi}} \int_1^{\infty} e^{-u^2} \, du = 0.157$$

27.
$$E_0 = 1.24 \text{ eV} = \tfrac{1}{2}\hbar\omega_0 \qquad \text{so} \qquad \hbar\omega_0 = 2.48 \text{ eV}$$

To $n = 2$:  $\Delta E = E_2 - E_0 = \tfrac{5}{2}\hbar\omega_0 - \tfrac{1}{2}\hbar\omega_0 = 2\hbar\omega_0 = 4.96 \text{ eV}$

To $n = 4$:  $\Delta E = E_4 - E_0 = \tfrac{9}{2}\hbar\omega_0 - \tfrac{1}{2}\hbar\omega_0 = 4\hbar\omega_0 = 9.92 \text{ eV}$

28.
$$Pdx = \psi^2 \, dx \qquad\qquad\qquad \psi(x) = A e^{-ax^2}$$

At $x = 0$   $\psi^2 = A^2$ $\qquad\qquad\qquad Pdx = A^2 \, dx$

At $x = \pm A_0$   $\psi^2 = A^2 e^{-2aA_0^2}$   with   $2aA_0^2 = 2\frac{\sqrt{km}}{2\hbar}\frac{\hbar\omega_0}{k} = 1$

so $Pdx = A^2 e^{-1} \, dx$

Probability at $x = \pm A_0$ is $e^{-1} = 0.368$ of probability at $x = 0$.

29.  (a)   The $x$ and $y$ motions are independent and each contributes an energy $\hbar\omega(n + \frac{1}{2})$, but the integer $n$ is not necessarily the same for the two independent motions.  Thus

$$E = \hbar\omega_0(n_x + \tfrac{1}{2}) + \hbar\omega_0(n_y + \tfrac{1}{2}) = \hbar\omega_0(n_x + n_y + 1)$$

(b)   $\underline{(0,3)}\ \underline{(1,2)}\ \underline{(2,1)}\ \underline{(3,0)}\ \ 4\hbar\omega_0$

$\underline{(0,2)}\ \underline{(1,1)}\ \underline{(2,0)}\ \ 3\hbar\omega_0$

$\underline{(0,1)}\ \underline{(1,0)}\ \ 2\hbar\omega_0$

$\underline{(0,0)}\ \ \hbar\omega_0$

$(n_x,n_y)\ \ E$

(c)   The level with energy $N\hbar\omega_0$ has $N$ different possible sets of quantum numbers $(n_x, n_y)$, with $n_x$ and $n_y$ ranging from 0 to $N-1$ but with their sum fixed to $N$.  The number of possible values of $n_x$ is then $N$ (0, 1, 2,3, ..., $N-2$, $N-1$) and for each $n_x$, the value of $n_y$ is fixed.  The total degeneracy of each level is therefore $N = n_x + n_y + 1$.

30.  $$\Delta x = \frac{1}{2}\sqrt{\frac{2K}{m}}\frac{\hbar}{U_0 - E + K}$$

$$\frac{d\Delta x}{dK} = \frac{\hbar}{2}\sqrt{\frac{2}{m}}\left[\frac{\frac{1}{2}K^{-1/2}}{U_0 - E + K} - \frac{K^{1/2}}{(U_0 - E + K)^2}\right] = 0$$

$$\frac{1}{2}K^{-1/2} = \frac{K^{1/2}}{U_0 - E + K} \quad\text{or}\quad K = U_0 - E$$

$$(\Delta x)_{max} = \frac{1}{2}\sqrt{\frac{2}{m}}\sqrt{U_0 - E}\frac{\hbar}{2(U_0 - E)} = \frac{1}{2}\frac{\hbar}{\sqrt{2m(U_0 - E)}}$$

31.

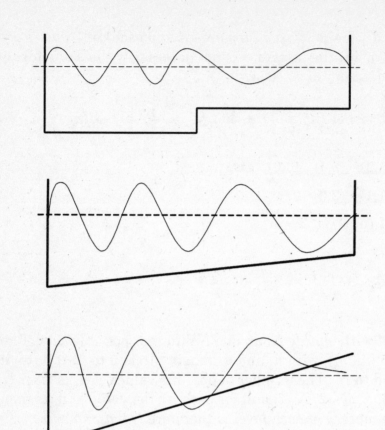

32.        $x < 0$:      $\psi_0(x) = A\sin k_0 x + B\cos k_0 x$      with      $k_0 = \sqrt{\dfrac{2mE}{\hbar^2}}$

           $x > 0$:      $\psi_1(x) = Ce^{k_1 x} + De^{-k_1 x}$      with      $k_1 = \sqrt{\dfrac{2m}{\hbar^2}(U_0 - E)}$

We set $C = 0$ to keep $\psi_1$ finite as $x \to \infty$.

At $x = 0$:

   $\psi_0(0) = \psi_1(0)$,    which gives    $B = D$

$$\left(\frac{d\psi_0}{dx}\right)_{x=0} = \left(\frac{d\psi_1}{dx}\right)_{x=0} \quad \text{which gives} \quad k_0 A = -k_1 D \quad \text{or} \quad D = -\frac{k_0}{k_1}A$$

So

$$D = B = -\sqrt{\frac{E}{U_0 - E}}\, A$$

33.  $x < 0:$  $\psi_0(x) = A' e^{ik_0 x} + B' e^{-ik_0 x}$  with  $k_0 = \sqrt{\frac{2m}{\hbar^2}E}$

$x > 0:$  $\psi_1(x) = C' e^{ik_1 x} + D' e^{-ik_1 x}$  with  $k_1 = \sqrt{\frac{2m}{\hbar^2}(E - U_0)}$

If the particles are incident from the negative $x$ direction, we set $D' = 0$.

$\psi_0(0) = \psi_1(0)$  gives  $A' + B' = C'$

$$\left(\frac{d\psi_0}{dx}\right)_{x=0} = \left(\frac{d\psi_1}{dx}\right)_{x=0} \quad \text{gives} \quad k_0(A' - B') = k_1 C'$$

Solving these two equations, we obtain

$$C' = \frac{2A'}{(1 + k_1/k_0)}$$

$$B' = C' - A' = \frac{2A'}{(1 + k_1/k_0)} - A' = \frac{(1 - k_1/k_0)}{(1 + k_1/k_0)}\, A'$$

The probabiity for the wave to be reflected is

$$\frac{|B'|^2}{|A'|^2} = \left[\frac{(1 - k_1/k_0)}{(1 + k_1/k_0)}\right]^2$$

and the probability for the wave to be transmitted into the $x > 0$ region is

$$\frac{|C'|^2}{|A'|^2} = \frac{4}{(1 + k_1/k_0)^2}$$

34.

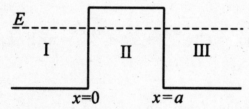

(a)   $x < 0$:     $\psi_{\text{I}}(x) = Ae^{ik_1x} + Be^{-ik_1x}$     with     $k_1 = \sqrt{\frac{2m}{\hbar^2}E}$

$0 < x < a$:     $\psi_{\text{II}}(x) = Ce^{k_2x} + De^{-k_2x}$   with   $k_2 = \sqrt{\frac{2m}{\hbar^2}(U_0 - E)}$

$x > a$:     $\psi_{\text{III}}(x) = Fe^{ik_1x} + Ge^{-ik_1x}$

(b)   At $x = 0$,

$\psi_{\text{I}}(0) = \psi_{\text{II}}(0)$   so   $A + B = C + D$

$\left(\frac{d\psi_{\text{I}}}{dx}\right)_{x=0} = \left(\frac{d\psi_{\text{II}}}{dx}\right)_{x=0}$   so   $ik_1(A - B) = k_2(C - D)$

At $x = a$

$$\psi_{\text{II}}(a) = \psi_{\text{III}}(a) \quad \text{so} \quad Ce^{k_2 a} + De^{-k_2 a} = Fe^{ik_1 a} + Ge^{-ik_1 a}$$

$$\left(\frac{d\psi_{\text{II}}}{dx}\right)_{x=a} = \left(\frac{d\psi_{\text{III}}}{dx}\right)_{x=a} \quad \text{so} \quad k_2(Ce^{k_2 a} - De^{-k_2 a}) = ik_1(Fe^{ik_1 a} - Ge^{-ik_1 a})$$

(c)     $G = 0$, because there can be no wave in region III traveling right to left.

35.

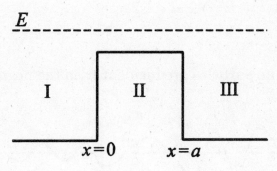

(a)     $x < 0$:     $\psi_{\text{I}}(x) = Ae^{ik_1 x} + Be^{-ik_1 x}$   with   $k_1 = \sqrt{\dfrac{2m}{\hbar^2} E}$

$0 < x < a$:     $\psi_{\text{II}}(x) = Ce^{ik_2 x} + De^{-ik_2 x}$   with   $k_2 = \sqrt{\dfrac{2m}{\hbar^2}(E - U_0)}$

$x > a$:     $\psi_{\text{III}}(x) = Fe^{ik_1 x} + Ge^{-ik_1 x}$

(b)     At $x = 0$,

$$\psi_I(0) = \psi_{II}(0) \quad \text{so} \quad A + B = C + D$$

$$\left(\frac{d\psi_I}{dx}\right)_{x=0} = \left(\frac{d\psi_{II}}{dx}\right)_{x=0} \quad \text{so} \quad k_1(A - B) = k_2(C - D)$$

At $x = a$

$$\psi_{II}(a) = \psi_{III}(a) \quad \text{so} \quad Ce^{ik_2 a} + De^{-ik_2 a} = Fe^{ik_1 a} + Ge^{-ik_1 a}$$

$$\left(\frac{d\psi_{II}}{dx}\right)_{x=a} = \left(\frac{d\psi_{III}}{dx}\right)_{x=a} \quad \text{so} \quad k_2(Ce^{ik_2 a} - De^{-ik_2 a}) = k_1(Fe^{ik_1 a} - Ge^{-ik_1 a})$$

(c)     $G = 0$ if the particles are incident from the negative $x$-direction.

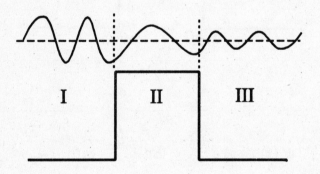

# Chapter 6

1.  $$\Delta p \sim \frac{\hbar}{\Delta x} = \frac{1}{c}\frac{\hbar c}{\Delta x} = \frac{1}{c}\frac{197 \text{ eV·nm}}{0.1 \text{ nm}} = 1970 \text{ eV}/c$$

$$K = \frac{(p_{av})^2}{2m} = \frac{(cp_{av})^2}{2mc^2} = \frac{(1970 \text{ eV})^2}{2(0.511 \times 10^6 \text{ eV})} = 3.8 \text{ eV}$$

This energy is consistent with the energies of electrons in atoms.

2.  (a) $$E(4\pi r^2) = \frac{q_{enclosed}}{\epsilon_0} = \frac{Ze}{\epsilon_0}\left(\frac{\frac{4}{3}\pi r^3}{\frac{4}{3}\pi R^3}\right) \qquad \text{or} \qquad E = \frac{1}{4\pi\epsilon_0}\frac{Ze}{R^3}r$$

(b) $$F = eE = \frac{1}{4\pi\epsilon_0}\frac{Ze^2}{R^3}r$$

3.  (a) $$\nu = \frac{1}{2\pi}\sqrt{\frac{k}{m}} = \frac{1}{2\pi}\sqrt{\frac{Ze^2}{4\pi\epsilon_0 R^3 m}} = \frac{1}{2\pi}\sqrt{\frac{Ze^2 c^2}{4\pi\epsilon_0 R^3 mc^2}}$$

$$= \frac{1}{2\pi}\sqrt{\frac{(1.440 \text{ eV·nm})(3\times10^8 \text{ m/s})^2(10^9 \text{ nm/m})^2}{(0.053 \text{ nm})^3(0.511\times10^6 \text{ eV})}} = 6.57\times10^{15} \text{ Hz}$$

$$\lambda = \frac{c}{\nu} = \frac{3.00\times10^8 \text{ m/s}}{6.57\times10^{15} \text{ Hz}} = 45.7 \text{ nm}$$

(b) With $Z = 11$ and $R = 0.18$ nm,

$$\nu = \frac{1}{2\pi}\sqrt{\frac{11(1.440 \text{ eV·nm})(3 \times 10^8 \text{ m/s})^2(10^9 \text{ nm/m})^2}{(0.18 \text{ nm})^3(0.511 \times 10^6 \text{ eV})}} = 3.48 \times 10^{15} \text{ Hz}$$

$$\lambda = \frac{c}{\nu} = \frac{3.00 \times 10^8 \text{ m/s}}{3.48 \times 10^{15} \text{ Hz}} = 86.2 \text{ nm}$$

4.

$$\theta = \frac{2zkb}{mv^2}\sqrt{R^2 - b^2}$$

$$\frac{d\theta}{db} = \frac{2zk}{mv^2}\sqrt{R^2 - b^2} + \frac{2zkb}{mv^2}\frac{1}{2}(R^2 - b^2)^{-1/2}(-2b) = 0$$

$$\sqrt{R^2 - b^2} = \frac{b^2}{\sqrt{R^2 - b^2}} \qquad \text{or} \qquad b = \frac{R}{\sqrt{2}}$$

$$\theta_{max} = \frac{2zk}{mv^2}\frac{R}{\sqrt{2}}\sqrt{\frac{R^2}{2}} = \frac{zkR^2}{mv^2}$$

5.     (a) The force on an electron at the radius $x$ due to the positive sphere is given by Equation 6.1 evaluated for $Z = 2$:

$$F_+ = \frac{1}{4\pi\epsilon_0}\frac{2e^2x}{R^3}$$

The force exerted on one electron by the other electron (located a distance $2x$ away) is

$$F_- = \frac{1}{4\pi\epsilon_0}\frac{e^2}{4x^2}$$

At equilibrium, $F_+ = F_-$ gives $\dfrac{2e^2x}{R^3} = \dfrac{e^2}{4x^2}$     or     $x = \dfrac{R}{2}$

6.  (a)  From Equation 6.13,

$$b = \frac{Zz}{2K} \frac{e^2}{4\pi\epsilon_0} \cot\frac{\theta}{2}$$

$$= \frac{2(79)}{2(5.00 \text{ MeV})} (1.440 \text{ MeV·fm}) \cot 45° = 22.8 \text{ fm}$$

(b)  From Equation 6.21,

$$\frac{1}{2}mv^2 = \frac{1}{2}mv^2 \frac{b^2}{r_{min}^2} + \frac{e^2}{4\pi\epsilon_0} \frac{Zz}{r_{min}}$$

$$(5.00 \text{ MeV}) r_{min}^2 = (5.00 \text{ MeV})(22.8 \text{ fm})^2 + (1.440 \text{ MeV·fm})(2)(79) r_{min}$$

$$r_{min}^2 - 45.5 r_{min} - 519.8 = 0 \quad \text{so} \quad r_{min} = 55.0 \text{ fm or } -9.5 \text{ fm}$$

Only the positive root is physically meaningful, so $r_{min} = 55.0$ fm.

(c)  $$U = \frac{e^2}{4\pi\epsilon_0} \frac{Zz}{r_{min}} = \frac{(1.440 \text{ MeV·fm})(2)(79)}{55.0 \text{ fm}} = 4.14 \text{ MeV}$$

$$K = E - U = 5.00 \text{ MeV} - 4.14 \text{ MeV} = 0.86 \text{ MeV}$$

7.  From Equation 6.22,

$$K = \frac{e^2}{4\pi\epsilon_0} \frac{Zz}{d} = \frac{(1.440 \text{ MeV·fm})(2)(79)}{7.0 \text{ fm}} = 33 \text{ MeV}$$

8.  $$d = \frac{e^2}{4\pi\epsilon_0} \frac{Zz}{K} = \frac{(1.440 \text{ MeV·fm})(2)(29)}{6.0 \text{ MeV}} = 14 \text{ fm}$$

9.    The density of silver is $\rho = 10.5$ g/cm$^3$ and its molar mass is $M = 107.9$ g/mole. Thus

$$n = \frac{N_A \rho}{M} = \frac{(6.02 \times 10^{23} \text{ atoms/mole})(10.5 \text{ g/cm}^3)}{107.9 \text{ g/mole}}$$

$$= 5.86 \times 10^{22} \text{ atoms/cm}^3 = 5.86 \times 10^{28} \text{ atoms/m}^3$$

(a)    At $\theta = 90°$,

$$b = \frac{Zz}{2K} \frac{e^2}{4\pi\epsilon_0} \cot\frac{\theta}{2} = \frac{(1)(47)}{2(5.0 \text{ MeV})}(1.440 \text{ MeV·fm}) \cot 45° = 6.77 \text{ fm}$$

$$f_{>90°} = nt\pi b^2$$

$$= (5.86 \times 10^{28} \text{ m}^{-3})(4.0 \times 10^{-6} \text{ m})(3.14)(6.77 \times 10^{-15} \text{ m})^2$$

$$= 3.37 \times 10^{-5}$$

(b)    At $\theta = 10°$,

$$b = \frac{(1)(47)}{2(5.0 \text{ MeV})}(1.440 \text{ MeV·fm}) \cot 5° = 77.4 \text{ fm}$$

$$f_{>10°} = (5.86 \times 10^{28} \text{ m}^{-3})(4.0 \times 10^{-6} \text{ m})(3.14)(77.4 \times 10^{-15} \text{ m})^2$$

$$= 4.41 \times 10^{-3}$$

(c)    At $\theta = 5°$,

$$b = \frac{(1)(47)}{2(5.0 \text{ MeV})}(1.440 \text{ MeV·fm}) \cot 2.5° = 155 \text{ fm}$$

$$f_{>5°} = (5.86 \times 10^{28} \text{ m}^{-3})(4.0 \times 10^{-6} \text{ m})(3.14)(155 \times 10^{-15} \text{ m})^2$$

$$= 1.77 \times 10^{-2}$$

$$f_{>5°} - f_{>10°} = 1.33 \times 10^{-2}$$

(d)    $f_{<5°} = 1 - f_{>5°} = 1 - 1.77 \times 10^{-2} = 0.982$

10. (a) From Equation 6.22

$$K = \frac{e^2}{4\pi\epsilon_0} \frac{Zz}{d} = \frac{(1.440 \text{ MeV·fm})(1)(29)}{5.0 \text{ fm}} = 8.4 \text{ MeV}$$

(b) $b = \dfrac{Zz}{2K} \dfrac{e^2}{4\pi\epsilon_0} \cot\dfrac{\theta}{2} = \dfrac{(1)(29)}{2(7.5 \text{ MeV})}(1.440 \text{ MeV·fm})\cot 60° = 1.61 \text{ fm}$

(c) From Equation 6.21, $\dfrac{1}{2}mv^2 = \dfrac{1}{2}mv^2\dfrac{b^2}{r_{min}^2} + \dfrac{e^2}{4\pi\epsilon_0}\dfrac{Zz}{r_{min}}$

$$(7.5 \text{ MeV})r_{min}^2 = (7.5 \text{ MeV})(1.61 \text{ fm})^2 + (1.440 \text{ MeV·fm})(1)(29)r_{min}$$

$$r_{min}^2 - 5.57r_{min} - 2.58 = 0 \quad \text{so} \quad r_{min} = 6.00 \text{ fm or } -0.43 \text{ fm}$$

Only the positive root is physically meaningful, so $r_{min} = 6.00$ fm.

(d) For copper, $M = 63.5$ g/mole and $\rho = 8.95$ g/cm$^3$, and

$$n = \frac{(6.02 \times 10^{23} \text{ atoms/mole})(8.95 \text{ g/cm}^3)}{63.5 \text{ g/mole}} = 8.49 \times 10^{28} \text{ atoms/m}^3$$

$f_{>120°} = nt\pi b^2$

$= (8.49 \times 10^{28} \text{ m}^{-3})(12 \times 10^{-6} \text{ m})(3.14)(1.61 \times 10^{-15} \text{ m})^2$

$= 8.3 \times 10^{-6}$

11. $R = \dfrac{f_{>90°}(\text{Au})}{f_{>90°}(\text{Ag})} = \dfrac{n_{Au}t_{Au}\pi b_{Au}^2}{n_{Ag}t_{Ag}\pi b_{Ag}^2} = \dfrac{\rho_{Au}M_{Ag}Z_{Au}^2}{\rho_{Ag}M_{Au}Z_{Ag}^2}$

$$= \frac{(19.3 \text{ g/cm}^3)(107.9 \text{ g/mole})(79)^2}{(10.5 \text{ g/cm}^3)(197.0 \text{ g/mole})(47)^2} = 2.84$$

12.    As a rough first approximation, we assume that the final momentum of the alpha particle is equal to its initial momentum.  The recoil momentum of the target nucleus is

$$p_{recoil} = p_i - p_f = p_i - (-p_i) = 2p_i$$

$$K_{recoil} = \frac{(p_{recoil})^2}{2M_{nucleus}} = \frac{4p_i^2}{2M_{nucleus}}$$

$$= \frac{4(2m_\alpha K_\alpha)}{2M_{nucleus}} = 4(8.0 \ \text{MeV}) \ \frac{m_\alpha}{M_{nucleus}} = 0.63 \ \text{MeV}$$

13.    Let $p_i$ and $p_f$ represent the initial and final momentum of the alpha particle, and let $K_i$ and $K_f$ be the initial and final kinetic energies of the alpha particle. Then conservation of momentum and kinetic energy give

$$p_i = p_f + p_e \qquad \text{and} \qquad K_i = K_f + K_e$$

$$\frac{p_i^2}{2m_\alpha} = \frac{p_f^2}{2m_\alpha} + \frac{p_e^2}{2m_e} = \frac{(p_i - p_e)^2}{2m_\alpha} + \frac{p_e^2}{2m_e}$$

$$\frac{2p_i p_e}{m_\alpha} = p_e^2 \left( \frac{1}{m_\alpha} + \frac{1}{m_e} \right) \qquad \text{or} \qquad p_e = \frac{2p_i}{1 + m_\alpha/m_e}$$

$$\Delta K = K_i - K_f = K_e = \frac{p_e^2}{2m_e} = \frac{4p_i^2}{2m_e(1 + m_\alpha/m_e)^2}$$

$$= \frac{p_i^2}{2m_\alpha} \frac{4m_\alpha/m_e}{(1 + m_\alpha/m_e)^2} = (8.0 \ \text{MeV})\frac{4(7294)}{(1 + 7294)^2} = 4.4 \times 10^{-3} \ \text{MeV}$$

14. The potential energy at minimum separation is $U = E - K = 4.8$ MeV, so

$$r_{min} = \frac{e^2}{4\pi\epsilon_0}\frac{Zz}{U} = \frac{(1.440 \text{ MeV·fm})(2)(47)}{4.8 \text{ MeV}} = 28.2 \text{ fm}$$

From Equation 6.20,

$$b = r_{min}\frac{v_{min}}{v} = r_{min}\sqrt{\frac{K_{min}}{K}} = 28.2 \text{ fm}\sqrt{\frac{4.8 \text{ MeV}}{9.6 \text{ MeV}}} = 19.9 \text{ fm}$$

$$\cot\frac{\theta}{2} = \frac{8\pi\epsilon_0 Kb}{Zze^2} = \frac{(2)(9.6 \text{ MeV})(19.9 \text{ fm})}{2(47)(1.440 \text{ MeV·fm})} = 2.828 \quad \text{or} \quad \theta = 38.9°$$

15.
$$n = \frac{N_A\rho}{M} = \frac{(6.02 \times 10^{23} \text{ atoms/mole})(19.3 \text{ g/cm}^3)}{197 \text{ g/mole}}$$

$$= 5.90 \times 10^{28} \text{ atoms/m}^3$$

$$N(\theta) = \frac{nt}{4r^2}\left(\frac{Zz}{2K}\right)^2\left(\frac{e^2}{4\pi\epsilon_0}\right)^2\frac{1}{\sin^4 \theta/2}$$

$$= \frac{(5.90 \times 10^{28} \text{ m}^{-3})(3.0 \times 10^{-6} \text{ m})}{4(0.12 \text{ m})^2}\left(\frac{2(79)}{2(6.0 \text{ MeV})}\right)^2\frac{(1.440 \text{ MeV·fm})^2}{\sin^4 15°}$$

$$= 0.2462 \text{ m}^{-2}$$

This gives the probability per unit area for an alpha particle to be scattered into the detector. The area of the detector is $\pi(0.5 \text{ cm})^2 = 7.96 \times 10^{-6} \text{ m}^2$. The total probability for an alpha particle to be scattered into the detector is $(0.2462 \text{ m}^{-2})(7.96 \times 10^{-6} \text{ m}^2) = 1.96 \times 10^{-6}$; that is, each alpha particle has a probability of $1.96 \times 10^{-6}$ to be scattered into the detector. If the rate of incident particles is $3.0 \times 10^7 \text{ s}^{-1}$, the rate at which they strike the detector is $(1.96 \times 10^{-6})(3.0 \times 10^7 \text{ s}^{-1}) = 59 \text{ s}^{-1}$.

16.       $r_3 = 9a_0 = 0.476$ nm

$$v = \frac{n\hbar}{mr} = c\frac{n\hbar c}{mc^2 r} = c\frac{3(1240/2\pi \ \text{eV·nm})}{(0.511 \times 10^6 \ \text{eV})(0.476 \ \text{nm})} = 2.43 \times 10^{-3}c$$

$$v = 7.30 \times 10^5 \ \text{m/s}$$

$$U = -\frac{e^2}{4\pi\epsilon_0}\frac{1}{r} = -\frac{1.440 \ \text{eV·nm}}{0.476 \ \text{nm}} = -3.02 \ \text{eV}$$

$$K = \frac{e^2}{8\pi\epsilon_0}\frac{1}{r} = \frac{1.440 \ \text{eV·nm}}{2(0.476 \ \text{nm})} = 1.51 \ \text{eV}$$

17.    The transitions of the Lyman series are those with $n_0 = 1$.

$$\Delta E = E_n - E_1 = -13.606 \ \text{eV}\left(\frac{1}{n^2} - 1\right) = h\nu = \frac{hc}{\lambda}$$

$$\lambda = \frac{hc}{13.606 \ \text{eV}}\frac{1}{1 - 1/n^2} = 91.13 \ \text{nm} \ \frac{n^2}{n^2 - 1}$$

$$\lambda_{\text{limit}} = 91.13 \ \text{nm}$$

The transistions of the Paschen series have $n_0 = 3$.

$$\Delta E = E_n - E_3 = -13.606 \ \text{eV}\left(\frac{1}{n^2} - \frac{1}{9}\right) = \frac{hc}{\lambda}$$

$$\lambda = \frac{hc}{13.606 \ \text{eV}}\frac{1}{1/9 - 1/n^2} = \frac{9hc}{13.606 \ \text{eV}}\frac{n^2}{n^2 - 9}$$

$$\lambda_{\text{limit}} = 820.1 \ \text{nm}$$

18. From Equation 6.29, $\quad v = \dfrac{n\hbar}{mr} = \dfrac{n\hbar}{mn^2 a_0}$

Using Equation 6.32 for $a_0$, we obtain

$$v = \dfrac{\hbar}{nm\left(\dfrac{4\pi\epsilon_0 \hbar^2}{me^2}\right)} = \dfrac{e^2}{4\pi\epsilon_0}\dfrac{1}{n\hbar} = \dfrac{\alpha c}{n}$$

When the nuclear charge is $Ze$, we must replace $e^2$ with $Ze^2$. Thus

$$v = \dfrac{Z\alpha c}{n}$$

19. The energy of the initial $n = 5$ state is

$$E_5 = \dfrac{-13.6 \text{ eV}}{25} = -0.544 \text{ eV}$$

This state can make transitions to any of the lower states with $n = 1, 2, 3,$ or 4. The energies of these states are

$$E_4 = \dfrac{-13.6 \text{ eV}}{16} = -0.850 \text{ eV}$$

Similarly, $\quad E_3 = -1.51 \text{ eV}, \quad E_2 = -3.40 \text{ eV}, \quad E_1 = -13.6 \text{ eV}$

The transition energies are

$5 \rightarrow 4$: $\quad \Delta E = E_5 - E_4 = -0.544 \text{ eV} - (-0.850 \text{ eV}) = 0.306 \text{ eV}$

$5 \rightarrow 3$: $\quad \Delta E = E_5 - E_3 = -0.544 \text{ eV} - (-1.51 \text{ eV}) = 0.97 \text{ eV}$

$5 \rightarrow 2$: $\quad \Delta E = E_5 - E_2 = -0.544 \text{ eV} - (-3.40 \text{ eV}) = 2.86 \text{ eV}$

$5 \rightarrow 1$: $\quad \Delta E = E_5 - E_1 = -0.544 \text{ eV} - (-13.6 \text{ eV}) = 13.1 \text{ eV}$

20.    (a)    15 different transitions are possible:

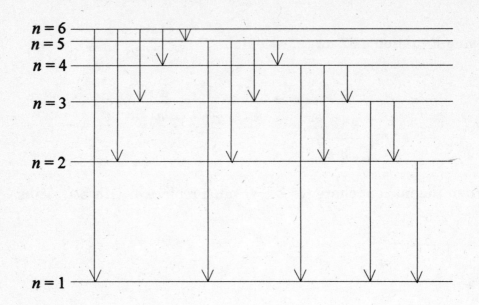

       (b)    Only 5 of the transitions change $n$ by one unit.

       (c)    One.

21.

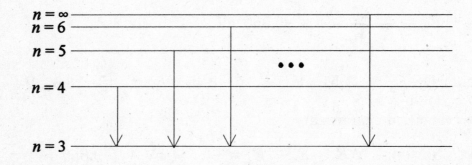

       The photon energies and wavelengths are

$4 \rightarrow 3:$ $\quad \Delta E = E_4 - E_3 = -13.606 \text{ eV} \left( \dfrac{1}{16} - \dfrac{1}{9} \right) = 0.6614 \text{ eV}$

$$\lambda = \frac{hc}{\Delta E} = \frac{1239.842 \text{ eV·nm}}{0.6614 \text{ eV}} = 1875 \text{ nm}$$

$5 \rightarrow 3:$ $\quad \Delta E = E_5 - E_3 = -13.606 \text{ eV} \left( \dfrac{1}{25} - \dfrac{1}{9} \right) = 0.9675 \text{ eV}$

$$\lambda = \frac{hc}{\Delta E} = \frac{1239.842 \text{ eV·nm}}{0.9675 \text{ eV}} = 1281 \text{ nm}$$

$6 \rightarrow 3:$ $\quad \Delta E = E_6 - E_3 = -13.606 \text{ eV} \left( \dfrac{1}{36} - \dfrac{1}{9} \right) = 1.134 \text{ eV}$

$$\lambda = \frac{hc}{\Delta E} = \frac{1239.842 \text{ eV·nm}}{1.134 \text{ eV}} = 1094 \text{ nm}$$

$\infty \rightarrow 3:$ $\quad \Delta E = E_\infty - E_3 = -13.606 \text{ eV} \left( 0 - \dfrac{1}{9} \right) = 1.512 \text{ eV}$

$$\lambda = \frac{hc}{\Delta E} = \frac{1239.842 \text{ eV·nm}}{1.512 \text{ eV}} = 820.1 \text{ nm} \qquad \text{(series limit)}$$

22.  The photon energies of the incident light are

$$E = \frac{hc}{\lambda} = \frac{1240 \text{ eV·nm}}{59.0 \text{ nm}} = 21.0 \text{ eV}$$

When an atom in the ground state absorbs a 21.0-eV photon, the atom is ionized (which takes 13.6 eV) and the excess energy, 21.0 eV − 13.6 eV = 7.4 eV, appears as the kinetic energy of the electron, which is now free of the atom. Thus, neglecting a small recoil kinetic energy given to the proton, the electrons will have a kinetic energy of 7.4 eV.

23. To remove an electron from an atom, we must give it at least enough energy to move from one of the negative energy bound states up to the free state ($n = \infty$) with $E = 0$. The ionization energy $E_i$ is thus

$$E_i = E_\infty - E_n = 0 - E_n = -E_n$$

(a) For the $n = 3$ level of hydrogen,

$$E_i = -E_3 = -\left(\frac{-13.6 \text{ eV}}{9}\right) = 1.51 \text{ eV}$$

(b) From Equation 6.42 with $Z = 2$ and $n = 2$,

$$E_i = -E_2 = -\left(-13.6 \text{ eV} \frac{Z^2}{n^2}\right) = 13.6 \text{ eV}$$

(c) $$E_i = -E_4 = -\left(-13.6 \text{ eV} \frac{Z^2}{n^2}\right) = 13.6 \text{ eV} \left(\frac{9}{16}\right) = 7.65 \text{ eV}$$

24. (a) $$E(4 \to 2) = E_4 - E_2 = -13.6 \text{ eV} \left(\frac{1}{16} - \frac{1}{4}\right) = 2.55 \text{ eV}$$

$$E(4 \to 3) = E_4 - E_3 = -13.6 \text{ eV} \left(\frac{1}{16} - \frac{1}{9}\right) = 0.661 \text{ eV}$$

$$E(3 \to 2) = E_3 - E_2 = -13.6 \text{ eV} \left(\frac{1}{9} - \frac{1}{4}\right) = 1.89 \text{ eV}$$

$$E(4 \to 3) + E(3 \to 2) = 0.661 \text{ eV} + 1.89 \text{ eV} = 2.55 \text{ eV} = E(4 \to 2)$$

(b) $$E(4 \to 1) = E_4 - E_1 = -13.6 \text{ eV} \left(\frac{1}{16} - 1\right) = 12.8 \text{ eV}$$

$$E(2 \rightarrow 1) = E_2 - E_1 = -13.6 \text{ eV} \left( \frac{1}{4} - 1 \right) = 10.2 \text{ eV}$$

$$E(4 \rightarrow 2) + E(2 \rightarrow 1) = 2.55 \text{ eV} + 10.2 \text{ eV} = 12.8 \text{ eV} = E(4 \rightarrow 1)$$

(c)    Because the photon energies are directly related to frequencies, the results of (a) and (b) can be written

$$\nu(4 \rightarrow 3) + \nu(3 \rightarrow 2) = \nu(4 \rightarrow 2)$$

$$\nu(4 \rightarrow 2) + \nu(2 \rightarrow 1) = \nu(4 \rightarrow 1)$$

These are examples of the Ritz combination principle. If a set of frequencies satisfies the Ritz combination principle, the corresponding energies $E = h\nu$ must also.

25.    The Rydberg constant in ordinary hydrogen ($M = 1.007825$ u) is

$$R_H = R_\infty \left( 1 + \frac{m}{M} \right) = R_\infty \left( 1 + \frac{5.48580 \times 10^{-4} \text{ u}}{1.007825 \text{ u}} \right) = R_\infty(1.000544)$$

and in "heavy" hydrogen or deuterium ($M = 2.014102$ u),

$$R_D = R_\infty \left( 1 + \frac{m}{M} \right) = R_\infty \left( 1 + \frac{5.48580 \times 10^{-4} \text{ u}}{2.014102 \text{ u}} \right) = R_\infty(1.000272)$$

From Equation 6.37, the difference in wavelength for the first line of the Balmer series ($n = 3$ to $n = 2$) is

$$\lambda_D - \lambda_H = \left( \frac{1}{R_D} - \frac{1}{R_H} \right) \left( \frac{3^2 2^2}{3^2 - 2^2} \right)$$

$$= \frac{1}{R_\infty} \left( \frac{3^2 2^2}{3^2 - 2^2} \right) \left( \frac{1}{1.000272} - \frac{1}{1.000544} \right) = 0.178 \text{ nm}$$

This small wavelength difference led to the discovery of deuterium in 1931 by Urey.

26.    The Lyman series consists of transitions that end in the $n = 1$ level. The
       smallest energy difference, corresponding to the longest wavelength, is $n = 2$
       to $n = 1$.

$$\Delta E = E_2 - E_1 = (-13.6 \text{ eV}) Z^2 (\tfrac{1}{4} - 1) = 40.8 \text{ eV}$$

$$\lambda = \frac{hc}{\Delta E} = \frac{1240 \text{ eV·nm}}{40.8 \text{ eV}} = 30.4 \text{ nm}$$

The largest energy difference would correspond to transitions from $n = \infty$ to
$n = 1$:

$$\Delta E = (-13.6 \text{ eV}) Z^2 (0 - 1) = 54.4 \text{ eV}$$

$$\lambda = \frac{hc}{\Delta E} = \frac{1240 \text{ eV·nm}}{54.4 \text{ eV}} = 22.8 \text{ nm}$$

27.    $$E_n = (-13.6 \text{ eV}) \left( \frac{Z^2}{n^2} \right) = \frac{-54.4 \text{ eV}}{n^2}$$

So $E_1 = -54.4$ eV, $E_2 = -13.6$ eV, $E_3 = -6.04$ eV, $E_4 = -3.40$ eV.

| | | |
|---|---|---|
| $4 \rightarrow 1$: | $\Delta E = E_4 - E_1 = 51.0 \text{ eV}$ | $\lambda = \dfrac{hc}{\Delta E} = 24.3 \text{ nm}$ |
| $4 \rightarrow 2$: | $\Delta E = E_4 - E_2 = 10.2 \text{ eV}$ | $\lambda = 122 \text{ nm}$ |
| $4 \rightarrow 3$: | $\Delta E = E_4 - E_3 = 2.64 \text{ eV}$ | $\lambda = 470 \text{ nm}$ |
| $3 \rightarrow 2$: | $\Delta E = E_3 - E_2 = 7.56 \text{ eV}$ | $\lambda = 164 \text{ nm}$ |
| $3 \rightarrow 1$: | $\Delta E = E_3 - E_1 = 48.4 \text{ eV}$ | $\lambda = 25.6 \text{ nm}$ |
| $2 \rightarrow 1$: | $\Delta E = E_2 - E_1 = 40.8 \text{ eV}$ | $\lambda = 30.4 \text{ nm}$ |

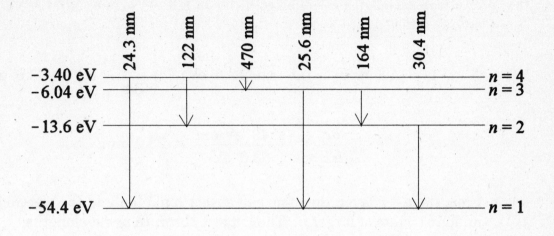

28.   (a)   From the $n = 8$ level, downward transitions are possible to any level of smaller $n$. The transitions with the longest wavelengths are those with the smallest energy differences.

$$8 \rightarrow 7: \quad \Delta E = E_8 - E_7 = (-13.6 \text{ eV}) Z^2 \left( \frac{1}{64} - \frac{1}{49} \right) = 0.260 \text{ eV}$$

$$\lambda = \frac{hc}{\Delta E} = \frac{1240 \text{ eV·nm}}{0.260 \text{ eV}} = 4.77 \text{ } \mu m$$

$$8 \rightarrow 6: \quad \Delta E = E_8 - E_6 = (-13.6 \text{ eV}) Z^2 \left( \frac{1}{64} - \frac{1}{36} \right) = 0.661 \text{ eV}$$

$$\lambda = \frac{hc}{\Delta E} = \frac{1240 \text{ eV·nm}}{0.661 \text{ eV}} = 1.88 \text{ } \mu m$$

$$8 \rightarrow 5: \quad \Delta E = E_8 - E_5 = (-13.6 \text{ eV}) Z^2 \left( \frac{1}{64} - \frac{1}{25} \right) = 1.33 \text{ eV}$$

$$\lambda = \frac{hc}{\Delta E} = \frac{1240 \text{ eV·nm}}{1.33 \text{ eV}} = 0.935 \text{ } \mu m$$

(b)     The transition with the shortest wavelength is the one with the largest energy difference.

$$8 \rightarrow 1: \quad \Delta E = E_8 - E_1 = (-13.6 \text{ eV}) Z^2 \left( \frac{1}{64} - 1 \right) = 53.6 \text{ eV}$$

$$\lambda = \frac{hc}{\Delta E} = \frac{1240 \text{ eV·nm}}{53.6 \text{ eV}} = 23.2 \text{ nm}$$

(c)     From the $n = 8$ level, the atom can absorb a photon and the electron will jump to a state of larger $n$. The longest absorption wavelengths correspond to the smallest energy differences.

$$8 \rightarrow 9: \quad \Delta E = E_9 - E_8 = (-13.6 \text{ eV}) Z^2 \left( \frac{1}{81} - \frac{1}{64} \right) = 0.178 \text{ eV}$$

$$\lambda = \frac{hc}{\Delta E} = \frac{1240 \text{ eV·nm}}{0.178 \text{ eV}} = 6.95 \text{ } \mu\text{m}$$

$$8 \rightarrow 10: \quad \Delta E = E_{10} - E_8 = (-13.6 \text{ eV}) Z^2 \left( \frac{1}{100} - \frac{1}{64} \right) = 0.306 \text{ eV}$$

$$\lambda = \frac{hc}{\Delta E} = \frac{1240 \text{ eV·nm}}{0.306 \text{ eV}} = 4.05 \text{ } \mu\text{m}$$

$$8 \rightarrow 11: \quad \Delta E = E_{11} - E_8 = (-13.6 \text{ eV}) Z^2 \left( \frac{1}{121} - \frac{1}{64} \right) = 0.400 \text{ eV}$$

$$\lambda = \frac{hc}{\Delta E} = \frac{1240 \text{ eV·nm}}{0.400 \text{ eV}} = 3.10 \text{ } \mu\text{m}$$

(d)     The shortest absorption wavelength corresponds to the largest energy difference.

$$8 \rightarrow \infty: \quad \Delta E = E_\infty - E_8 = (-13.6 \text{ eV}) Z^2 \left( 0 - \frac{1}{64} \right) = 0.850 \text{ eV}$$

$$\lambda = \frac{hc}{\Delta E} = \frac{1240 \text{ eV·nm}}{0.850 \text{ eV}} = 1.46 \text{ } \mu\text{m}$$

29.  The time $\Delta t$ in which we must measure the energy of the state is no greater than the lifetime of that state, and the energy measurement must be uncertain by an amount $\Delta E$ given by the uncertainty principle.

$$\Delta E \sim \frac{\hbar}{\Delta t} = \frac{6.58 \times 10^{-16} \text{ eV·s}}{10^{-8} \text{ s}} \cong 7 \times 10^{-8} \text{ eV}$$

This energy uncertainty is negligible compared with the energies of the states, which are typically of the order of eV. This energy uncertainty is therefore unlikely to be observed if we measure the energies of transitions between the states (unless we could measure the transition energies to about 1 part in $10^8$).

30.  $$\Delta E = (-13.6 \text{ eV})Z^2 \left( \frac{1}{n^2} - \frac{1}{n_0^2} \right) = 54.4 \text{ eV} \frac{n^2 - n_0^2}{n^2 n_0^2}$$

$$\lambda = \frac{hc}{\Delta E} = \frac{1240 \text{ eV·nm}}{54.4 \text{ eV}} \frac{n^2 n_0^2}{n^2 - n_0^2} = 22.78 \text{ nm} \frac{n^2 n_0^2}{n^2 - n_0^2}$$

The Lyman series has $n_0 = 1$ and $n \geq 2$.

| $n$ | $n_0$ | $\lambda$ (nm) | |
|---|---|---|---|
| 2 | 1 | 30.38 | ultraviolet |
| 3 | 1 | 25.63 | ultraviolet |
| 4 | 1 | 24.30 | ultraviolet |
| 5 | 1 | 23.73 | ultraviolet |
| $\infty$ | 1 | 22.78 | series limit |

The Balmer series has $n_0 = 2$ and $n \geq 3$.

| $n$ | $n_0$ | $\lambda$ (nm) | |
| --- | --- | --- | --- |
| 3 | 2 | 164.0 | ultraviolet |
| 4 | 2 | 121.5 | ultraviolet |
| 5 | 2 | 108.5 | ultraviolet |
| 6 | 2 | 102.5 | ultraviolet |
| $\infty$ | 2 | 91.13 | series limit |

The Paschen series has $n_0 = 3$ and $n \geq 4$.

| $n$ | $n_0$ | $\lambda$ (nm) | |
| --- | --- | --- | --- |
| 4 | 3 | 468.6 | visible |
| 5 | 3 | 320.4 | ultraviolet |
| 6 | 3 | 273.4 | ultraviolet |
| 7 | 3 | 251.2 | ultraviolet |
| 8 | 3 | 238.6 | ultraviolet |
| $\infty$ | 3 | 205.0 | series limit |

The Brackett series has $n_0 = 4$ and $n \geq 5$.

| $n$ | $n_0$ | $\lambda$ (nm) | |
| --- | --- | --- | --- |
| 5 | 4 | 1012.5 | infrared |
| 6 | 4 | 656.1 | visible |
| 7 | 4 | 541.2 | visible |
| $\infty$ | 4 | 364.5 | series limit |

The Pfund series has $n_0 = 5$ and $n \geq 6$.

| $n$ | $n_0$ | $\lambda$ (nm) | |
| --- | --- | --- | --- |
| 6 | 5 | 1863.9 | infrared |
| 7 | 5 | 1162.8 | infrared |
| $\infty$ | 5 | 569.5 | series limit |

31.
$$\Delta E = (-13.606 \text{ eV}) Z^2 \left( \frac{1}{n^2} - \frac{1}{n_0^2} \right)$$

$$\lambda = \frac{hc}{\Delta E} = \frac{1239.842 \text{ eV·nm}}{(13.606 \text{ eV}) Z^2} \left( \frac{n^2 n_0^2}{n^2 - n_0^2} \right) = 10.13 \text{ nm} \left( \frac{n^2 n_0^2}{n^2 - n_0^2} \right)$$

Lyman series ($n_0 = 1$)

| $n$ | $n_0$ | $\lambda$ (nm) | |
|---|---|---|---|
| 2 | 1 | 13.50 | ultraviolet |
| 3 | 1 | 11.39 | ultraviolet |
| $\infty$ | 1 | 10.13 | series limit |

Balmer series ($n_0 = 2$)

| $n$ | $n_0$ | $\lambda$ (nm) | |
|---|---|---|---|
| 3 | 2 | 72.90 | ultraviolet |
| 4 | 2 | 54.00 | ultraviolet |
| $\infty$ | 2 | 40.50 | series limit |

32. Let $p$ and $E$ be the momentum and the energy of the photon. Then:

Conservation of momentum $\quad p = p_R$

Conservation of energy $\quad E_1 = E_2 + E + K_R$

$$= E_2 + cp + K_R = E_2 + cp_R + K_R$$

Using nonrelativistic kinetic energy $p_R = \sqrt{2MK_R}$ for the atom, we obtain

$$K_R + \sqrt{2Mc^2 K_R} = E_1 - E_2$$

Because we expect $K_R \ll Mc^2$, the first term on the left is negligible, and so

$$\sqrt{2Mc^2K_R} \cong E_1 - E_2 \qquad \text{or} \qquad K_R \cong \frac{(E_1 - E_2)^2}{2Mc^2}$$

The $n = 2$ to $n = 1$ transition in hydrogen has energy $-3.4$ eV $- (-13.6$ eV$) = 10.2$ eV, and the atomic mass is $1.007825$ u $= 939$ MeV/$c^2$.

$$K_R = \frac{(10.2 \text{ eV})^2}{2(939 \text{ MeV})} = 5.5 \times 10^{-8} \text{ eV}$$

33.  The gravitational force law is $F = Gm_e m_p / r^2$ instead of $F = e^2 / 4\pi\epsilon_0 r^2$. The Bohr theory can thus be directly applied if we substitute $Gm_e m_p$ for $e^2/4\pi\epsilon_0$. Equation 6.32 becomes

$$a_0 = \frac{\hbar^2}{Gm_e^2 m_p}$$

$$= \frac{(1.05 \times 10^{-34} \text{ J·s})^2}{(6.67 \times 10^{-11} \text{ N·m}^2/\text{kg}^2)(9.11 \times 10^{-31} \text{ kg})^2(1.67 \times 10^{-27} \text{ kg})}$$

$$= 1.19 \times 10^{29} \text{ m}$$

$$E_n = -\frac{m_e}{2\hbar^2}\frac{(Gm_e m_p)^2}{n^2}$$

$$E_2 - E_1 = -\frac{m_e}{2\hbar^2}(Gm_e m_p)^2\left(\frac{1}{4} - 1\right) = \frac{3G^2 m_e^3 m_p^2}{8\hbar^2}$$

$$= \frac{3(6.67 \times 10^{-11} \text{ N·m}^2/\text{kg}^2)^2(9.11 \times 10^{-31} \text{ kg})^3(1.67 \times 10^{-27} \text{ kg})^2}{8(1.05 \times 10^{-34} \text{ J·s})^2}$$

$$= 3.2 \times 10^{-97} \text{ J} = 2.0 \times 10^{-78} \text{ eV}$$

34.    (a)    Using the fine structure constant $\alpha = e^2/4\pi\epsilon_0 \hbar c$, we obtain

$$a_0 = \frac{4\pi\epsilon_0 \hbar^2}{me^2} = \frac{4\pi\epsilon_0 \hbar c}{e^2}\frac{\hbar c}{mc^2} = \frac{1}{\alpha}\frac{\hbar c}{mc^2} = \frac{1}{2\pi\alpha}\frac{hc}{mc^2}$$

(b)    $$E_1 = \frac{-me^4}{32\pi^2\epsilon_0^2\hbar^2} = -\left(\frac{e^2}{4\pi\epsilon_0}\right)^2\frac{m}{2\hbar^2} = -(\alpha^2\hbar^2 c^2)\frac{m}{2\hbar^2} = -\frac{1}{2}\alpha^2 mc^2$$

35.    The shortest wavelength (largest energy) of the Lyman series corresponds to $n = \infty$ to $n = 1$ and has an energy (in ordinary hydrogen) of 13.6 eV. From Equation 6.33 it can be seen that the energy levels are proportional to the mass of the electron, and so if the electron is replaced with a heavier particle, the energies will increase in direct proportion to the mass.

$$\frac{E(\text{muonic})}{E(\text{electronic})} = \frac{m_\mu}{m_e} = 207$$

Thus

$$E = (13.6 \text{ eV})(207) = 2.82 \text{ keV}$$

$$\lambda = \frac{hc}{E} = \frac{1240 \text{ eV·nm}}{2.82 \text{ keV}} = 0.440 \text{ nm}$$

This is in the X-ray region of the electromagnetic spectrum.

36.    Because $r \propto Z^{-1}$ and $r \propto m^{-1}$, with $Z = 82$ and $m = m_\mu = 207m_e$ we obtain

$$r = \frac{a_0}{(82)(207)} = 3.11 \times 10^{-15} \text{ m} = 3.11 \text{ fm}$$

This suggests that the muon orbit is inside the nucleus! (It also suggests that we must do this calculation more carefully, since the use of the Coulomb potential requires that the orbiting particle always be outside the nucleus.)

37.   (a)      $2\pi r = n\lambda$                    $n = 1, 2, 3, \cdots$

If the circumference is an integral number of de Broglie waves, then after each orbit the wave will align, peak to peak and valley to valley, to give standing waves.

(b)      With $\lambda = h/p$ for the de Broglie wavelength,

$$2\pi r = n\lambda = \frac{nh}{p} = \frac{nh}{mv} \qquad \text{so} \qquad mvr = \frac{nh}{2\pi} = n\hbar$$

38.   From Equation 6.47,

$$\Delta E = h\nu = \frac{hme^4}{32\pi^3\epsilon_0^2\hbar^3}\frac{1}{n^3} = mc^2\left(\frac{e^2}{4\pi\epsilon_0\hbar c}\right)^2\frac{1}{n^3} = \frac{\alpha^2 mc^2}{n^3}$$

39.   The energy uncertainty of a state whose lifetime is $10^{-8}$ s is

$$\Delta E \sim \frac{\hbar}{\Delta t} = \frac{6.58 \times 10^{-16} \text{ eV·s}}{10^{-8} \text{ s}} = 6.58 \times 10^{-8} \text{ eV}$$

This energy uncertainty will be equal to the spacing $\alpha^2 mc^2/n^3$ when

$$n = \sqrt[3]{\frac{\alpha^2 mc^2}{6.58 \times 10^{-8} \text{ eV}}} = \sqrt[3]{\frac{0.511 \times 10^6 \text{ eV}}{(137)^2(6.58 \times 10^{-8} \text{ eV})}} = 745$$

$$r = n^2 a_0 = (745)^2(5.29 \times 10^{-11} \text{ m}) = 29 \text{ μm}$$

Such highly excited states, with atomic sizes of the order μm to mm, are known as Rydberg states.

40. The frequency of revolution can be found from Equation 6.45:

$$\nu_R = \frac{me^4}{32\pi^3\epsilon_0^2\hbar^3}\frac{1}{n^3} = \frac{1}{\pi\hbar}\frac{me^4}{32\pi^2\epsilon_0^2\hbar^2}\frac{1}{n^3} = \frac{13.6 \text{ eV}}{\pi\hbar}\frac{1}{n^3} = \frac{6.58\times10^{15}\text{ Hz}}{n^3}$$

(a)   For $n = 10$, $\nu_R = 6.58\times10^{12}$ Hz.

The transition frequency is

$$\nu_T = \frac{\Delta E}{h} = \frac{E_{10} - E_9}{h} = \frac{-13.6\text{ eV}\left(\dfrac{1}{10^2} - \dfrac{1}{9^2}\right)}{4.136\times10^{-15}\text{ eV·s}} = 7.71\times10^{12}\text{ Hz}$$

(b)   For $n = 100$, $\nu_R = 6.58\times10^9$ Hz and

$$\nu_T = \frac{-13.6\text{ eV}\left(\dfrac{1}{100^2} - \dfrac{1}{99^2}\right)}{4.136\times10^{-15}\text{ eV·s}} = 6.68\times10^9\text{ Hz}$$

(c)   For $n = 1000$, $\nu_R = 6.58\times10^6$ Hz and

$$\nu_T = \frac{-13.6\text{ eV}\left(\dfrac{1}{1000^2} - \dfrac{1}{999^2}\right)}{4.136\times10^{-15}\text{ eV·s}} = 6.59\times10^6\text{ Hz}$$

(d)   For $n = 10{,}000$, $\nu_R = 6.58\times10^3$ Hz and

$$\nu_T = \frac{-13.6\text{ eV}\left(\dfrac{1}{10{,}000^2} - \dfrac{1}{9999^2}\right)}{4.136\times10^{-15}\text{ eV·s}} = 6.58\times10^3\text{ Hz}$$

Notice that $\nu_T$ approaches $\nu_R$ as $n$ increases, in accordance with the correspondence principle.

41.    Let $V_1 = 4$ volts, $V_2 = 7$ volts, and $V_3 = 9$ volts.  Then decreases in the current should occur near the following voltages:

| | | |
|---|---|---|
| $V_1 = 4$ volts | $3V_1 = 12$ volts | $2V_1 + V_3 = 17$ volts |
| $V_2 = 7$ volts | $V_1 + V_3 = 13$ volts | $2V_3 = 18$ volts |
| $2V_1 = 8$ volts | $2V_2 = 14$ volts | $3V_1 + V_3 = 19$ volts |
| $V_3 = 9$ volts | $2V_1 + V_2 = 15$ volts | $5V_1 = 20$ volts |
| $V_1 + V_2 = 11$ volts | $4V_1 = 16$ volts | |

42.    The energy difference between the ground state and the first excited state is

$$E = \frac{hc}{\lambda} = \frac{1240 \text{ eV·nm}}{590 \text{ nm}} = 2.10 \text{ eV}$$

At $V = 2.10$ volts, we expect to see a decrease in the current, as atoms are raised to the first excited state.

# Chapter 7

1.

| $l = 0$ | $l = 1$ | $l = 2$ | $l = 3$ |
|---------|---------|---------|---------|
| (4,0,0) | (4,1,+1) | (4,2,+2) | (4,3,+3) |
|  | (4,1,0) | (4,2,+1) | (4,3,+2) |
|  | (4,1,-1) | (4,2,0) | (4,3,+1) |
|  |  | (4,2,-1) | (4,3,0) |
|  |  | (4,2,-2) | (4,3,-1) |
|  |  |  | (4,3,-2) |
|  |  |  | (4,3,-3) |

2.   (a)   $l_{max} = n - 1 = 5$

so $l = 0, 1, 2, 3, 4, 5$   for $n = 6$

(b)   $m_l = +l$ to $-l$ in integer steps

so $m_l = +6, +5, +4, +3, +2, +1, 0, -1, -2, -3, -4, -5, -6$

(c)   $l \leq n - 1$

$n \geq l + 1 = 5$ for $l = 4$, so the smallest value of $n$ is 5

(d)   $|m_l| \leq l$

For $m_l = 4$, $l \geq 4$ so the smallest possible $l$ is 4

3.   (a)   degeneracy $= 2n^2 = 50$

(b)   For each $l$-value, degeneracy $= 2(2l + 1)$

| $l = 0$ | $2 \times 1 = 2$ |
|---------|------------------|
| $l = 1$ | $2 \times 3 = 6$ |
| $l = 2$ | $2 \times 5 = 10$ |
| $l = 3$ | $2 \times 7 = 14$ |
| $l = 4$ | $2 \times 9 = 18$ |
|  | total = 50 |

4.
$$\sum_{l=0}^{n-1} 2(2l + 1) = 4\sum_{l=0}^{n-1} l + 2\sum_{l=0}^{n-1} 1 = 4\frac{n(n - 1)}{2} + 2n = 2n^2$$

5.   (a)   $l_{max} = n - 1 = 1$          (b)   $m_l = +2$ not permitted for $l = 1$ (max. $m_l = +1$)

     (c)   $m_s = \pm 1/2$ only; $m_s = -3/2$ not allowed          (d)   $l$ is never negative

6.   (a)   $|\mathbf{L}| = \hbar\sqrt{l(l + 1)} = \hbar\sqrt{3(4)} = \sqrt{12}\,\hbar$

     (b)   There are $2l + 1 = 7$ possible $z$ components:

           $L_z = m_l\hbar = +3\hbar,\ +2\hbar,\ +\hbar,\ 0,\ -\hbar,\ -2\hbar,\ -3\hbar$

     (c)   $\cos\theta = \dfrac{L_z}{|\mathbf{L}|} = \dfrac{m_l}{\sqrt{12}}$

           | | | |
           |---|---|---|
           | $m_l = +3$ | $\cos\theta = \frac{1}{2}\sqrt{3}$ | $\theta = 30°$ |
           | $m_l = +2$ | $\cos\theta = \dfrac{1}{\sqrt{3}}$ | $\theta = 55°$ |
           | $m_l = +1$ | $\cos\theta = \dfrac{1}{\sqrt{12}}$ | $\theta = 73°$ |
           | $m_l = 0$ | $\cos\theta = 0$ | $\theta = 90°$ |
           | $m_l = -1$ | $\cos\theta = -\dfrac{1}{\sqrt{12}}$ | $\theta = 107°$ |
           | $m_l = -2$ | $\cos\theta = -\dfrac{1}{\sqrt{3}}$ | $\theta = 125°$ |
           | $m_l = -3$ | $\cos\theta = -\frac{1}{2}\sqrt{3}$ | $\theta = 150°$ |

     (d)   None of these results depend on $n$.

7.  For $l = 2$, $m_l = +2, +1, 0, -1, -2$

$$\cos\theta = \frac{L_z}{|\mathbf{L}|} = \frac{m_l\hbar}{\hbar\sqrt{l(l+1)}} = \frac{m_l}{\sqrt{6}}$$

$m_l = +2$ $\qquad$ $\cos\theta = \sqrt{\dfrac{2}{3}}$ $\qquad$ $\theta = 35°$

$m_l = +1$ $\qquad$ $\cos\theta = \dfrac{1}{\sqrt{6}}$ $\qquad$ $\theta = 66°$

$m_l = 0$ $\qquad$ $\cos\theta = 0$ $\qquad$ $\theta = 90°$

$m_l = -1$ $\qquad$ $\cos\theta = -\dfrac{1}{\sqrt{6}}$ $\qquad$ $\theta = 114°$

$m_l = -2$ $\qquad$ $\cos\theta = -\sqrt{\dfrac{2}{3}}$ $\qquad$ $\theta = 145°$

8.  For $\quad \psi_{100}(r,\theta,\phi) = \dfrac{1}{\sqrt{4\pi}}\dfrac{2}{\sqrt{a_0^3}}\, e^{-r/a_0}$ the normalization is

$$\int_0^\infty r^2\,dr \int_0^\pi \sin\theta\,d\theta \int_0^{2\pi} d\phi\ |\psi(r,\theta,\phi)|^2$$

$$= \frac{1}{4\pi}\frac{4}{a_0^3}\int_0^\infty e^{-2r/a_0}r^2\,dr \int_0^\pi \sin\theta\,d\theta \int_0^{2\pi} d\phi = \frac{4}{a_0^3}\int_0^\infty e^{-2r/a_0}r^2\,dr$$

$$= \frac{4}{a_0^3}\frac{2!}{(2/a_0)^3} = 1 \qquad\qquad \text{using} \quad \int_0^\infty x^n e^{-ax}\,dx = \frac{n!}{a^{n+1}}$$

For $\quad \psi_{200}(r,\theta,\phi) = \dfrac{1}{\sqrt{4\pi}}\dfrac{1}{\sqrt{8a_0^3}}\left(2 - \dfrac{r}{a_0}\right)e^{-r/2a_0}$ the normalization is

$$\frac{1}{4\pi}\frac{1}{8a_0^3}\int_0^\infty e^{-r/a_0}\left(2 - \frac{r}{a_0}\right)^2 r^2\,dr \int_0^\pi \sin\theta\,d\theta \int_0^{2\pi} d\phi$$

$$= \frac{1}{8a_0^3} \int_0^\infty e^{-2r/a_0} \left( 4r^2 - \frac{4}{a_0}r^3 + \frac{r^4}{a_0^2} \right) dr$$

$$= \frac{1}{8a_0^3} \left[ 4\frac{2!}{(1/a_0)^3} - \frac{4}{a_0}\frac{3!}{(1/a_0)^4} + \frac{1}{a_0^2}\frac{4!}{(1/a_0)^5} \right] = \frac{1}{8}(8 - 24 + 24) = 1$$

9.
$$\psi_{200}(r,\theta,\phi) = \frac{1}{\sqrt{4\pi}} \frac{1}{\sqrt{8a_0^3}} \left( 2 - \frac{r}{a_0} \right) e^{-r/2a_0}$$

$$\frac{\partial\psi}{\partial\theta} = 0 \qquad \text{and} \qquad \frac{\partial\psi}{\partial\phi} = 0$$

$$\frac{\partial\psi}{\partial r} = \frac{1}{\sqrt{32\pi a_0^3}} \left[ -\frac{1}{a_0}e^{-r/2a_0} - \frac{1}{2a_0}\left( 2 - \frac{r}{a_0} \right) e^{-r/2a_0} \right]$$

$$\frac{\partial^2\psi}{\partial r^2} = \frac{1}{\sqrt{32\pi a_0^3}} \left[ \frac{1}{2a_0^2}e^{-r/2a_0} + \frac{1}{2a_0^2}e^{-r/2a_0} + \frac{1}{4a_0^2}\left( 2 - \frac{r}{a_0} \right) e^{-r/2a_0} \right]$$

From Equation 7.3 we get

$$-\frac{\hbar^2}{2m} \left[ \frac{1}{\sqrt{32\pi a_0^3}} e^{-r/2a_0} \left( \frac{3}{2a_0^2} - \frac{r}{4a_0^3} \right) + \frac{2}{r}\frac{1}{\sqrt{32\pi a_0^3}} \left( -\frac{2}{a_0} + \frac{r}{2a_0^2} \right) e^{-r/2a_0} \right]$$

$$- \frac{e^2}{4\pi\epsilon_0 r}\frac{1}{\sqrt{32\pi a_0^3}} \left( 2 - \frac{r}{a_0} \right) e^{-r/2a_0}$$

$$= \frac{1}{\sqrt{32\pi a_0^3}} e^{-r/2a_0} \left[ -\frac{\hbar^2}{2m}\left( \frac{3}{2a_0^2} - \frac{r}{4a_0^3} - \frac{4}{ra_0} + \frac{1}{a_0^2} \right) - \frac{e^2}{2\pi\epsilon_0 r} + \frac{e^2}{4\pi\epsilon_0 a_0} \right]$$

$$= \frac{1}{\sqrt{32\pi a_0^3}} e^{-r/2a_0} \frac{e^2}{4\pi\epsilon_0} \left( -\frac{5}{4a_0} + \frac{r}{8a_0^2} + \frac{2}{r} - \frac{2}{r} + \frac{1}{a_0} \right)$$

$$= \frac{1}{\sqrt{32\pi a_0^3}} e^{-r/2a_0} \frac{e^2}{4\pi\epsilon_0} \left( -\frac{1}{4a_0} + \frac{r}{8a_0^2} \right) = \frac{e^2}{4\pi\epsilon_0} \left( -\frac{1}{8a_0} \right) \psi_{200}(r,\theta,\phi)$$

Thus Equation 7.3 is satisfied if

$$E = \frac{e^2}{4\pi\epsilon_0} \left( -\frac{1}{8a_0} \right) = \frac{e^2}{4\pi\epsilon_0} \left( -\frac{me^2}{32\pi\epsilon_0\hbar^2} \right) = \frac{1}{4} \left( -\frac{me^4}{32\pi^2\epsilon_0^2\hbar^2} \right)$$

which is just the energy $E_2$ as defined in Equation 7.6.

For the $n = 2$, $l = 1$, $m_l = 0$ wave function,

$$\psi_{210}(r,\theta,\phi) = \frac{1}{\sqrt{32\pi a_0^5}} r e^{-r/2a_0} \cos\theta$$

$$\frac{\partial\psi}{\partial r} = \frac{1}{\sqrt{32\pi a_0^5}} \left( e^{-r/2a_0} - \frac{r}{2a_0} e^{-r/2a_0} \right) \cos\theta$$

$$\frac{\partial^2\psi}{\partial r^2} = \frac{1}{\sqrt{32\pi a_0^5}} \left( -\frac{1}{2a_0} e^{-r/2a_0} - \frac{1}{2a_0} e^{-r/2a_0} + \frac{r}{4a_0^2} e^{-r/2a_0} \right) \cos\theta$$

$$\frac{\partial\psi}{\partial\theta} = \frac{1}{\sqrt{32\pi a_0^5}} r e^{-r/2a_0} (-\sin\theta)$$

$$\frac{\partial}{\partial\theta} \left( \sin\theta \frac{\partial\psi}{\partial\theta} \right) = -\frac{1}{\sqrt{32\pi a_0^5}} r e^{-r/2a_0} (2\sin\theta \, \cos\theta)$$

Equation 7.3 then gives

$$\frac{\cos\theta}{\sqrt{32\pi a_0^5}}\, e^{-r/2a_0}\left(-\frac{\hbar^2}{2m}\left[-\frac{1}{a_0}+\frac{r}{4a_0^2}+\frac{2}{r}\left(1-\frac{r}{2a_0}\right)-\frac{2}{r}\right]-\frac{e^2}{4\pi\epsilon_0}\right)$$

$$=\frac{e^2}{4\pi\epsilon_0}\,\psi_{210}(r,\theta,\phi)\left(\frac{1}{2r}-\frac{1}{8a_0}+\frac{1}{2r}-\frac{1}{r}\right)$$

$$=\frac{e^2}{4\pi\epsilon_0}\left(-\frac{1}{8a_0}\right)\psi_{210}(r,\theta,\phi)=E_2\,\psi_{210}(r,\theta,\phi)$$

10.  $$\psi_{100}(r,\theta,\phi)=\frac{1}{\sqrt{\pi a_0^3}}\,e^{-r/a_0}$$

$$\frac{\partial\psi}{\partial r}=\frac{1}{\sqrt{\pi a_0^3}}\left(-\frac{1}{a_0}\right)e^{-r/a_0}\qquad\text{and}\qquad\frac{\partial^2\psi}{\partial r^2}=\frac{1}{\sqrt{\pi a_0^3}}\left(\frac{1}{a_0^2}\right)e^{-r/a_0}$$

Substituting into Equation 7.3, we obtain

$$\frac{1}{\sqrt{\pi a_0^3}}\left[-\frac{\hbar^2}{2m}\left(\frac{1}{a_0^2}e^{-r/a_0}-\frac{2}{a_0 r}e^{-r/a_0}\right)-\frac{e^2}{4\pi\epsilon_0 r}e^{-r/a_0}\right]$$

$$=\frac{1}{\sqrt{\pi a_0^3}}\,e^{-r/a_0}\frac{e^2}{4\pi\epsilon_0}\left(-\frac{1}{2a_0}+\frac{1}{r}-\frac{1}{r}\right)$$

$$=-\frac{1}{2a_0}\frac{e^2}{4\pi\epsilon_0}\,\psi_{100}(r,\theta,\phi)=E\psi_{100}(r,\theta,\phi)$$

with

$$E=-\frac{1}{2a_0}\frac{e^2}{4\pi\epsilon_0}=-\frac{1}{2}\frac{e^2}{4\pi\epsilon_0}\frac{me^2}{4\pi\epsilon_0\hbar^2}=-\frac{me^4}{32\pi^2\epsilon_0^2\hbar^2}$$

which is exactly $E_1$ from Equation 7.6.

11.      $$P(r) = r^2|R_{n,l}(r)|^2 = r^2 \frac{4}{a_0^3} e^{-2r/a_0} \qquad\qquad \text{for } n = 1,\ l = 0$$

To find the maximum, we set $dP/dr$ to zero:

$$\frac{dP}{dr} = \frac{4}{a_0^3}\left[2re^{-2r/a_0} - r^2\left(\frac{2}{a_0}\right)e^{-2r/a_0}\right] = \frac{8r}{a_0^3}e^{-2r/a_0}\left(1 - \frac{r}{a_0}\right) = 0$$

There are 3 solutions to this equation: $r = 0$, $r = \infty$, $r = a_0$. The first two solutions correspond to minima of $P(r)$; only $r = a_0$ gives a maximum.

12.     $$P(r) = r^2|R_{n,l}(r)|^2 = r^2 \frac{1}{8a_0^3}\left(2 - \frac{r}{a_0}\right)^2 e^{-r/a_0} \qquad\qquad \text{for } n = 2,\ l = 1$$

$$= \frac{1}{8a_0^3}\left(4r^2 - \frac{4r^3}{a_0} + \frac{r^4}{a_0^2}\right)e^{-r/a_0}$$

Setting $dP/dr$ to 0, we find

$$\frac{1}{8a_0^3}re^{-r/a_0}\left[8 - \frac{16r}{a_0} + \frac{8r^2}{a_0^2} - \frac{r^3}{a_0^3}\right] = 0$$

The polynomial can be factored as $(2 - r/a_0)[(r/a_0)^2 - 6r/a_0 + 4]$ and the solutions are therefore $r = 0$, $r = \infty$, $r = 2a_0$, $r = (3\pm\sqrt{5})a_0$. The first 3 solutions give minima and the last two give maxima.

13.         $$P(r) = r^2 |R_{n,l}(r)|^2 = r^2 \frac{1}{24 a_0^3} \frac{r^2}{a_0^2} e^{-r/a_0}$$

The total probability between $a_0$ and $2a_0$ is

$$P = \int_{a_0}^{2a_0} P(r)\, dr = \frac{1}{24 a_0^5} \int_{a_0}^{2a_0} r^4 e^{-r/a_0}\, dr = \frac{1}{24} \int_1^2 x^4 e^{-x}\, dx$$

where $x = r/a_0$. Integrating by parts, we obtain

$$\int_1^2 x^4 e^{-x}\, dx = -x^4 e^{-x}\Big|_1^2 + 4\int_1^2 x^3 e^{-x}\, dx$$

$$\int_1^2 x^3 e^{-x}\, dx = -x^3 e^{-x}\Big|_1^2 + 3\int_1^2 x^2 e^{-x}\, dx$$

$$\int_1^2 x^2 e^{-x}\, dx = -x^2 e^{-x}\Big|_1^2 + 2\int_1^2 x e^{-x}\, dx$$

$$\int_1^2 x e^{-x}\, dx = e^{-x}(-x - 1)\Big|_1^2$$

Thus

$$P = \frac{1}{24}(-x^4 - 4x^3 - 12x^2 - 24x - 24)e^{-x}\Big|_1^2 = 0.0490$$

14.      $$P(r) = r^2 |R_{n,l}(r)|^2 = r^2 \frac{1}{8 a_0^3}\left(2 - \frac{r}{a_0}\right)^2 e^{-r/a_0}$$

for $n = 2$, $l = 0$. The total probability to find the electron beyond $5a_0$ is

$$P = \frac{1}{8a_0^3} \int_{5a_0}^{\infty} \left( 4r^2 - \frac{4r^3}{a_0} + \frac{r^4}{a_0^2} \right) e^{-r/a_0} dr$$

$$= \frac{1}{8} \int_5^{\infty} (4x^2 - 4x^3 + x^4) e^{-x} dx \qquad \text{with} \quad x = \frac{r}{a_0}$$

Using the integrals from Problem 13, we obtain

$$\int_5^{\infty} x^4 e^{-x} dx = (-x^4 - 4x^3 - 12x^2 - 24x - 24)e^{-x} \Big|_5^{\infty} = 10.5718$$

$$\int_5^{\infty} x^3 e^{-x} dx = (-x^3 - 3x^2 - 6x - 6)e^{-x} \Big|_5^{\infty} = 1.5902$$

$$\int_5^{\infty} x^2 e^{-x} dx = (-x^2 - 2x - 2)e^{-x} \Big|_5^{\infty} = 0.2493$$

Thus

$$P = \frac{1}{8}[10.5718 - 4(1.5902) + 4(0.2493)] = 0.651$$

For $n = 2$, $l = 1$

$$P(r) = r^2 \frac{1}{24a_0^3} \frac{r^2}{a_0^2} e^{-r/a_0}$$

$$P = \frac{1}{24a_0^5} \int_{5a_0}^{\infty} r^4 e^{-r/a_0} dr = \frac{1}{24} \int_5^{\infty} x^4 e^{-x} dx = 0.440$$

Thus the $n = 2$, $l = 0$ electron is more likely to be found beyond $5a_0$ than the $n = 2$, $l = 1$ electron.

15.
$$P(r)\,dr = r^2|R_{1,0}(r)|^2\,dr = (1.00\,a_0)^2\,\frac{4}{a_0^3}\,e^{-2}(0.01\,a_0) = 5.4 \times 10^{-3}$$

16.
$$r_{av} = \int_0^\infty rP(r)\,dr = \int_0^\infty r^3|R_{n,l}(r)|^2\,dr = \frac{4}{a_0^3}\int_0^\infty r^3 e^{-2r/a_0}\,dr$$

$$= 4a_0\int_0^\infty x^3 e^{-2x}\,dx = 4a_0\,\frac{3!}{2^4} = \frac{3}{2}\,a_0$$

The mean radius is larger than $a_0$ because the electron wave function can extend to large $r$.

17.    2s level:

$$r_{av} = \int_0^\infty rP(r)\,dr = \int_0^\infty r^3|R_{2,0}(r)|^2\,dr = \frac{1}{8a_0^3}\int_0^\infty r^3\left(2 - \frac{r}{a_0}\right)^2 e^{-r/a_0}\,dr$$

$$= \frac{a_0}{8}\int_0^\infty (4x^3 - 4x^4 + x^5)e^{-x}\,dx = \frac{a_0}{8}[4(3!) - 4(4!) + 5!] = 6a_0$$

2p level:

$$r_{av} = \frac{1}{24a_0^5}\int_0^\infty r^5 e^{-r/a_0}\,dr = \frac{a_0}{24}\int_0^\infty x^5 e^{-x}\,dx = \frac{a_0}{24}(5!) = 5a_0$$

18.
$$U_{av} = \int_0^\infty U(r)P(r)\,dr = \int_0^\infty \left(-\frac{e^2}{4\pi\epsilon_0 r}\right) r^2 |R_{1,0}(r)|^2\,dr$$

$$= -\frac{e^2}{4\pi\epsilon_0}\frac{4}{a_0^3}\int_0^\infty r e^{-2r/a_0}\,dr = -\frac{e^2}{4\pi\epsilon_0}\frac{4}{a_0^3}\frac{1}{(2/a_0)^2} = -\frac{e^2}{4\pi\epsilon_0 a_0}$$

In the Bohr model, $U = -e^2/4\pi\epsilon_0 r$ and $r = a_0$ in the $n = 1$ state, so the Bohr model gives the same potential energy as the rigorous calculation. (This is a general result that is true for all states if we use $r = a_0 n^2$.)

19. (a)
$$(r^{-1})_{av} = \int_0^\infty r^{-1} P(r)\,dr = \int_0^\infty r|R_{n,l}(r)|^2\,dr$$

For 1s:
$$(r^{-1})_{av} = \int_0^\infty r\frac{4}{a_0^3}e^{-2r/a_0}\,dr = \frac{4}{a_0^3}\frac{1}{(2/a_0)^2} = \frac{1}{a_0}$$

For 2s:
$$(r^{-1})_{av} = \int_0^\infty r\frac{1}{8a_0^3}\left(2-\frac{r}{a_0}\right)^2 e^{-2r/a_0}\,dr = \frac{1}{8a_0}\int_0^\infty x(2-x)^2 e^{-x}\,dx$$

$$= \frac{1}{8a_0}\int_0^\infty (4x - 4x^2 + x^3)e^{-x}\,dx = \frac{1}{8a_0}(4 - 8 + 6) = \frac{1}{4a_0}$$

For 2p:
$$(r^{-1})_{av} = \int_0^\infty r\frac{1}{24a_0^3}\frac{r^2}{a_0^2}e^{-r/a_0}\,dr = \frac{1}{24a_0}\int_0^\infty x^3 e^{-x}\,dx = \frac{1}{4a_0}$$

20.    Assuming a beam of silver atoms ($m \cong 108$ u) and estimating the magnetic moment to be about one Bohr magneton, we have

$$F_z = \mu_z \left( \frac{dB}{dz} \right) = (9.27 \times 10^{-24} \text{ J/T})(10 \text{ T/m}) = 9.3 \times 10^{-23} \text{ N}$$

The acceleration in the region of the field is

$$a_z = \frac{F_z}{m} = \frac{9.3 \times 10^{-23} \text{ N}}{(108 \text{ u})(1.66 \times 10^{-27} \text{ kg/u})} = 518 \text{ m/s}^2$$

For an oven temperature of 1000 K, the kinetic energy of the atoms is

$$K = \tfrac{3}{2}kT = \tfrac{3}{2}(1.38 \times 10^{-23} \text{ J/K})(1000 \text{ K}) = 2.1 \times 10^{-20} \text{ J}$$

and the speed of these atoms is

$$v = \sqrt{\frac{2K}{m}} = \sqrt{\frac{2(2.1 \times 10^{-20} \text{ J})}{(108 \text{ u})(1.66 \times 10^{-27} \text{ kg/u})}} = 480 \text{ m/s}$$

The time for an atom to travel 1 meter through the magnetic field region is

$$t = \frac{1 \text{ m}}{480 \text{ m/s}} = 2.1 \times 10^{-3} \text{ s}$$

Let the atoms enter the field with $z = 0$, $v_z = 0$. Then after passing through the 1-meter field region,

$$z = \tfrac{1}{2}a_z t^2 = \tfrac{1}{2}(518 \text{ m/s}^2)(2.1 \times 10^{-3} \text{ s})^2 = 1.1 \text{ mm}$$

$$v_z = a_z t = (518 \text{ m/s}^2)(2.1 \times 10^{-3} \text{ s}) = 1.1 \text{ m/s}$$

After leaving the region of the field there is no longer an acceleration, but the $z$-component of the velocity causes an additional displacement in the $z$-direction. The horizontal velocity is unchanged, so it will take $2.1 \times 10^{-3}$ s to pass the field-free region, and the additional displacement is

$$z = v_z t = (1.1 \text{ m/s})(2.1 \times 10^{-3} \text{ s}) = 2.2 \text{ mm}$$

The total displacement is then 1.1 mm + 2.2 mm = 3.3 mm. We would expect to see the images separated on the screen by a few millimeters.

21.     The selection rule is $\Delta l = \pm 1$, so the $4p$ state can make transitions to any lower $s$ state ($\Delta l = -1$) or $d$ state ($\Delta l = +1$):

$$4p \rightarrow 3s, \ 4p \rightarrow 2s, \ 4p \rightarrow 1s, \ \text{and} \ 4p \rightarrow 3d$$

22.     (a)     The transitions that change $l$ by one unit are

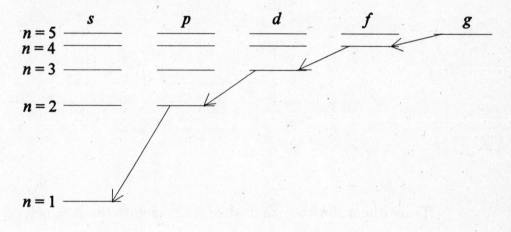

    (b)     Starting instead with $5d$,

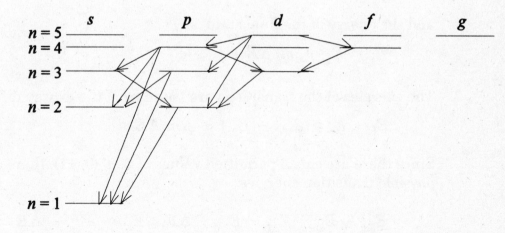

23.    (a) and (b)

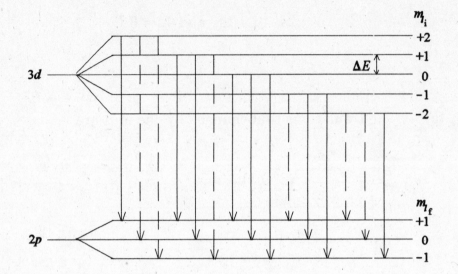

Transitions shown with dashed lines violate the $\Delta m_l$ selection rule.

(c)    The energy of the initial state is

$$E_i = E_{3d} + m_{l_i} \Delta E$$

and the energy of the final state is

$$E_f = E_{2p} + m_{l_f} \Delta E$$

The energies of the transitions are found from the energy difference:

$$E_i - E_f = (E_{3d} - E_{2p}) + \Delta m_l \Delta E$$

Since there are only 3 permitted values of $\Delta m_l$ (0, ±1), there are only 3 possible transition energies:

$$E_{3d} - E_{2p}, \quad E_{3d} - E_{2p} + \Delta E, \quad E_{3d} - E_{2p} - \Delta E$$

24.    (a)    In the absence of a magnetic field, the $3d$ to $2p$ energy difference is

$$E = -13.6057 \text{ eV}\left(\frac{1}{9} - \frac{1}{4}\right) = 1.88968 \text{ eV}$$

and the wavelength is

$$\lambda = \frac{hc}{E} = \frac{1239.842 \text{ eV·nm}}{1.88968 \text{ eV}} = 656.112 \text{ nm}$$

The magnetic field gives a change in wavelength of

$$\Delta\lambda = \frac{\lambda^2}{hc}\Delta E = \frac{(656.112 \text{ nm})^2}{1239.842 \text{ eV·nm}}(5.79 \times 10^{-5} \text{ eV/T})(3.50 \text{ T}) = 0.0703 \text{ nm}$$

The wavelengths of the 3 normal Zeeman components are

$$656.112 \text{ nm}, \qquad 656.112 \text{ nm} \pm 0.070 \text{ nm}$$

     (b)    Since the $3s$ energy is the same as the $3d$ energy, the above calculation will also hold for the Zeeman splitting of the $3s$ to $2p$ transition.

25.    The $2p$ fine structure splitting was computed to be $4.5 \times 10^{-5}$ eV.

The $2p$ to $1s$ Lyman transition has an energy of

$$E = -13.60570 \text{ eV}\left(\frac{1}{4} - 1\right) = 10.20428 \text{ eV}$$

and the wavelength is (in the absence of fine structure),

$$\lambda = \frac{hc}{E} = \frac{1239.842 \text{ eV·nm}}{10.20428 \text{ eV}} = 121.5022 \text{ nm}$$

The wavelength splitting arising from the fine structure is

$$\Delta\lambda = \frac{\lambda^2}{hc}\Delta E = \frac{(121.5 \text{ nm})^2}{1240 \text{ eV·nm}}(4.5 \times 10^{-5} \text{ eV}) = 0.00054 \text{ nm}$$

The fine structure splits one level up by $\frac{1}{2}\Delta E$ and the other down by the same amount. so the wavelengths are

$$\lambda + \frac{1}{2}\Delta\lambda = 121.5024 \text{ nm} \qquad \text{and} \qquad \lambda - \frac{1}{2}\Delta\lambda = 121.5019 \text{ nm}$$

26.    The $3d$ fine structure splitting is roughly

$$\Delta E = mc^2\alpha^4\frac{1}{3^5} = 6.0 \times 10^{-6} \text{ eV}$$

Assuming that the parallel and antiparallel states are affected equally by this splitting, the $3d$ fine structure levels have energies

$$-1.51 \text{ eV} \pm 3.0 \times 10^{-6} \text{ eV}$$

and the $2p$ energies are

$$-3.40 \text{ eV} \pm 2.2 \times 10^{-5} \text{ eV}$$

so that the energy differences are

$$1.89 \text{ eV} \pm 2.5 \times 10^{-5} \text{ eV} \qquad \text{and} \qquad 1.89 \text{ eV} \pm 1.9 \times 10^{-5} \text{ eV}$$

The wavelength differences are

$$\Delta\lambda = \frac{\lambda^2}{hc}\Delta E = \frac{(656 \text{ nm})^2}{1240 \text{ eV·nm}}(2.5 \times 10^{-5} \text{ eV}) = 0.0087 \text{ nm}$$

$$\Delta\lambda = \frac{\lambda^2}{hc}\Delta E = \frac{(656 \text{ nm})^2}{1240 \text{ eV·nm}}(1.9 \times 10^{-5} \text{ eV}) = 0.0066 \text{ nm}$$

There might therefore be as many as 4 component wavelengths,

$$656.1123 \text{ nm} \pm 0.0087 \text{ nm} \qquad \text{and} \qquad 656.1123 \text{ nm} \pm 0.0066 \text{ nm}$$

# Chapter 8

1.  (a)  From Figure 8.2 we have:

    $2p^3$ – N          $4p^3$ – As          $6p^3$ – Bi

    $3p^3$ – P          $5p^3$ – Sb

    (b)  $3d^7$ – Co          $4d^7$ – Rh          $5d^7$ – Ir

2.  (a)  [Ne] $3s^2 3p^3$          (b)  [Ar] $4s^2 3d^3$

    (c)  [Kr] $5s^2 4d^{10} 5p^3$          (d)  [Xe] $6s^2 4f^{14} 5d^{10} 6p^2$

3.  Ionization energy = 5.14 eV for sodium

    $$E = (-13.6 \ eV)\frac{Z_{eff}^2}{n^2}$$

    $$Z_{eff} = 3\sqrt{\frac{5.14 \ eV}{13.6 \ eV}} = 1.8 \qquad for \quad n = 3$$

    For potassium, ionization energy = 4.34 eV

    $$Z_{eff} = 4\sqrt{\frac{4.34 \ eV}{13.6 \ eV}} = 2.3$$

    For complete screening by the inner shells, we expect $Z_{eff} = 1$ in the Bohr model.

4.  Applying Equation 6.42 to an atom with $Z-1$ nuclear charge, we obtain

$$E_n = -(Z-1)^2 \frac{me^4}{32\pi^2\epsilon_0^2\hbar^2} \frac{1}{n^2} = -(Z-1)^2 \frac{hcR_\infty}{n^2}$$

using Equation 6.40 for $R_\infty$. The frequency of the emitted radiation is

$$\nu = \frac{E_2 - E_1}{h} = -(Z-1)^2 cR_\infty \left(\frac{1}{4} - 1\right) = \frac{3cR_\infty}{4}(Z-1)^2$$

5.  Solving Equation 8.1 with $\lambda = c/\nu$, we obtain

$$Z-1 = \sqrt{\frac{4}{3R_\infty \lambda}} = \sqrt{\frac{1.33}{(1.0974 \times 10^7 \text{ m}^{-1})(0.1940 \times 10^{-9} \text{ m})}} = 25.02$$

Thus $Z = 26$ and the element is iron.

6.  Calcium ($Z = 20$):

$$E = h\nu = \frac{3hcR_\infty}{4}(Z-1)^2$$

$$= \frac{3(1240 \text{ eV·nm})(1.097 \times 10^7 \text{ m}^{-1})(19)^2}{4} = 3.68 \text{ keV}$$

Zirconium ($Z = 40$):

$$E = \frac{3(1240 \text{ eV·nm})(1.097 \times 10^7 \text{ m}^{-1})(39)^2}{4} = 15.5 \text{ keV}$$

Mercury ($Z = 80$):

$$E = \frac{3(1240 \text{ eV·nm})(1.097 \times 10^7 \text{ m}^{-1})(79)^2}{4} = 63.7 \text{ keV}$$

The values computed from Moseley's Law are smaller than the measured values.

7.    The values of $\nu^{1/2}$ in $Hz^{1/2}$ can be found as follows:

| | | | |
|---|---|---|---|
| Ne (Z=10) | $4.55 \times 10^8$ | Mn (Z=25) | $1.25 \times 10^9$ | Zr (Z=40) | $2.07 \times 10^9$ |
| P (Z=15) | $7.19 \times 10^8$ | Zn (Z=30) | $1.52 \times 10^9$ | Rh (Z=45) | $2.35 \times 10^9$ |
| Ca (Z=20) | $9.86 \times 10^8$ | Br (Z=35) | $1.79 \times 10^9$ | Sn (Z=50) | $2.62 \times 10^9$ |

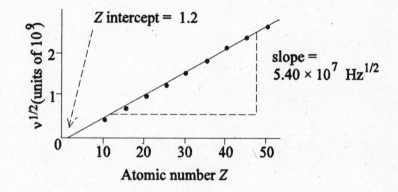

The $K_\beta$ x rays originate with the $n = 3$ shell, so we have

$$\nu = \frac{E_3 - E_1}{h} = -(Z-1)^2 c R_\infty \left( \frac{1}{3^2} - 1 \right) = \frac{8 c R_\infty}{9} (Z-1)^2$$

If we plot $\nu^{1/2}$ against $Z$, we should obtain a straight line of slope

$$\sqrt{\frac{8 c R_\infty}{9}} = 5.41 \times 10^7 \; Hz^{1/2}$$

and intercept $Z = 1$. The expected values are very close to the measured values.

8.    The values of $\nu^{1/2}$ in $Hz^{1/2}$ are:

| Mn ($Z=25$) | $4.18\times10^8$ | Rh ($Z=45$) | $8.36\times10^8$ |
| Zn ($Z=30$) | $5.18\times10^8$ | Sn ($Z=50$) | $9.47\times10^8$ |
| Br ($Z=35$) | $6.22\times10^8$ | Cs ($Z=55$) | $1.06\times10^9$ |
| Zr ($Z=40$) | $7.06\times10^8$ | Nd ($Z=60$) | $1.18\times10^9$ |

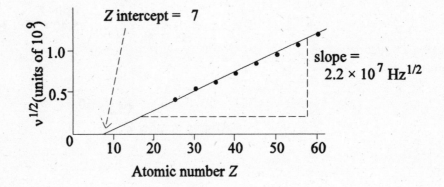

The $L_\alpha$ X rays begin with the $n = 3$ level and end with the $n = 2$ level. It is difficult to calculate the screening effect of the $1s$, $2s$, and $2p$ electrons on the $n = 3$ electron that makes the transition, but as a rough approximation we may assume that the screening is caused by the two $n = 1$ ($1s$) electrons and by the seven $n = 2$ ($2s + 2p$) electrons. Thus $Z_{eff} \cong Z-9$, and

$$\nu = \frac{E_3 - E_2}{h} = -(Z-9)^2 cR_\infty\left(\frac{1}{3^2} - \frac{1}{2^2}\right) = \frac{5cR_\infty}{36}(Z-9)^2$$

The expected slope of $\nu^{1/2}$ plotted against $Z$ is

$$\sqrt{\frac{5cR_\infty}{36}} = 2.14 \times 10^7 \; Hz^{1/2}$$

The expected slope is fairly close to the measured value, and the measured intercept of 7 is consistent with the screening effect of many $n = 1$ and $n = 2$ electrons.

9.    In order to observe a $K$ X ray, it is first necessary to remove one of the $K$ electrons.  The binding energy of the $K$ electron is approximately

$$E_n = -13.6 \text{ eV} \left( \frac{Z^2}{n^2} \right)$$

if we neglect the screening effect of the other $K$ electron (which is probably not negligible) and the other electrons (whose effect may be smaller).  For the $K$ electron of copper ($Z = 29$),

$$E_1 \cong 11 \text{ keV}$$

Electrons with energies in excess of 11 keV should be able to knock loose a $K$ electron, after which $K$ X rays will be emitted.  The necessary voltage is thus about 11 kV.

10.   Cr:  $[\text{Ar}]4s^1 3d^5$
There is nothing that prevents all 6 electrons from having $m_s = +\frac{1}{2}$, and thus $s = +\frac{1}{2} + \frac{1}{2} + \frac{1}{2} + \frac{1}{2} + \frac{1}{2} + \frac{1}{2} = 3$.  According to the Pauli principle, the five $3d$ electrons must all have different $m_l$ values, which are +2, +1, 0, −1, −2; the $4s$ electron has $m_l = 0$ only.  The total $L$ is therefore $+2 + 1 + 0 - 1 - 2 + 0 = 0$.  The configuration is thus $L = 0$, $S = 3$.

11.   (a)    Ce:  $[\text{Xe}]6s^2 4f^1 5d^1$
The two $6s$ electrons have opposite spins so the only contributions to the total $S$ come from the other two electrons, each of which has a maximum $m_s$ of $+\frac{1}{2}$. Thus $S = 1$.  The Pauli principle does not prevent the $m_l$ values of these two electrons from having their maximum possible values of +3 (for $4f$) and +2 (for $5d$).  The $6s$ electrons do not contribute to $L$, so $L = 2 + 3 = 5$.  The ground state is thus $L = 5$, $S = 1$.

(b)    Gd:  $[\text{Xe}]6s^2 4f^7 5d^1$
The two $6s$ electrons contribute neither to $L$ nor to $S$.  To maximize $S$, we give all seven $4f$ electrons $m_s = +\frac{1}{2}$ (which is possible, because the $4f$ shell has a capacity of 14) and we also give $m_s = +\frac{1}{2}$ to the $5d$ electron.  Thus $S = 8(\frac{1}{2}) = 4$.  The Pauli principle requires that all seven of the $4f$ electrons have different $m_l$ values, which are +3, +2, +1, 0, −1, −2, and −3, for a total of 0. The only contribution to $L$ comes from the $5d$ electron, which contributes $m_l = 2$.  The ground state is therefore $L = 2$, $S = 4$.

(c)    Pt:  $[Xe]6s^1 4f^{14} 5d^9$

There is no contribution to $L$ or $S$ from the filled $4f$ subshell. The spin of the nine $5d$ electrons is maximized by giving five of them $m_s = +\frac{1}{2}$ and the remaining four $m_s = -\frac{1}{2}$. The $6s$ electron also contributes $m_s = +\frac{1}{2}$, for a total of $S = 1$. The $6s$ electron doesn't contribute to $L$, and the five $5d$ electrons with $m_s = +\frac{1}{2}$ have $m_l$ of $+2, +1, 0, -1, -2$ and also don't contribute to $L$. We therefore maximize the contribution to $L$ of the remaining four $5d$ electrons by assigning them $m_l$ of $+2, +1, 0, -1$ for a net total of $L = 2$. The ground state is thus $L = 2$, $S = 1$.

12.   (a)    F:  $[He]2s^2 2p^5$

Only the five $2p$ electrons contribute to $L$ or $S$. The total spin is maximized with three having $m_s = +\frac{1}{2}$ and two $m_s = -\frac{1}{2}$, for a total of $S = 1/2$. The three $m_s = +\frac{1}{2}$ electrons must, according to the Pauli principle, have $m_l$ of $+1, 0, -1$ for a total of zero. The two $m_s = -\frac{1}{2}$ electrons maximize $L$ if assigned $m_l$ of $+1, 0$. Thus, $L = 1$, $S = 1/2$.

(b)    Mg:  $[Ne]2s^2$

The $2s$ electrons do not contribute to $L$, and their spins must be opposite. Thus $L = 0$, $S = 0$.

(c)    Ti:  $[Ar]4s^2 3d^2$

The $4s$ electrons do not contribute to $L$ or $S$. Maximizing $S$ for the $3d$ electrons gives $S = +\frac{1}{2} + \frac{1}{2} = 1$. The $3d$ electrons must have different $m_l$, and so $L$ is maximized with $m_l = +2, +1$. Thus $L = 3$, $S = 1$.

(d)    Fe:  $[Ar]4s^2 3d^6$

Maximizing $S$ for the $3d$ electrons gives $S = +\frac{1}{2} + \frac{1}{2} + \frac{1}{2} + \frac{1}{2} + \frac{1}{2} - \frac{1}{2} = 2$. The five electrons with $m_s = +\frac{1}{2}$ are assigned $m_l = +2, +1, 0, -1, -2$, and the electron with $m_s = -\frac{1}{2}$ has $m_l = +2$. Thus $L = 2$, $S = 2$.

13.   Each electron has $s = \frac{1}{2}$, so the total possible $S$ is 0 or 1. The two $d$ electrons, each with $l = 2$, can couple to give $L = 0, 1, 2, 3, 4$.

14.  The difference in wavelength between the components of the fine structure doublet is 0.6 nm. With $E = hc/\lambda$,

$$\Delta E = \frac{hc}{\lambda^2} \Delta \lambda = \frac{1240 \text{ eV·nm}}{(590 \text{ nm})^2}(0.6 \text{ nm}) = 2.1 \times 10^{-3} \text{ eV}$$

If we assume this energy difference comes from the interaction of a magnetic field $B$ with a magnetic moment $\mu = 1 \mu_B$, then $\Delta E = 2\mu_B B$ and

$$B = \frac{\Delta E}{2\mu_B} = \frac{2.1 \times 10^{-3} \text{ eV}}{2(5.8 \times 10^{-5} \text{ eV/T})^2} = 18 \text{ T}$$

This is quite a large magnetic field, of the order of the largest that can be produced in the laboratory with superconducting electromagnets.

15.  In sodium,

$3d \rightarrow 3p$      $\lambda = 819$ nm      $\Delta E = \dfrac{hc}{\lambda} = \dfrac{1240 \text{ eV·nm}}{819 \text{ nm}} = 1.51$ eV

$4d \rightarrow 3p$      $\lambda = 568.5$ nm      $\Delta E = \dfrac{hc}{\lambda} = \dfrac{1240 \text{ eV·nm}}{568.5 \text{ nm}} = 2.18$ eV

$\Delta E(4d \rightarrow 3d) = \Delta E(4d \rightarrow 3p) - \Delta E(3d \rightarrow 3p) = 2.18 \text{ eV} - 1.51 \text{ eV} = 0.67 \text{ eV}$

In lithium,

$3d \rightarrow 3p$      $\lambda = 610.4$ nm      $\Delta E = \dfrac{hc}{\lambda} = \dfrac{1240 \text{ eV·nm}}{610.4 \text{ nm}} = 2.03$ eV

$4d \rightarrow 3p$      $\lambda = 460.3$ nm      $\Delta E = \dfrac{hc}{\lambda} = \dfrac{1240 \text{ eV·nm}}{460.3 \text{ nm}} = 2.69$ eV

$\Delta E(4d \rightarrow 3d) = \Delta E(4d \rightarrow 3p) - \Delta E(3d \rightarrow 3p) = 2.69 \text{ eV} - 2.03 \text{ eV} = 0.66 \text{ eV}$

In hydrogen,

$$\Delta E(4 \rightarrow 3) = -13.6 \text{ eV} \left( \frac{1}{4^2} - \frac{1}{3^2} \right) = 0.66 \text{ eV}$$

The agreement is good, because in sodium and lithium the outer electron is screened by the $Z-1$ inner electrons, and so the energy levels are well approximated by the hydrogenic levels with $Z = 1$.

16.  (a)   From Figure 8.10, we can find the $3d \rightarrow 3p$ energy difference as follows:

$$\Delta E(3d \rightarrow 3p) = \Delta E(3d \rightarrow 2s) - \Delta E(3p \rightarrow 2s)$$

$$= \Delta E(3d \rightarrow 2p) + \Delta E(2p \rightarrow 2s) - \Delta E(3p \rightarrow 2s)$$

$$= \frac{hc}{\lambda(3d \rightarrow 2p)} + \frac{hc}{\lambda(2p \rightarrow 2s)} - \frac{hc}{\lambda(3p \rightarrow 2s)}$$

$$= \frac{1240 \text{ eV·nm}}{610.4 \text{ nm}} + \frac{1240 \text{ eV·nm}}{670.8 \text{ nm}} - \frac{1240 \text{ eV·nm}}{323.3 \text{ nm}} = 0.045 \text{ eV}$$

(b)   $\Delta E(ns \rightarrow 2s) = \Delta E(ns \rightarrow 2p) + \Delta E(2p \rightarrow 2s)$

$$= \frac{hc}{\lambda(ns \rightarrow 2p)} + \frac{hc}{\lambda(2p \rightarrow 2s)}$$

$$\Delta E(3s \rightarrow 2s) = \frac{1240 \text{ eV·nm}}{812.7 \text{ nm}} + \frac{1240 \text{ eV·nm}}{670.8 \text{ nm}} = 3.374 \text{ eV}$$

$$\Delta E(4s \rightarrow 2s) = \frac{1240 \text{ eV·nm}}{491.2 \text{ nm}} + \frac{1240 \text{ eV·nm}}{670.8 \text{ nm}} = 4.373 \text{ eV}$$

$$\Delta E(5s \rightarrow 2s) = \frac{1240 \text{ eV·nm}}{427.3 \text{ nm}} + \frac{1240 \text{ eV·nm}}{670.8 \text{ nm}} = 4.750 \text{ eV}$$

(c)   $\Delta E(2p \rightarrow 2s) = E(2p) - E(2s)$

$$E(2p) = E(2s) + \Delta E(2p \rightarrow 2s) = E(2s) + \frac{hc}{\lambda(2p \rightarrow 2s)}$$

$$= -5.39 \text{ eV} + \frac{1240 \text{ eV·nm}}{670.8 \text{ nm}} = -3.54 \text{ eV}$$

The 2p ionization energy is therefore 3.54 eV.

$$E(3s) = E(2s) + \Delta E(3s \rightarrow 2s) = -5.39 \text{ eV} + 3.37 \text{ eV} = -2.02 \text{ eV}$$

The 3s ionization energy is 2.02 eV.

17.        $$E = \frac{hc}{\lambda} \quad \text{so} \quad \Delta E = \frac{hc}{\lambda^2} \Delta \lambda$$

The fine structure splittings are

3p:   $$\Delta E = \frac{1240 \text{ eV·nm}}{(589 \text{ nm})^2} (589.592 \text{ nm} - 588.995 \text{ nm}) = 2.1 \times 10^{-3} \text{ eV}$$

4p:   $$\Delta E = \frac{1240 \text{ eV·nm}}{(330 \text{ nm})^2} (330.303 \text{ nm} - 330.241 \text{ nm}) = 7.1 \times 10^{-4} \text{ eV}$$

5p:   $$\Delta E = \frac{1240 \text{ eV·nm}}{(285 \text{ nm})^2} (285.307 \text{ nm} - 285.286 \text{ nm}) = 3.2 \times 10^{-4} \text{ eV}$$

6p:   $$\Delta E = \frac{1240 \text{ eV·nm}}{(268 \text{ nm})^2} (268.047 \text{ nm} - 268.038 \text{ nm}) = 1.6 \times 10^{-4} \text{ eV}$$

The theory of Section 7.8 ascribes the fine structure splitting to the apparent motion of the nucleus, and so we should scale the effective magnetic field by a factor of $Z$. The expressions for $r$ and $E$ should take into account the electron screening, and so $Z = 1$ formulas should be used. The result is

$$\Delta E = \frac{Zmc^2\alpha^4}{n^5} = \frac{1.60 \times 10^{-2} \text{ eV}}{n^5}$$

The calculated values range from $6.6 \times 10^{-5}$ eV for $n = 3$ to $2.1 \times 10^{-6}$ for $n = 6$ and are thus two orders of magnitude too small. The simple theory does not work well here. (The correct calculation gives $\Delta E$ proportional to $Z^2$, and the $n^{-5}$ dependence is also not correct according to the complete calculation.)

18.          $$\Delta E(4p \rightarrow 3p) = \Delta E(4p \rightarrow 2s) - \Delta E(3p \rightarrow 2s)$$

$$= \frac{hc}{\lambda(4p \rightarrow 2s)} - \frac{hc}{\lambda(3p \rightarrow 2s)}$$

$$= \frac{1240 \text{ eV·nm}}{396.5 \text{ nm}} - \frac{1240 \text{ eV·nm}}{501.6 \text{ nm}} = 0.655 \text{ eV}$$

In hydrogen,

$$\Delta E(4 \rightarrow 3) = -13.6 \text{ eV} \left( \frac{1}{4^2} - \frac{1}{3^2} \right) = 0.661 \text{ eV}$$

(The agreement is so good, because the $4p$ electron in helium is screened by the $1s$ electron, so that $Z_{eff} = 2 - 1 = 1$.)

$$\Delta E(4d \rightarrow 3d) = \Delta E(4d \rightarrow 2p) - \Delta E(3d \rightarrow 2p)$$

$$= \frac{hc}{\lambda(4d \rightarrow 2p)} - \frac{hc}{\lambda(3d \rightarrow 2p)}$$

$$= \frac{1240 \text{ eV·nm}}{447.1 \text{ nm}} - \frac{1240 \text{ eV·nm}}{587.6 \text{ nm}} = 0.663 \text{ eV}$$

Again, the agreement with hydrogen is very good.

19.    (a)    For a $2p$ electron $n = 2$, $l = 1$; thus $m_l = \pm 1$ and $m_s = \pm\frac{1}{2}$.

$$(n,l,m_l,m_s) = (2,1,+1,+\tfrac{1}{2}), \ (2,1,+1,-\tfrac{1}{2}), \ (2,1,0,+\tfrac{1}{2}),$$
$$(2,1,0,-\tfrac{1}{2}), \ (2,1,-1,+\tfrac{1}{2}), \ (2,1,-1,-\tfrac{1}{2})$$

      (b)    Since there are 6 possible sets for each electron, the total number of possibilities for 2 electrons is $6 \times 6 = 36$.

      (c)    The Pauli principle prevents the two sets from being identical. There will be 6 combinations in which the sets are identical, which must be eliminated, leaving 30 allowed combinations.

      (d)    Since the $n$ values are different, the Pauli principle does not restrict the number of possible combinations, so there will be 36 possible sets.

20.    Figure 8.14 shows 6 states with different $L$ and $S$ values that make up the $2p^1 3p^1$ group. Each state has a degeneracy of $(2S + 1)(2L + 1)$:

|  | degeneracy |
|---|---|
| $L = 0$, $S = 0$ | 1 |
| $L = 1$, $S = 0$ | 3 |
| $L = 2$, $S = 0$ | 5 |
| $L = 0$, $S = 1$ | 3 |
| $L = 1$, $S = 1$ | 9 |
| $L = 2$, $S = 1$ | 15 |
|  | total = 36 |

The total number of individual states is 36, as we found in Problem 19(d).

21.    (a)    Figure 8.10 shows that the longest absorption wavelength from the ground state is 670.8 nm, in the visible region of the spectrum.

      (b)    From Figure 8.13, the longest ground-state absorption wavelength is 58.4 nm, in the ultraviolet region.

(c)     The shortest absorption wavelengths (largest absorption energies) are those which ionize the atom.  For lithium, this is

$$\lambda = \frac{hc}{E} = \frac{1240 \ eV \cdot nm}{5.39 \ eV} = 230 \ nm$$

in the near ultraviolet region.  For helium,

$$\lambda = \frac{1240 \ eV \cdot nm}{24.5 \ eV} = 50.6 \ nm$$

in the ultraviolet.

22.     (a)     For $\lambda = 632.8$ nm,

$$E = \frac{hc}{\lambda} = \frac{1240 \ eV \cdot nm}{632.8 \ nm} = 1.96 \ eV = 3.14 \times 10^{-19} \ J$$

$$P = \frac{3.5 \times 10^{-3} \ J/s}{3.14 \times 10^{-19} \ J/photon} = 1.12 \times 10^{16} \ photon/s$$

(b)     From Equation 3.10,

$$E = \sqrt{\frac{2\mu_0 c P_{av}}{A}}$$

$$= \sqrt{\frac{2(4\pi \times 10^{-7} \ T \cdot m/A)(3.00 \times 10^8 \ m/s)(3.5 \times 10^{-3} \ W)}{\pi(1.2 \times 10^{-3} \ m)^2}} = 763 \ V/m$$

For the incandescent bulb:

$$E = \sqrt{\frac{2(4\pi \times 10^{-7} \ T \cdot m/A)(3.00 \times 10^8 \ m/s)(100 \ W)}{\pi(1 \ m)^2}} = 77 \ V/m$$

# Chapter 9

1. The binding energy of $H_2^+$ is 2.7 eV, and the binding energy of $H_2$ is 4.5 eV. The ionization energy of $H_2$ is thus

$$E_{ion}(H_2) = E(H_2^+) - E(H_2) = -16.3 \text{ eV} + 31.7 \text{ eV} = 15.4 \text{ eV}$$

2. The equilibrium separation of KBr is 0.282 nm.

$$U = \frac{e^2}{4\pi\epsilon_0} \frac{1}{R} = \frac{1.44 \text{ eV·nm}}{0.282 \text{ nm}} = 5.11 \text{ eV}$$

3. The difference between the ionization energy of K and the electron affinity of I is

$$4.34 \text{ eV} - 3.06 \text{ eV} = 1.28 \text{ eV}$$

The potential energy will be 1.28 eV when $R$ is

$$R = \frac{e^2}{4\pi\epsilon_0} \frac{1}{U} = \frac{1.44 \text{ eV·nm}}{1.28 \text{ eV}} = 1.13 \text{ nm}$$

Whenever $R$ is less than 1.13 nm it is advantageous to have $K^+$ and $I^-$ ions.

4. (a) Each mole contains $6.022 \times 10^{23}$ molecules, so

$$E = \frac{410 \times 10^3 \text{ J/mole}}{6.022 \times 10^{23} \text{ molecules/mole}} \frac{1}{1.60 \times 10^{-19} \text{ J/eV}}$$

$$= 4.25 \text{ eV/molecule}$$

(b)    $E = \dfrac{106 \times 10^3 \text{ J/mole}}{6.022 \times 10^{23} \text{ molecules/mole}} \dfrac{1}{1.60 \times 10^{-19} \text{ J/eV}}$

$= 1.10 \text{ eV/molecule}$

(c)    $E = \dfrac{945 \times 10^3 \text{ J/mole}}{6.022 \times 10^{23} \text{ molecules/mole}} \dfrac{1}{1.60 \times 10^{-19} \text{ J/eV}}$

$= 9.80 \text{ eV/molecule}$

5.    (a)    $p = eR_{eq} = (1.60 \times 10^{-19} \text{ C})(0.193 \times 10^{-9} \text{ m}) = 30.9 \times 10^{-30} \text{ C·m}$

(b)    $\dfrac{p_{meas}}{p} = \dfrac{27.2 \times 10^{-30} \text{ C·m}}{30.9 \times 10^{-30} \text{ C·m}} = 0.88$

Thus NaF is 88% ionic.

6.    $p = eR_{eq} = (1.60 \times 10^{-19} \text{ C})(0.160 \times 10^{-9} \text{ m}) = 25.6 \times 10^{-30} \text{ C·m}$

$\dfrac{p_{meas}}{p} = \dfrac{1.47 \times 10^{-30} \text{ C·m}}{25.6 \times 10^{-30} \text{ C·m}} = 0.057 = 5.7\% \text{ ionic}$

7.    $p = 2er = 2(1.60 \times 10^{-19} \text{ C})(0.194 \times 10^{-9} \text{ m}) = 62.1 \times 10^{-30} \text{ C·m}$

$\dfrac{p_{meas}}{p} = \dfrac{26.5 \times 10^{-30} \text{ C·m}}{62.1 \times 10^{-30} \text{ C·m}} = 0.427 = 42.7\% \text{ ionic}$

8. At $R = R_{eq}$, $E = -E_0 = \dfrac{A}{R_{eq}^9} - \dfrac{B}{R_{eq}}$

$$\left(\frac{dE}{dR}\right)_{R \cdot R_{eq}} = \frac{-9A}{R_{eq}^{10}} + \frac{B}{R_{eq}^2} = 0$$

Solving these two equations simultaneously, we obtain

$$A = \frac{E_0 R_{eq}^9}{8} \qquad \text{and} \qquad B = \frac{9A}{R_{eq}^8} = \frac{9}{8}E_0 R_{eq}$$

9.

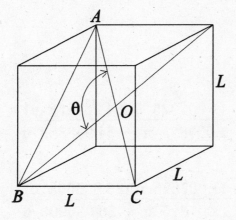

$$AB = \sqrt{2}\,L \quad \text{and} \quad AC = \sqrt{(AB)^2 + (BC)^2} = \sqrt{2L^2 + L^2} = \sqrt{3}\,L$$

Use the law of cosines on triangle $OAB$:

$$(AB)^2 = (AO)^2 + (OB)^2 - 2(AO)(OB)\cos\theta$$

But $AO = OB = \frac{1}{2}AC$, so

$$(AB)^2 = 2\left(\tfrac{1}{2}AC\right)^2 - 2\left(\tfrac{1}{2}AC\right)^2\cos\theta$$

$$\theta = \cos^{-1}\left[1 - \frac{(AB)^2}{\frac{1}{2}(AC)^2}\right] = \cos^{-1}\left[1 - \frac{2\,L^2}{\frac{1}{2}(3L^2)}\right] = \cos^{-1}\left(-\frac{1}{3}\right) = 109.5°$$

10.
$$I = m_1 x_1^2 + m_2 x_2^2 = (m_1 x_1^2 + m_2 x_2^2)\left(\frac{m_1 + m_2}{m_1 + m_2}\right)$$

$$= \frac{m_1^2 x_1^2 + m_1 m_2 x_2^2 + m_1 m_2 x_1^2 + m_2^2 x_2^2}{m_1 + m_2}$$

$$= \frac{m_1 m_2 x_1^2 + 2m_1 m_2 x_1 x_2 + m_1 m_2 x_2^2}{m_1 + m_2} \qquad \text{using} \quad m_1 x_1 = m_2 x_2$$

$$= \frac{m_1 m_2}{m_1 + m_2}(x_1^2 + 2x_1 x_2 + x_2^2) = mR_{eq}^2$$

11.    The reduced masses are

$$m_{35} = \frac{m_1 m_2}{m_1 + m_2} = \frac{(1.007825 \text{ u})(34.968853 \text{ u})}{1.007825 \text{ u} + 34.968853 \text{ u}} = 0.979593 \text{ u}$$

$$m_{37} = \frac{m_1 m_2}{m_1 + m_2} = \frac{(1.007825 \text{ u})(36.965903 \text{ u})}{1.007825 \text{ u} + 36.965903 \text{ u}} = 0.981077 \text{ u}$$

$$\Delta E = \frac{\hbar^2}{R^2}\left(\frac{1}{m_{35}} - \frac{1}{m_{37}}\right) = \frac{\hbar^2 c^2}{R^2}\left(\frac{1}{m_{35}c^2} - \frac{1}{m_{37}c^2}\right)$$

$$= \left(\frac{197.3 \text{ eV·nm}}{0.127 \text{ nm}}\right)^2 (1.65768 \times 10^{-6} \text{ MeV}^{-1}) = 4.00 \times 10^{-6} \text{ eV}$$

12. $$k = \frac{2\,(0.25\ \text{eV})}{(0.040\ \text{nm})^2} = 310\ \text{eV/nm}^2 = 310 \times 10^{18}\ \text{eV/m}^2$$

$$m = \frac{m_1 m_2}{m_1 + m_2} = \frac{(23\ \text{u})(35.5\ \text{u})}{23\ \text{u} + 35.5\ \text{u}} = 13.96\ \text{u} \quad \text{using average mass of Cl}$$

$$\nu = \frac{1}{2\pi}\sqrt{\frac{kc^2}{mc^2}} = \frac{1}{2\pi}\sqrt{\frac{(310 \times 10^{18}\ \text{eV/m}^2)(9.0 \times 10^{16}\ \text{m}^2/\text{s}^2)}{(13.96\ \text{u})(931.5\ \text{MeV/u})}}$$

$$= 7.4 \times 10^{12}\ \text{Hz}$$

$$\lambda = \frac{c}{\nu} = \frac{3 \times 10^8\ \text{m/s}}{7.4 \times 10^{12}\ \text{Hz}} = 40\ \mu\text{m} \quad \text{(infrared region)}$$

$$h\nu = 0.031\ \text{eV}$$

The approximation is valid for an energy range of about 0.25 eV, so up to about $N = 8$.

13. For $H_2$ $\quad m = \dfrac{m_1 m_2}{m_1 + m_2} = \dfrac{(m_H)(m_H)}{2m_H} = \dfrac{m_H}{2}$

For HD $\quad m = \dfrac{(m_H)(2m_H)}{3m_H} = \dfrac{2}{3}m_H$

For $D_2$ $\quad m = \dfrac{(2m_H)(2m_H)}{4m_H} = m_H$

$$\nu \propto \frac{1}{\sqrt{m}} \quad \text{so} \quad \frac{\nu_{HD}}{\nu_{H_2}} = \frac{\sqrt{m_H/2}}{\sqrt{2m_H/3}} = \sqrt{\frac{3}{4}} = 0.866$$

$$\nu_{HD} = 0.866(1.32 \times 10^{14} \text{ Hz}) = 1.14 \times 10^{14} \text{ Hz}$$

$$\frac{\nu_{D_2}}{\nu_{H_2}} = \frac{\sqrt{m/2}}{\sqrt{m}} = \sqrt{\frac{1}{2}} = 0.707$$

$$\nu_{D_2} = 0.707(1.32 \times 10^{14} \text{ Hz}) = 9.33 \times 10^{13} \text{ Hz}$$

$R_{eq}$ does not depend on the nuclear mass, so HD and $D_2$ should have the same $R_{eq}$ as $H_2$.

The rotational parameters can be found from the mass ratios:

For HD $\qquad \dfrac{\hbar^2}{mR_{eq}^2} = (0.0152 \text{ eV}) \dfrac{m_H/2}{(2/3)m_H} = 0.0114 \text{ eV}$

For $D_2$ $\qquad \dfrac{\hbar^2}{mR_{eq}^2} = (0.0152 \text{ eV}) \dfrac{m_H/2}{m_H} = 0.0076 \text{ eV}$

14.    For $H_2$, $\qquad E_{vib} = 0.54 \text{ eV} = h\nu \qquad$ with $\quad \nu \propto 1/\sqrt{m}$

For HD, $\qquad E_{vib} = 0.54 \text{ eV} \sqrt{\dfrac{3}{4}} = 0.47 \text{ eV}$

For $D_2$, $\qquad E_{vib} = 0.54 \text{ eV} \sqrt{\dfrac{1}{2}} = 0.38 \text{ eV}$

The zero-point energy is half the vibrational energy, so the dissociation energy for HD is

$$4.52 \text{ eV} - \frac{1}{2}E_{vib,H_2} + \frac{1}{2}E_{vib,HD}$$

$$= 4.52 \text{ eV} - \frac{1}{2}(0.54 \text{ eV}) + \frac{1}{2}(0.47 \text{ eV}) = 4.56 \text{ eV}$$

For $D_2$ the dissociation energy is

$$4.52 \text{ eV} - \frac{1}{2}E_{\text{vib,H}_2} + \frac{1}{2}E_{\text{vib,D}_2}$$

$$= 4.52 \text{ eV} - \frac{1}{2}(0.54 \text{ eV}) + \frac{1}{2}(0.38 \text{ eV}) = 4.60 \text{ eV}$$

15.    For NaCl (using the average mass of 35.5 u for Cl)

$$m = \frac{m_1 m_2}{m_1 + m_2} = \frac{(23 \text{ u})(35.5 \text{ u})}{23 \text{ u} + 35.5 \text{ u}} = 13.96 \text{ u}$$

$$R_{\text{eq}} = 0.236 \text{ nm}$$

$$\frac{\hbar^2}{mR_{\text{eq}}^2} = \frac{\hbar^2 c^2}{mc^2 R_{\text{eq}}^2} = \frac{(197 \text{ eV·nm})^2}{(13.96 \text{ u})(931.5 \text{ MeV/u})(0.236 \text{ nm})^2}$$

$$= 53.6 \times 10^{-6} \text{ eV}$$

$L = 1$ to $L = 0$:

$$\Delta E = \frac{\hbar^2}{mR_{\text{eq}}^2} = 53.6 \times 10^{-6} \text{ eV} \quad \text{and} \quad \lambda = \frac{hc}{\Delta E} = 23.1 \text{ mm}$$

$L = 2$ to $L = 1$:

$$\Delta E = 2\frac{\hbar^2}{mR_{\text{eq}}^2} = 107.2 \times 10^{-6} \text{ eV} \quad \text{and} \quad \lambda = 11.6 \text{ mm}$$

$L = 3$ to $L = 2$

$$\Delta E = 3\frac{\hbar^2}{mR_{\text{eq}}^2} = 160.8 \times 10^{-6} \text{ eV} \quad \text{and} \quad \lambda = 7.71 \text{ mm}$$

16.  (a)  For $H_2$,   $E_{vib} = 0.54$ eV   and   $\dfrac{\hbar^2}{mR_{eq}^2} = 0.0152$ eV

From Equation 9.13,  $L(L + 1) = \dfrac{2E_{vib}}{\hbar^2/mR_{eq}^2} = \dfrac{2(0.54 \text{ eV})}{0.0152 \text{ eV}} = 71$

$L \cong 8$

so 9 rotational states ($L = 0$ to 8) are between the vibrational states.

(b)  For HCl,   $E_{vib} = 0.358$ eV   and   $\dfrac{\hbar^2}{mR_{eq}^2} = 0.00265$ eV

$L(L + 1) = \dfrac{2E_{vib}}{\hbar^2/mR_{eq}^2} = \dfrac{2(0.358 \text{ eV})}{0.00265 \text{ eV}} = 270$

$L \cong 16$

so 17 rotational states are between the vibrational states.

(c)  For NaCl,  $E_{vib} = 0.030$ eV   and   $\dfrac{\hbar^2}{mR_{eq}^2} = 53.6 \times 10^{-6}$ eV

$L(L + 1) = \dfrac{2(0.030 \text{ eV})}{53.6 \times 10^{-6} \text{ eV}} = 1119$

$L \cong 33$

so 34 rotational states are between the vibrational states.

17. $$E_{NL} = (N + 1/2)h\nu + L(L + 1)\frac{\hbar^2}{2mR_{eq}^2} = 2(N + 1/2) + 10L(L + 1)$$

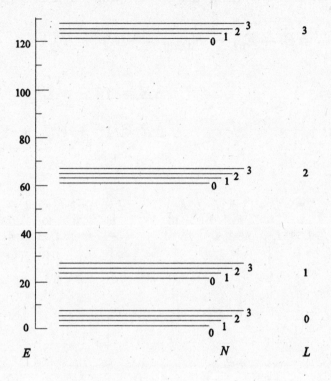

18. (a)

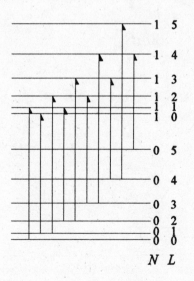

(b)     $E_{NL} = (N + 1/2)h\nu + L(L + 1)\dfrac{\hbar^2}{2mR_{eq}^2} = 10(N + 1/2) + \dfrac{1}{4}L(L + 1)$

For $N = 0$ to $N = 1$, there are two sequences of absorption lines:

$$\Delta E = \left| E_{0L} - E_{1L \pm 1} \right| = -E_{0L} + E_{1L \pm 1}$$

$L \to L - 1$                      $\Delta E = 10 - \frac{1}{2}L$

$L \to L + 1$                      $\Delta E = 10 + \frac{1}{2}(L + 1)$

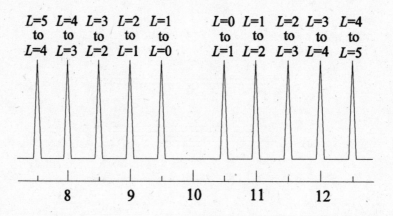

19.          $E_{NL} = (N + \frac{1}{2})h\nu + L(L + 1)\dfrac{\hbar^2}{2mR_{eq}^2}$

For emission transitions $N \to N - 1$ and $L \to L \pm 1$, $\Delta E = E_{NL} - E_{N-1L \pm 1}$

$L \to L + 1$:    $\Delta E = h\nu + L(L + 1)\dfrac{\hbar^2}{2mR_{eq}^2} - (L + 1)(L + 2)\dfrac{\hbar^2}{2mR_{eq}^2}$

$$= h\nu - (L + 1)\dfrac{\hbar^2}{mR_{eq}^2}$$

$$L \to L - 1: \quad \Delta E = h\nu + L(L + 1)\frac{\hbar^2}{2mR_{eq}^2} - (L - 1)(L)\frac{\hbar^2}{2mR_{eq}^2}$$

$$= h\nu + L\frac{\hbar^2}{mR_{eq}^2}$$

20.    (a)    $m = \dfrac{m_K m_{Cl}}{m_K + m_{Cl}} = \dfrac{(39.1 \text{ u})(35.5 \text{ u})}{39.1 \text{ u} + 35.5 \text{ u}} = 18.6 \text{ u} = 1.73 \times 10^4 \text{ MeV}/c^2$

      (b)    $\dfrac{\hbar^2}{mR_{eq}^2} = \dfrac{\hbar^2 c^2}{mc^2 R_{eq}^2} = \dfrac{(197.3 \text{ eV·nm})^2}{(1.73 \times 10^{10} \text{ eV})(0.267 \text{ nm})^2} = 3.16 \times 10^{-5} \text{ eV}$

21.    (a)    The "missing" transition is at an energy of about 0.317 eV.

      (b)    $\nu = \dfrac{E}{h} = \dfrac{0.317 \text{ eV}}{4.14 \times 10^{-15} \text{ eV·s}} = 7.66 \times 10^{13} \text{ Hz}$

$$m = \frac{m_H m_{Br}}{m_H + m_{Br}} = \frac{(1 \text{ u})(80 \text{ u})}{81 \text{ u}} = 0.988 \text{ u} = 920 \text{ MeV}/c^2$$

$$k = \frac{mc^2(2\pi\nu)^2}{c^2} = \frac{(920 \times 10^6 \text{ eV})(2\pi)^2(7.66 \times 10^{13} \text{ Hz})^2}{9 \times 10^{16} \text{ m}^2/\text{s}^2}$$

$$= 2.37 \times 10^{21} \text{ eV/m}^2$$

      (c)    With $R_{eq} = 0.141$ nm,

$$\frac{\hbar^2}{mR_{eq}^2} = \frac{\hbar^2 c^2}{mc^2 R_{eq}^2} = \frac{(197.3 \ eV \cdot nm)^2}{(920 \times 10^6 \ eV)(0.141 \ nm)^2} = 2.1 \times 10^{-3} \ eV$$

This value agrees nicely with with the spacing of the lines in the spectrum, estimated to be about 0.002 eV.

22.

$$p(E_{NL}) = (2L + 1)e^{-E_{NL}/kT} = (2L + 1)e^{-[(N + \frac{1}{2})h\nu + L(L + 1)\hbar^2/2mR_{eq}^2]/kT}$$

$$\frac{dp}{dL} = 2e^{-[\ ]} - (2L + 1)e^{-[\ ]}(2L + 1)\frac{\hbar^2}{2mR_{eq}^2 kT} = 0$$

$$2L + 1 = \sqrt{\frac{4kT}{\hbar^2/mR_{eq}^2}}$$

23. (a)   The vibrational energy is $h\nu = 0.54$ eV. Since the vibrational states are non-degenerate,

$$\frac{p(N = 1)}{p(N = 0)} = \frac{e^{-(3/2)h\nu/kT}}{e^{-(1/2)h\nu/kT}} = e^{-h\nu/kT}$$

At $T = 293$ K, $kT = 0.02525$ eV.

$$\frac{p(N = 1)}{p(N = 0)} = e^{-0.54 \ eV/0.02525 \ eV} = 5.15 \times 10^{-10}$$

(b)   In the $N = 2$ state,

$$\frac{p(N = 2)}{p(N = 0)} = \frac{e^{-(5/2)h\nu/kT}}{e^{-(1/2)h\nu/kT}} = e^{-2h\nu/kT} = \left(e^{-h\nu/kT}\right)^2 = 2.65 \times 10^{-19}$$

24.    (a)     For NaCl, $h\nu = 0.063$ eV.

$$\frac{p(N=1)}{p(N=0)} = e^{-h\nu/kT} = e^{-0.063 \text{ eV}/0.02525 \text{ eV}} = 8.2 \times 10^{-2}$$

      (b)

$$\frac{p(N=2)}{p(N=0)} = e^{-2h\nu/kT} = \left(e^{-h\nu/kT}\right)^2 = 6.8 \times 10^{-3}$$

25.    (a)     For $H_2$, $\hbar^2/mR_{eq}^2 = 0.0152$ eV. At $T = 293$ K,

$$\frac{p(L)}{p(0)} = (2L+1)e^{-L(L+1)\hbar^2/2mR_{eq}^2 kT} = (2L+1)e^{-0.301L(L+1)}$$

$$\frac{p(1)}{p(0)} = 1.64, \qquad \frac{p(2)}{p(0)} = 0.822, \qquad \frac{p(3)}{p(0)} = 0.189$$

      (b)     At $T = 30$ K, $kT = 0.002585$ eV

$$\frac{p(L)}{p(0)} = (2L+1)e^{-2.94L(L+1)}$$

$$\frac{p(1)}{p(0)} = 8.38 \times 10^{-3}, \qquad \frac{p(2)}{p(0)} = 1.09 \times 10^{-7}, \qquad \frac{p(3)}{p(0)} = 3.33 \times 10^{-15}$$

26.    (a)     For NaCl, $\hbar^2/mR_{eq}^2 = 53.6 \times 10^{-6}$ eV. With $kT = 0.02525$ eV,

$$\frac{p(L)}{p(0)} = (2L+1)e^{-L(L+1)\hbar^2/2mR_{eq}^2 kT} = (2L+1)e^{-L(L+1)(1.06 \times 10^{-3})}$$

$$\frac{p(1)}{p(0)} = 2.99, \qquad \frac{p(2)}{p(0)} = 4.97, \qquad \frac{p(3)}{p(0)} = 6.91$$

(b)     At $T = 30$ K, $kT = 0.002585$ eV

$$\frac{p(L)}{p(0)} = (2L + 1)\,e^{-L(L+1)(1.04 \times 10^{-2})}$$

$$\frac{p(1)}{p(0)} = 2.94, \qquad \frac{p(2)}{p(0)} = 4.70, \qquad \frac{p(3)}{p(0)} = 6.31$$

27.     $$\frac{p(N=1)}{p(N=0)} = \frac{e^{-(3/2)h\nu/kT}}{e^{-(1/2)h\nu/kT}} = e^{-h\nu/kT}$$

$$T = \frac{-h\nu}{k\,\ln[p(N=1)/p(N=0)]} = \frac{-0.358\ \text{eV}}{(8.617 \times 10^{-5}\ \text{eV/K})\,\ln(1/3)} = 3780\ \text{K}$$

28.     For CO,

$$m = \frac{m_C m_O}{m_C + m_O} = \frac{(12\ \text{u})(16\ \text{u})}{28\ \text{u}} = 6.86\ \text{u} = 6.39 \times 10^3\ \text{MeV}/c^2$$

$$\frac{\hbar^2}{mR_{eq}^2} = \frac{\hbar^2 c^2}{mc^2 R_{eq}^2} = \frac{(197.3\ \text{eV·nm})^2}{(6.39 \times 10^9\ \text{eV})(0.113\ \text{nm})^2} = 4.77 \times 10^{-4}\ \text{eV}$$

$$2L + 1 = \sqrt{\frac{4kT}{\hbar^2/mR_{eq}^2}} = \sqrt{\frac{4(0.025\ \text{eV})}{(4.77 \times 10^{-4}\ \text{eV})}} = 14.5$$

$$L = 7$$

# Chapter 10

1. $p(0) = \dfrac{4{\times}5+3{\times}20+3{\times}20+2{\times}30+3{\times}10+2{\times}60+2{\times}10+1{\times}20+1{\times}30+0{\times}5}{5 \times 210} = 0.400$

$p(1) = \dfrac{0{\times}5+1{\times}20+0{\times}20+2{\times}30+0{\times}10+1{\times}60+0{\times}10+3{\times}20+2{\times}30+4{\times}5}{5 \times 210} = 0.267$

$p(2) = \dfrac{0{\times}5+0{\times}20+1{\times}20+0{\times}30+0{\times}10+1{\times}60+3{\times}10+0{\times}20+2{\times}30+1{\times}5}{5 \times 210} = 0.167$

$p(3) = \dfrac{0{\times}5+0{\times}20+0{\times}20+0{\times}30+2{\times}10+1{\times}60+0{\times}10+1{\times}20+0{\times}30+0{\times}5}{5 \times 210} = 0.095$

$p(4) = \dfrac{0{\times}5+0{\times}20+1{\times}20+1{\times}30+0{\times}10+0{\times}60+0{\times}10+0{\times}20+0{\times}30+0{\times}5}{5 \times 210} = 0.048$

$p(5) = \dfrac{0{\times}5+1{\times}20+0{\times}20+0{\times}30+0{\times}10+0{\times}60+0{\times}10+0{\times}20+0{\times}30+0{\times}5}{5 \times 210} = 0.019$

$p(6) = \dfrac{1{\times}5+0{\times}20+0{\times}20+0{\times}30+0{\times}10+0{\times}60+0{\times}10+0{\times}20+0{\times}30+0{\times}5}{5 \times 210} = 0.005$

2.

$v_p = 0.35$ m/s

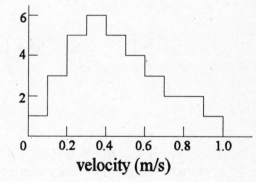

$v_m = \dfrac{1}{32}[1 \times 0.05 \text{ m/s} + 3 \times 0.15 \text{ m/s} + 5 \times 0.25 \text{ m/s} + 6 \times 0.35 \text{ m/s}$

$+ 5 \times 0.45 \text{ m/s} + 4 \times 0.55 \text{ m/s} + 3 \times 0.65 \text{ m/s} + 2 \times 0.75 \text{ m/s}$

$+ 2 \times 0.85 \text{ m/s} + 1 \times 0.95 \text{ m/s}] = 0.45 \text{ m/s}$

$$(v^2)_m = \frac{1}{32}[(0.05 \text{ m/s})^2 + 3(0.15 \text{ m/s})^2 + 5(0.25 \text{ m/s})^2 + 6(0.35 \text{ m/s})^2$$

$$+ 5(0.45 \text{ m/s})^2 + 4(0.55 \text{ m/s})^2 + 3(0.65 \text{ m/s})^2 + 2(0.75 \text{ m/s})^2$$

$$+ 2(0.85 \text{ m/s})^2 + (0.95 \text{ m/s})^2] = 0.2525 \text{ m}^2/\text{s}^2$$

$$v_{rms} = \sqrt{(v^2)_m} = 0.50 \text{ m/s}$$

3.  $$n = \int_0^\infty f(v)\,dv = \frac{4\pi}{A}\int_0^\infty e^{-bv^2}v^2\,dv = \frac{4\pi}{A}\frac{1}{4b}\sqrt{\frac{\pi}{b}} \quad \text{or} \quad A = \frac{1}{n}\left(\frac{\pi}{b}\right)^{3/2}$$

$$K_m = \tfrac{3}{2}kT = \frac{1}{n}\int_0^\infty \tfrac{1}{2}mv^2 f(v)\,dv = \frac{m}{2}\frac{4\pi}{nA}\int_0^\infty e^{-bv^2}v^4\,dv = \frac{2\pi m}{nA}\frac{3}{8b^2}\sqrt{\frac{\pi}{b}}$$

$$\tfrac{3}{2}kT = \frac{2\pi m}{(\pi/b)^{3/2}}\frac{3}{8b^2}\sqrt{\frac{\pi}{b}} \quad \text{or} \quad b = \frac{m}{2kT}$$

$$\frac{1}{A} = n\left(\frac{\pi}{b}\right)^{-3/2} = n\left(\frac{2\pi kT}{m}\right)^{-3/2} = n\left(\frac{m}{2\pi kT}\right)^{3/2}$$

4.  $v_p$ occurs where $f(v)$ has its maximum value.

$$\frac{df}{dv} = 4\pi n\left(\frac{m}{2\pi kT}\right)^{3/2}\left[2v\,e^{-mv^2/2kT} - \left(\frac{mv}{kT}\right)v^2 e^{-mv^2/2kT}\right] = 0 \quad \text{at} \quad v = v_p$$

$$2v_p - \frac{mv_p^3}{kT} = 0 \quad \text{or} \quad v_p = \sqrt{\frac{2kT}{m}}$$

5. Using the results of Example 10.1, we have

$$\Delta v = \sqrt{(v^2)_m - (v_m)^2} = \sqrt{\frac{3kT}{m} - \frac{8kT}{\pi m}} = \left(\frac{kT}{m}\right)^{1/2}\sqrt{3 - 8/\pi}$$

$\Delta v$ gives the width or "spread" of the velocity distribution.

6. (a) The most probable kinetic energy occurs where $f(K)$ has a maximum.

$$\frac{df}{dK} = \frac{2n}{\pi^{1/2}(kT)^{3/2}}\left[\frac{1}{2}K^{-1/2}e^{-K/kT} - \frac{1}{kT}K^{1/2}e^{-K/kT}\right] = 0 \quad \text{at} \quad K = K_p$$

$$\frac{1}{2}K_p^{-1/2} = \frac{1}{kT}K_p^{1/2} \qquad \text{or} \qquad K_p = \frac{1}{2}kT$$

(b) $$K_m = \frac{1}{n}\int_0^\infty Kf(K)\,dK = \frac{2}{\pi^{1/2}(kT)^{3/2}}\int_0^\infty K^{3/2}e^{-K/kT}\,dK$$

Let $K = x^2$, $dK = 2x\,dx$.

$$K_m = \frac{4}{\pi^{1/2}(kT)^{3/2}}\int_0^\infty x^4 e^{-x^2/kT}\,dx = \frac{4}{\pi^{1/2}(kT)^{3/2}}\frac{3}{8(1/kT)^2}\sqrt{\pi kT} = \frac{3}{2}kT$$

(c) $$(K^2)_m = \frac{1}{n}\int_0^\infty K^2 f(K)\,dK = \frac{2}{\pi^{1/2}(kT)^{3/2}}\int_0^\infty K^{5/2}e^{-K/kT}\,dK$$

$$= \frac{4}{\pi^{1/2}(kT)^{3/2}}\int_0^\infty x^6 e^{-x^2/kT}\,dx \quad \text{with} \quad K = x^2,\ dK = 2x\,dx$$

$$= \frac{4}{\pi^{1/2}(kT)^{3/2}}\frac{15}{16(1/kT)^3}\sqrt{\pi kT} = \frac{15}{4}(kT)^2$$

$$K_{\text{rms}} = \sqrt{(K^2)_{\text{m}}} = \sqrt{\frac{15}{4}}\, kT$$

(d) $\quad \Delta K = \sqrt{(K^2)_{\text{m}} - (K_{\text{m}})^2} = \sqrt{(15/4)(kT)^2 - (3/2)^2(kT)^2} = \sqrt{\frac{3}{2}}\, kT$

7.  (a)  Let $E_2 = E$, $E_1 = 0$. The states are nondegenerate, so $g(E_2) = g(E_1) = 1$. If $N_1$ is the number with energy $E_1$ and $N_2$ is the number with energy $E_2$, then $N_1 = Np(E_1)$ and $N_2 = Np(E_2)$ and

$$\frac{N_2}{N_1} = \frac{p(E_2)}{p(E_1)} = \frac{g(E_2)}{g(E_1)} \frac{f_{\text{MB}}(E_2)}{f_{\text{MB}}(E_1)} = e^{-E/kT}$$

(b) $\quad E_{\text{m}} = \dfrac{N_1 E_1 + N_2 E_2}{N_1 + N_2} = \dfrac{E_1 + (N_2/N_1)E_2}{1 + (N_2/N_1)} = \dfrac{0 + e^{-E/kT} E}{1 + e^{-E/kT}} = \dfrac{E}{e^{E/kT} + 1}$

(c) $\quad E_{\text{total}} = N_1 E_1 + N_2 E_2 = N E_{\text{m}} = \dfrac{NE}{e^{E/kT} + 1}$

(d)  Assume $N = N_A$ (corresponding to one mole of the substance)

$$\frac{dE_{\text{total}}}{dT} = N_A E \frac{1}{(e^{E/kT} + 1)^2} \left( -\frac{E}{kT^2} e^{E/kT} \right) = k N_A (E/kT)^2 \frac{e^{E/kT}}{(e^{E/kT} + 1)^2}$$

$$C = \frac{dE_{\text{total}}}{dT} = R (E/kT)^2 \frac{e^{E/kT}}{(e^{E/kT} + 1)^2}$$

8.  (a)  At height $h$, $E = K + mgh$

$$\frac{p(E_2)}{p(E_1)} = \frac{g(E_2)}{g(E_1)} \frac{e^{-E_2/kT}}{e^{-E_1/kT}} = \frac{e^{-(K + mgh)/kT}}{e^{-K/kT}} = e^{-mgh/kT}$$

(b)   The density at height $h$ is proportional to the probability to find a molecule at height $h$, which is given by $p(mgh)$. Thus

$$\frac{\rho(h)}{\rho(0)} = e^{-mgh/kT}$$

(c)   Probably not, because of the assumption of thermal equilibrium.

9.   (a)   $\Delta E = \mu_B B = (9.27 \times 10^{-24} \text{ J/T})(5.0 \text{ T}) = 4.64 \times 10^{-23} \text{ J}$

Because the degeneracies are identical,

$$\frac{p(0)}{p(-1)} = e^{-\Delta E/kT} = e^{-(4.64 \times 10^{-23} \text{ J})/(1.38 \times 10^{-23} \text{ J/K})(293 \text{ K})} = 0.9886$$

The energy difference between the $m_l = +1$ and $m_l = 0$ states is also $\Delta E$, so

$$\frac{p(+1)}{p(0)} = 0.9886$$

The fraction of atoms in the $m_l = +1$ state is

$$f(+1) = \frac{p(+1)}{p(+1) + p(0) + p(-1)} = \frac{p(+1)/p(0)}{p(+1)/p(0) + 1 + p(-1)/p(0)}$$

$$= \frac{0.9886}{0.9886 + 1 + 1/0.9886} = 0.3295$$

$$f(0) = \frac{p(0)}{p(+1) + p(0) + p(-1)} = \frac{1}{p(+1)/p(0) + 1 + p(-1)/p(0)}$$

$$= \frac{1}{0.9886 + 1 + 1/0.9886} = 0.3333$$

$$f(-1) = 1 - f(0) - f(+1) = 1 - 0.3333 - 0.3295 = 0.3372$$

(b)

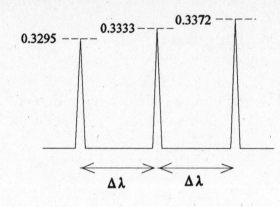

10.  Consider a molecule of the liquid at the point $x$.  The "centrifugal" force on it
     is $F = mx\omega^2$.  Let us assume that the forces in the liquid that give rise to this
     force can be associated with a potential energy $U(x)$, where $F = -dU/dx$:

$$U = -\int F dx = -\int_0^x mx\omega^2\,dx = -\frac{m\omega^2 x^2}{2}$$

where we take $U = 0$ at $x = 0$ (on the axis of rotation).  The Boltzmann factors
then give

$$\frac{\rho(x)}{\rho(0)} = \frac{f_{MB}(x)}{f_{MB}(0)} = e^{-U/kT} = e^{m\omega^2 x^2/2kT}$$

$$\rho(x) = \rho_0 e^{m\omega^2 x^2/2kT} \qquad \text{where } \rho_0 = \rho(0).$$

11.  (a)  $K_m = \frac{1}{2}m(v^2)_m = \frac{1}{2}m\left(\dfrac{3kT}{m}\right) = \frac{3}{2}kT$

$$= \frac{3}{2}(8.617 \times 10^{-5}\ \text{eV/K})(293\ \text{K}) = 0.0379\ \text{eV}$$

(b)   $n = \dfrac{1 \text{ mole}}{V} = \dfrac{6.02 \times 10^{23} \text{ molecules}}{(0.12 \text{ m})^3} = 3.48 \times 10^{26} \text{ molecules/m}^3$

$$f(E)\,dE = \frac{2(3.48 \times 10^{26} \text{ m}^{-3})}{\pi^{1/2}[(8.617 \times 10^{-5} \text{ eV/K})(293 \text{ K})]^{3/2}}$$

$$\times \ (0.0379 \text{ eV})^{1/2} e^{-1.5}(3.79 \times 10^{-4} \text{ eV}) = 1.61 \times 10^{24} \text{ m}^{-3}$$

To find the total number of molecules, we multiply by the volume:

$$(1.61 \times 10^{24} \text{ m}^{-3})(0.12 \text{ m})^3 = 2.79 \times 10^{21}$$

12.   $u(E) = \dfrac{Ep(E)}{L^3} = E \dfrac{\pi}{(\hbar c \pi)^3} E^2 \dfrac{1}{e^{E/kT} - 1} = \dfrac{\pi E^3}{(\hbar c \pi)^3} \dfrac{1}{e^{E/kT} - 1}$

With $E = \dfrac{hc}{\lambda}$,   then   $dE = -\dfrac{hc}{\lambda^2} d\lambda$

$u(E)|dE| = u(\lambda)|d\lambda|$

$u(\lambda) = u(E)\left|\dfrac{dE}{d\lambda}\right| = \dfrac{\pi(hc/\lambda)^3}{(\hbar c \pi)^3} \dfrac{1}{e^{hc/\lambda kT} - 1} \dfrac{hc}{\lambda^2} = \dfrac{8\pi hc}{\lambda^5} \dfrac{1}{e^{hc/\lambda kT} - 1}$

13   (a)   From Problem 12,

$$u(E) = \frac{8\pi E^3}{(hc)^3} \frac{1}{e^{E/kT} - 1}$$

This gives the energy density of photons with energy $E$. The number density of photons at that energy is $n(E)$, and so $u(E) = En(E)$:

$$n(E) = \frac{u(E)}{E} = \frac{8\pi E^2}{(hc)^3} \frac{1}{e^{E/kT} - 1}$$

(b)   To find the total number of photons at all energies, we integrate this result over all $E$ using the substitution $x = E/kT$:

$$N = \int_0^\infty n(E)\,dE = \frac{8\pi}{(hc)^3} \int_0^\infty \frac{E^2\,dE}{e^{E/kT} - 1} = \frac{8\pi(kT)^3}{(hc)^3} \int_0^\infty \frac{x^2\,dx}{e^x - 1}$$

(c)   At $T = 300$ K, $kT = 0.02585$ eV and so

$$N = \frac{8\pi(0.02585 \text{ eV})^3}{(1240 \text{ eV·nm})^3(10^{-7} \text{ cm/nm})^3}(2.404) = 5.47 \times 10^8 \text{ photons/cm}^3$$

Every cubic centimeter of your room contains about $10^9$ photons!  At 3 K, the number is reduced by $(100)^3 = 10^6$ to $5.47 \times 10^2$ photons/cm$^3$.

14.        $$u(E) = \frac{8\pi E^3}{(hc)^3} \frac{1}{e^{E/kT} - 1}$$

$$\frac{du}{dE} = \frac{8\pi}{(hc)^3}\left[\frac{3E^2}{e^{E/kT} - 1} - \frac{E^3}{(e^{E/kT} - 1)^2}\frac{e^{E/kT}}{kT}\right] = 0 \quad \text{at} \quad E = E_{max}$$

$$3(e^x - 1) = xe^x \qquad \text{with} \qquad x = E_{max}/kT$$

This equation cannot be solved exactly, but an approximate result can be found numerically:

$$x = 2.8214 = \frac{E_{max}}{kT}$$

$$E_{max} = (2.8214)(8.617 \times 10^{-5} \text{ eV/K})\,T = (2.4313 \times 10^{-4} \text{ eV/K})\,T$$

Note that

$$\frac{hc}{\lambda_{max}} = \frac{1240 \ eV \cdot nm}{(2.898 \times 10^{-3} \ mK)/T} = (4.279 \times 10^{-4} \ eV/K) \, T$$

and thus

$$E_{max} \neq \frac{hc}{\lambda_{max}}$$

This happens because $u(E)$ and $u(\lambda)$ do not simultaneously reach their maximum values. As we did in Problem 12, we can write

$$u(\lambda) = u(E) \left| \frac{dE}{d\lambda} \right| = u(E) \frac{hc}{\lambda^2} = u(E) \frac{E^2}{hc}$$

$$\frac{du}{d\lambda} = \frac{d}{d\lambda} \left[ u(E) \frac{E^2}{hc} \right] = \frac{d}{dE} \left[ u(E) \frac{E^2}{hc} \right] \left| \frac{dE}{d\lambda} \right| = \left[ \frac{du}{dE} \frac{E^2}{hc} + u(E) \frac{2E}{hc} \right] \frac{hc}{\lambda^2}$$

It is thus clear that $du/d\lambda \neq 0$ when $du/dE = 0$.

15. (a) The total energy density $U$ is

$$U = \int_0^\infty u(E) \, dE = \frac{1}{c/4} \sigma T^4$$

$$= \frac{4}{3.00 \times 10^8 \ m/s} (5.67 \times 10^{-8} \ W/m^2 \cdot K^4)(2.50 \times 10^3 \ K)^4$$

$$= 0.0295 \ J/m^3 = 1.84 \times 10^{17} \ eV/m^3$$

(b) At $T = 2.50 \times 10^3$ K, $kT = 0.215$ eV. The energy emitted in the $dE = 0.05$ eV interval at $E = 1.00$ eV is

$$u(E) \, dE = \frac{8\pi}{(hc)^3} \frac{E^3}{e^{E/kT} - 1} \, dE = \frac{8\pi}{(1240 \ eV \cdot nm)^3} \frac{(1.00 \ eV)^3 (0.05 \ eV)}{e^{1.00 \ eV/0.215 \ eV} - 1}$$

$$= 6.36 \times 10^{-12} \text{ eV/nm}^3 = 6.36 \times 10^{15} \text{ eV/m}^3$$

The fraction of the total energy density this represents is

$$\frac{u(E)\,dE}{U} = \frac{6.36 \times 10^{15} \text{ eV/m}^3}{1.84 \times 10^{17} \text{ eV/m}^3} = 0.0346$$

(c)     At 10.00 eV,

$$u(E)\,dE = \frac{8\pi}{(1240 \text{ eV·nm})^3} \frac{(10.00 \text{ eV})^3(0.05 \text{ eV})}{e^{10.00 \text{ eV}/0.215 \text{ eV}} - 1} = 4.16 \text{ eV/m}^3$$

$$\frac{u(E)\,dE}{U} = \frac{4.16 \text{ eV/m}^3}{1.84 \times 10^{17} \text{ eV/m}^3} = 2.26 \times 10^{-17}$$

16.   (a)     $$N = \frac{8\sqrt{2}\,\pi L^3 m^{3/2}}{h^3} \int_0^{E_F} E^{1/2}\,dE = \frac{8\sqrt{2}\,\pi L^3 m^{3/2}}{h^3} \frac{2}{3} E_F^{3/2}$$

$$E_F^{3/2} = \frac{h^3}{m^{3/2}} \frac{3N}{16\sqrt{2}\,\pi V} \qquad \text{where } V = L^3$$

$$E_F = \left[\frac{h^3}{m^{3/2}} \frac{3N}{16\sqrt{2}\,\pi V}\right]^{2/3} = \frac{h^2}{2m}\left(\frac{3N}{8\pi V}\right)^{2/3}$$

(b)     $$E_m = \frac{1}{N}\int_0^\infty E p(E)\,dE = \frac{8\sqrt{2}\,\pi L^3 m^{3/2}}{N h^3}\int_0^{E_F} E^{3/2}\,dE$$

$$= \frac{8\sqrt{2}\,\pi V m^{3/2}}{N h^3}\frac{2}{5}E_F^{5/2} = \frac{8\sqrt{2}\,\pi V m^{3/2}}{N h^3}\frac{2}{5}\left(\frac{h^2}{2m}\right)^{5/2}\left(\frac{3N}{8\pi V}\right)^{5/3}$$

$$= \frac{3}{5}\frac{h^2}{2m}\left(\frac{3N}{8\pi V}\right)^{2/3} = \frac{3}{5}E_F$$

17.    We assume each copper atom contributes one free electron to the metal.

$$\frac{N}{V} = \frac{\rho N_A}{M} = \frac{(8.95 \ \text{g/cm}^3)(6.02 \times 10^{23} \ \text{atoms/mole})}{63.5 \ \text{g/mole}}$$

$$= 8.48 \times 10^{28} \ \text{atoms/m}^3$$

$$E_F = \frac{h^2}{2m}\left(\frac{3}{8\pi}\frac{N}{V}\right)^{2/3} = \frac{h^2 c^2}{2mc^2}\left(\frac{3}{8\pi}\frac{N}{V}\right)^{2/3}$$

$$= \frac{(1240 \ \text{eV}\cdot\text{nm})^2}{2(0.511 \times 10^6 \ \text{eV})}\left(\frac{3}{8\pi}8.48 \times 10^{28} \ \text{m}^{-3}\right)^{2/3} = 7.04 \ \text{eV}$$

$$E_m = \tfrac{3}{5}E_F = \tfrac{3}{5}(7.04 \ \text{eV}) = 4.22 \ \text{eV}$$

18.    $$\frac{N}{V} = (2 \ \text{electrons/atom})\frac{\rho N_A}{M}$$

$$= (2/\text{atom})\frac{(1.74 \ \text{g/cm}^3)(6.02 \times 10^{23} \ \text{atoms/mole})}{24.3 \ \text{g/mole}} = 8.62 \times 10^{28} \ \text{m}^{-3}$$

$$E_F = \frac{h^2 c^2}{2mc^2}\left(\frac{3}{8\pi}\frac{N}{V}\right)^{2/3}$$

$$= \frac{(1240 \ \text{eV}\cdot\text{nm})^2}{2(0.511 \times 10^6 \ \text{eV})}\left(\frac{3}{8\pi}8.62 \times 10^{28} \ \text{m}^{-3}\right)^{2/3} = 7.12 \ \text{eV}$$

19.    At room temperature (293 K), $kT = 0.02525$ eV.  For sodium, $E_F = 3.15$ eV.

$$f_{FD}(E) = \frac{1}{e^{(E - E_F)/kT} + 1} = 0.1$$

$$e^{(E - E_F)/kT} = 9 \qquad \text{or} \qquad \frac{E - E_F}{kT} = \ln 9 = 2.20$$

$$E = E_F + 2.20kT = 3.15 \text{ eV} + 2.20(0.02525 \text{ eV}) = 3.21 \text{ eV}$$

$$f_{FD}(E) = \frac{1}{e^{(E - E_F)/kT} + 1} = 0.9$$

$$e^{(E - E_F)/kT} = \frac{1}{9} \qquad \text{or} \qquad \frac{E - E_F}{kT} = -\ln 9 = -2.20$$

$$E = E_F - 2.20kT = 3.15 \text{ eV} - 2.20(0.02525 \text{ eV}) = 3.09 \text{ eV}$$

The energy difference is 3.21 eV – 3.09 eV = 0.12 eV, so the distribution is reasonably sharp.  The occupation probability drops from near maximum (0.9) to near minimum (0.1) within ±2% of $E_F$.

20.    The Fermi-Dirac function is

$$\frac{1}{e^{(E - E_F)/kT} + 1} = \frac{1}{e^{(1.89 \text{ eV} - 3.15 \text{ eV})/(2.52 \times 10^{-2} \text{ eV})} + 1} \cong 1.000$$

$$\frac{p(E)\,dE}{V} = \frac{8\sqrt{2}\,\pi\,(mc^2)^{3/2}}{h^3 c^3} E_m^{1/2}(0.01E_F)$$

$$= \frac{8\sqrt{2}\,\pi\,(0.511 \times 10^6 \text{ eV})^{3/2}}{(1240 \text{ eV·nm})^3} (1.89 \text{ eV})^{1/2}(0.0315 \text{ eV})$$

$$= 0.295 \text{ nm}^{-3} = 0.295 \times 10^{27} \text{ m}^{-3}$$

21. (a) At $T = 295$ K, $kT = 0.0254$ eV.

With $E_F^{3/2} = \dfrac{h^3}{2\sqrt{2}\,m^{3/2}}\dfrac{3N}{8\pi V}$ and $V = L^3$,

$$\frac{p(E)\,dE}{N} = \frac{3}{2}\frac{E^{1/2}\,dE}{E_F^{3/2}}\frac{1}{e^{(E-E_F)/kT}+1}$$

$$= \frac{3}{2}\frac{(5.00\ \text{eV})^{1/2}(0.10\ \text{eV})}{(3.00\ \text{eV})^{3/2}}\frac{1}{e^{2.00\ \text{eV}/0.0254\ \text{eV}}+1} = 4.37\times10^{-36}$$

(b) At $T = 2500$ K, $kT = 0.215$ eV.

$$\frac{p(E)\,dE}{N} = \frac{3}{2}\frac{(5.00\ \text{eV})^{1/2}(0.10\ \text{eV})}{(3.00\ \text{eV})^{3/2}}\frac{1}{e^{2.00\ \text{eV}/0.215\ \text{eV}}+1} = 6.00\times10^{-6}$$

22. There are 20 protons and 20 neutrons in the nuclear volume, which is

$$V = \tfrac{4}{3}\pi R^3 = \tfrac{4}{3}\pi(4.1\ \text{fm})^3 = 289\ \text{fm}^3$$

$$E_F = \frac{h^2}{2m}\left(\frac{3}{8\pi}\frac{N}{V}\right)^{2/3} = \frac{h^2c^2}{2mc^2}\left(\frac{3}{8\pi}\frac{N}{V}\right)^{2/3}$$

$$= \frac{(1240\ \text{eV·nm})^2}{2(940\ \text{MeV})}\left(\frac{3}{8\pi}\right)^{2/3}\left(\frac{20}{289\ \text{fm}^3}\right)^{2/3} = 33.4\ \text{MeV}$$

$$E_m = \tfrac{3}{5}E_F = 20.1\ \text{MeV}$$

These are quite reasonable numbers for the motion of nucleons in the nucleus.

23.    For a mass of $2.00 \times 10^{30}$ kg, the number of nucleons is about

$$N = \frac{2.00 \times 10^{30} \text{ kg}}{1.67 \times 10^{-27} \text{ kg/nucleon}} = 1.20 \times 10^{57} \text{ nucleons}$$

The number of electrons is thus about $6 \times 10^{56}$, and the electron density is

$$\frac{N}{V} = \frac{6.00 \times 10^{56}}{\frac{4}{3}\pi (6.40 \times 10^{6} \text{ m})^{3}} = 5.46 \times 10^{35} \text{ m}^{-3}$$

$$E_{F} = \frac{h^{2}c^{2}}{2mc^{2}} \left( \frac{3}{8\pi} \right)^{2/3} \left( \frac{N}{V} \right)^{2/3}$$

$$= \frac{(1240 \text{ eV·nm})^{2}}{2(0.511 \times 10^{6} \text{ eV})} \left( \frac{3}{8\pi} \right)^{2/3} (5.46 \times 10^{35} \text{ m}^{-3})^{2/3} = 244 \text{ keV}$$

(This is rather close to the electron's rest energy of 511 keV, and thus the nonrelativistic expression $E = p^{2}/2m$ used to derive Equation 10.35 may not be valid.)

24.    $$N = \frac{2m_{\text{Sun}}}{m_{\text{nucleon}}} = \frac{4.00 \times 10^{30} \text{ kg}}{1.67 \times 10^{-27} \text{ kg}} = 2.40 \times 10^{57}$$

$$\frac{N}{V} = \frac{2.40 \times 10^{57}}{\frac{4}{3}\pi (10^{4} \text{ m})^{3}} = 5.72 \times 10^{44} \text{ m}^{-3}$$

$$E_{F} = \frac{h^{2}c^{2}}{2mc^{2}} \left( \frac{3}{8\pi} \right)^{2/3} \left( \frac{N}{V} \right)^{2/3}$$

$$= \frac{(1240 \text{ MeV·fm})^{2}}{2(940 \text{ MeV})} \left( \frac{3}{8\pi} \right)^{2/3} (5.72 \times 10^{44} \text{ m}^{-3})^{2/3} = 137 \text{ MeV}$$

# Chapter 11

1. (a) 1/8

   (b) If the spheres are in contact, then $a = 2r$.

   (c) $V_{cube} = a^3 = 8r^3$

   $$V_{spheres} = 8 \times \frac{1}{8} \times \frac{4}{3}\pi r^3 = \frac{4}{3}\pi r^3$$

   $$\text{packing fraction} = \frac{V_{spheres}}{V_{cube}} = \frac{\frac{4}{3}\pi r^3}{8r^3} = \frac{\pi}{6} = 0.5236$$

2. <u>fcc lattice</u>:  The basic cube has 1/8 of a sphere at each of the 8 corners, and 1/2 of a sphere at each of its 6 faces.  Thus

   $$V_{spheres} = \left( 8 \times \frac{1}{8} + 6 \times \frac{1}{2} \right) \frac{4}{3}\pi r^3 = \frac{16}{3}\pi r^3$$

   The diagonal along any face of the cube has length $a\sqrt{2}$ ; if the spheres are touching on the faces, then this diagonal also has length $4r$.  With $a\sqrt{2} = 4r$,

   $$V_{cube} = a^3 = \left( \frac{4r}{\sqrt{2}} \right)^3 = 16\sqrt{2}\, r^3$$

   $$\text{packing fraction} = \frac{V_{spheres}}{V_{cube}} = \frac{\frac{16}{3}\pi r^3}{16\sqrt{2}r^3} = \frac{\pi}{3\sqrt{2}} = 0.7405$$

   <u>bcc lattice</u>:

   $$V_{spheres} = \left( 8 \times \frac{1}{8} + 1 \right) \frac{4}{3}\pi r^3 = \frac{8}{3}\pi r^3$$

   The spheres are touching along the body diagonal, which has length $a\sqrt{3} = 4r$ :

$$V_{cube} = a^3 = \left(\frac{4r}{\sqrt{3}}\right)^3 = \frac{64}{3\sqrt{3}}r^3$$

$$\text{packing fraction} = \frac{V_{spheres}}{V_{cube}} = \frac{\frac{8}{3}\pi r^3}{\frac{64}{3\sqrt{3}}r^3} = \frac{\sqrt{3}\,\pi}{8} = 0.6802$$

3.
$$E = -\alpha\frac{e^2}{4\pi\epsilon_0}\frac{1}{R} + \frac{A}{R^n}$$

$$\frac{dE}{dr} = \alpha\frac{e^2}{4\pi\epsilon_0}\frac{1}{R^2} - \frac{nA}{R^{n+1}} = 0 \qquad \text{at} \qquad R = R_0$$

$$\alpha\frac{e^2}{4\pi\epsilon_0}\frac{1}{R_0^2} = \frac{nA}{R_0^{n+1}} \qquad \text{or} \qquad A = \alpha\frac{e^2}{4\pi\epsilon_0}\frac{R_0^{n-1}}{n}$$

$$E = -\alpha\frac{e^2}{4\pi\epsilon_0}\frac{1}{R} + \alpha\frac{e^2}{4\pi\epsilon_0}\frac{R_0^{n-1}}{nR^n} = -\frac{\alpha e^2}{4\pi\epsilon_0 R}\left[1 - \frac{1}{n}\left(\frac{R_0}{R}\right)^{n-1}\right]$$

$$B = -E(R_0) = \frac{\alpha e^2}{4\pi\epsilon_0 R_0}\left[1 - \frac{1}{n}\right]$$

4.

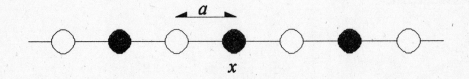

Consider the ion at $x$. It feels an attractive potential energy from its two nearest neighbors

$$U_1 = -2\frac{e^2}{4\pi\epsilon_0}\frac{1}{a}$$

and a repulsive potential energy from the next two, at a distance of $2a$:

$$U_2 = +2\frac{e^2}{4\pi\epsilon_0}\frac{1}{2a}$$

and so forth:

$$U_3 = -2\frac{e^2}{4\pi\epsilon_0}\frac{1}{3a} \qquad U_4 = +2\frac{e^2}{4\pi\epsilon_0}\frac{1}{4a}$$

The total potential energy is

$$U = U_1 + U_2 + U_3 + U_4 + ... = -2\frac{e^2}{4\pi\epsilon_0}\left[\frac{1}{a} - \frac{1}{2a} + \frac{1}{3a} - \frac{1}{4a} + ...\right]$$

$$= -2\frac{e^2}{4\pi\epsilon_0 a}\sum_{n=1}^{\infty}\frac{(-1)^{n+1}}{n} = -2\frac{e^2}{4\pi\epsilon_0 a}\ln 2 = -\alpha\frac{e^2}{4\pi\epsilon_0}\frac{1}{a}$$

where $\alpha = 2\ln 2$.

5. In the CsCl structure, a $Cs^+$ ion at the center of the cube is surrounded by 8 $Cl^-$ ions at a distance $R$, which contribute a potential energy

$$U_1 = -8\frac{e^2}{4\pi\epsilon_0}\frac{1}{R}$$

At the centers of the adjacent cubes are 6 $Cs^+$ ions. Their distance from the original $Cs^+$ ion is equal to the cube edge, or $2R/\sqrt{3}$.

$$U_2 = +6 \frac{e^2}{4\pi\epsilon_0} \frac{1}{2R/\sqrt{3}}$$

At the far corners of the 6 adjacent cubes are 24 Cl$^-$ ions at distances $R\sqrt{11/3}$ :

$$U_3 = -24 \frac{e^2}{4\pi\epsilon_0} \frac{1}{R\sqrt{11/3}}$$

$$U = U_1 + U_2 + U_3 + ... = -\frac{e^2}{4\pi\epsilon_0} \frac{1}{R} \left( 8 - \frac{6}{2/\sqrt{3}} + \frac{24}{\sqrt{11/3}} - ... \right)$$

6.    Although there is considerable scatter in the points, the data show a rough proportionality between the boiling points and the cohesive energy -- the larger the cohesive energy, the higher the boiling point.

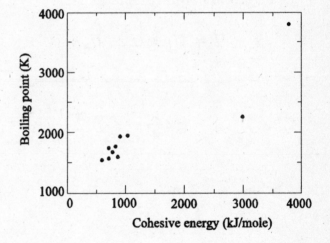

7.    (a)    $B = \dfrac{C}{N_A} = \dfrac{657 \times 10^3 \text{ J/mol}}{(6.02 \times 10^{23} \text{ ions/mole})(1.60 \times 10^{-19} \text{ J/eV})} = 6.82$ eV

      (b)    $B = \dfrac{\alpha e^2}{4\pi\epsilon_0 R_0} \left( 1 - \dfrac{1}{n} \right)$

             $= \dfrac{(1.7627)(1.440 \text{ eV·nm})}{0.356 \text{ nm}} \left( 1 - \dfrac{1}{10.5} \right) = 6.45$ eV

(c)    Binding energy per atom pair = binding energy per ion pair
$$+ \text{electron affinity of Cl}$$
$$- \text{ionization energy of Cs}$$

$$= 6.82 \text{ eV} + 3.61 \text{ eV} - 3.89 \text{ eV} = 6.54 \text{ eV}$$

Binding energy per atom $= \frac{1}{2}(6.54 \text{ eV}) = 3.27 \text{ eV}$

8.    (a)    $B = \dfrac{C}{N_A} = \dfrac{1030 \times 10^3 \text{ J/mole}}{(6.02 \times 10^{23} \text{ ions/mole})(1.60 \times 10^{-19} \text{ J/eV})} = 10.69 \text{ eV}$

(b)    $B = \dfrac{\alpha e^2}{4\pi\epsilon_0 R_0}\left(1 - \dfrac{1}{n}\right)$

$$= \dfrac{(1.7476)(1.440 \text{ eV·nm})}{0.201 \text{ nm}}\left(1 - \dfrac{1}{6}\right) = 10.4 \text{ eV}$$

(c)    Binding energy per atom pair =

$$10.69 \text{ eV} + 3.45 \text{ eV} - 5.39 \text{ eV} = 8.75 \text{ eV}$$

Binding energy per atom $= \frac{1}{2}(8.75 \text{ eV}) = 4.38 \text{ eV}$

9.    $U_C = -\alpha \dfrac{e^2}{4\pi\epsilon_0}\dfrac{1}{R_0} = \dfrac{-(1.7476)(1.440 \text{ eV·nm})}{0.281 \text{ nm}} = -8.96 \text{ eV}$

$$U_R = \dfrac{A}{R_0^n} = \dfrac{\alpha e^2}{4\pi\epsilon_0 R_0 n} = \dfrac{1}{n}(-U_C) = 1.00 \text{ eV}$$

10.    From Equation 11.11,

$$k = \frac{\alpha e^2}{4\pi\epsilon_0 R_0^3}(n-1) = \frac{(1.7627)(1.440 \text{ eV·nm})}{(0.395 \text{ nm})^3}(12-1) = 453 \text{ eV/nm}^2$$

The vibrational frequency of an I ion is (with $m = 127 \text{ u} = 1.18 \times 10^{11} \text{ eV}/c^2$):

$$\nu = \frac{1}{2\pi}\sqrt{\frac{k}{m}} = \frac{1}{2\pi}\sqrt{\frac{(453 \text{ eV/nm}^2)(10^{18} \text{ nm}^2/\text{m}^2)}{(1.18 \times 10^{11} \text{ eV})/(3.00 \times 10^8 \text{ m/s})^2}}$$

$$= 2.96 \times 10^{12} \text{ Hz}$$

$$\lambda = \frac{c}{\nu} = \frac{3.00 \times 10^8 \text{ m/s}}{2.96 \times 10^{12} \text{ Hz}} = 101 \text{ } \mu\text{m}$$

For an ion of Cs ($m = 133 \text{ u} = 1.24 \times 10^{11} \text{ eV}/c^2$),

$$\nu = \frac{1}{2\pi}\sqrt{\frac{(453 \text{ eV/nm}^2)(10^{18} \text{ nm}^2/\text{m}^2)}{(1.24 \times 10^{11} \text{ eV})/(3.00 \times 10^8 \text{ m/s})^2}} = 2.89 \times 10^{12} \text{ Hz}$$

$$\lambda = \frac{c}{\nu} = \frac{3.00 \times 10^8 \text{ m/s}}{2.89 \times 10^{12} \text{ Hz}} = 103 \text{ } \mu\text{m}$$

11.        $$U = -\mathbf{p}_2 \cdot \mathbf{E}_1$$

where $\mathbf{p}_2$ is the moment of dipole 2 and $\mathbf{E}_1$ is the electric field of dipole 1. Because $E_1 \propto r^{-3}$ and $p_2$ is proportional to $E_1$, $p_2$ is also proportional to $r^{-3}$. Thus

$$U \propto r^{-6}$$

$$F = -\frac{dU}{dr} \propto r^{-7}$$

12. The density of atoms is

$$n = \frac{\rho N_A}{M} = \frac{(0.971 \text{ g/cm}^3)(6.02 \times 10^{23} \text{ atoms/mole})}{23.0 \text{ g/mole}}$$

$$= 2.54 \times 10^{22} \text{ atoms/cm}^3$$

In the bcc structure, each basic cube contains 2 atoms (see Problem 2) in a volume $a^3$

$$\frac{2 \text{ atoms}}{a^3} = 2.54 \times 10^{22} \text{ atoms/cm}^3$$

$$a = \left( \frac{2 \text{ atoms}}{2.54 \times 10^{22} \text{ atoms/cm}^3} \right)^{1/3} = 4.29 \times 10^{-8} \text{ cm} = 0.429 \text{ nm}$$

The atomic spacing is $d = 2r = \dfrac{a\sqrt{3}}{2} = 0.371$ nm

13.

$$n = \frac{\rho N_A}{M} = \frac{(8.96 \text{ g/cm}^3)(6.02 \times 10^{23} \text{ atoms/mole})}{63.5 \text{ g/mole}}$$

$$= 8.49 \times 10^{22} \text{ atoms/cm}^3$$

In the fcc structure, there are 4 atoms per basic cube of volume $a^3$ (see Problem 2)

$$\frac{4 \text{ atoms}}{a^3} = 8.49 \times 10^{22} \text{ atoms/cm}^3$$

$$a = \left( \frac{4 \text{ atoms}}{8.49 \times 10^{22} \text{ atoms/cm}^3} \right)^{1/3} = 3.61 \times 10^{-8} \text{ cm} = 0.361 \text{ nm}$$

The atomic spacing is $d = 2r = \dfrac{a\sqrt{2}}{2} = 0.255$ nm

14.   Na:

$$B = \frac{C}{N_A} = \frac{107 \times 10^3 \text{ J/mole}}{(6.02 \times 10^{23} \text{ atoms/mole})(1.60 \times 10^{-19} \text{ J/eV})} = 1.11 \text{ eV}$$

Cu:

$$B = \frac{C}{N_A} = \frac{337 \times 10^3 \text{ J/mole}}{(6.02 \times 10^{23} \text{ atoms/mole})(1.60 \times 10^{-19} \text{ J/eV})} = 3.50 \text{ eV}$$

15.   (a)   $f_{FD}(E) = \dfrac{1}{e^{(E - E_F)/kT} + 1} = 0.1$

$$e^{(E - E_F)/kT} + 1 = 10 \qquad \text{so} \qquad \frac{E - E_F}{kT} = \ln 9 = 2.20$$

At room temperature (293 K), $kT = 0.0252$ eV.

$$E = E_F + 2.20kT = 7.03 \text{ eV} + 2.20(0.0252 \text{ eV}) = 7.09 \text{ eV}$$

(b)   $E - E_F$ is 2.20 times $kT$.

16.   An electron at the Fermi energy of 7.03 eV has momentum

$$p = \sqrt{2mK} = \frac{1}{c}\sqrt{2mc^2 K}$$

$$= \frac{1}{c}\sqrt{2(0.511 \times 10^6 \text{ eV})(7.03 \text{ eV})} = 2.68 \times 10^3 \text{ eV}/c$$

$$\lambda = \frac{h}{p} = \frac{hc}{pc} = \frac{1240 \text{ eV·nm}}{2.68 \times 10^3 \text{ eV}} = 0.463 \text{ nm}$$

This is comparable to the atomic spacing of copper (0.256 nm).

17.
$$\frac{p(E)\,dE}{V} = \frac{8\sqrt{2}\,\pi m^{3/2}}{h^3} \frac{E^{1/2}}{e^{(E-E_F)/kT}+1}\,dE = \frac{8\sqrt{2}\,\pi (mc^2)^{3/2}}{(hc)^3} \frac{E^{1/2}}{e^{(E-E_F)/kT}+1}\,dE$$

$$= \frac{8\sqrt{2}\,\pi (0.511 \times 10^6 \text{ eV})^{3/2}}{(1240 \text{ eV·nm})^3} \frac{(3.25 \text{ eV})^{1/2}}{e^{0.1 \text{ eV}/0.0238 \text{ eV}}+1} (0.01 \text{ eV})$$

$$= 0.23 \times 10^{25} \text{ m}^{-3}$$

18.
$$E_F = \frac{h^2}{2m}\left(\frac{3N}{8\pi V}\right)^{2/3}$$

The density of free electrons is

$$\frac{N}{V} = \frac{8\pi}{3}\left(\frac{2mE_F}{h^2}\right)^{2/3} = \frac{8\pi}{3}\left(\frac{2(0.511 \times 10^6 \text{ eV})(7.11 \text{ eV})}{(1240 \text{ eV·nm})^2}\right)^{2/3}$$

$$= 86.1 \text{ nm}^{-3} = 86.1 \times 10^{27} \text{ m}^{-3}$$

The atomic density is

$$n = \frac{\rho N_A}{M} = \frac{(1.74 \text{ g/cm}^3)(6.02 \times 10^{23} \text{ atoms/mole})}{24.3 \text{ g/mole}}$$

$$= 4.31 \times 10^{22} \text{ cm}^{-3} = 4.31 \times 10^{28} \text{ m}^{-3}$$

The number of free electrons per atom is thus

$$\frac{8.61 \times 10^{27} \text{ electrons/m}^3}{4.31 \times 10^{28} \text{ atoms/m}^3} = 2.00 \text{ electrons/atom}$$

19.  $$\frac{E_F(T)}{E_F(0)} = 0.99 = 1 - \frac{\pi^2}{12}\left(\frac{kT}{E_F(0)}\right)^2$$

$$kT = E_F(0)\sqrt{\frac{(12)(0.01)}{\pi^2}} = (5.53 \text{ eV})\sqrt{\frac{0.12}{\pi^2}} = 0.610 \text{ eV}$$

$$T = 7076 \text{ K}$$

20.  $$\frac{N}{V} = 2n = 2\frac{\rho N_A}{M} = \frac{2(6.51 \text{ g/cm}^3)(6.02 \times 10^{23} \text{ mole}^{-1})}{91.22 \text{ g/mole}}$$

$$= 8.59 \times 10^{22} \text{ cm}^{-3} = 8.59 \times 10^{28} \text{ m}^{-3}$$

$$E_F = \frac{(hc)^2}{2mc^2}\left(\frac{3N}{8\pi V}\right)^{2/3}$$

$$= \frac{(1240 \text{ eV·nm})^2}{2(0.511 \times 10^6 \text{ eV})}\left(\frac{3}{8\pi} 8.59 \times 10^{28} \text{ m}^{-3}\right)^{2/3} = 7.10 \text{ eV}$$

**21.**
$$L = \frac{\pi^2 k^2}{3e^2} = \frac{\pi^2 (1.38066 \times 10^{-23} \text{ J/K})^2}{3(1.6022 \times 10^{-19} \text{ C})^2} = 2.44 \times 10^{-8} \text{ J}^2/\text{C}^2 \cdot \text{K}^2$$

The units are reduced as follows:

$$\frac{\text{J}^2}{\text{C}^2 \cdot \text{K}^2} = \frac{\text{J/s}}{\text{C/s}} \frac{\text{J}}{\text{C}} \frac{1}{\text{K}^2} = \frac{\text{W} \cdot \text{V}}{\text{A} \cdot \text{K}^2} = \frac{\text{W} \cdot \Omega}{\text{K}^2}$$

Thus $L = 2.44 \times 10^{-8} \text{ W} \cdot \Omega/\text{K}^2$.

**22.**
$$\frac{K}{\sigma} = (2.44 \times 10^{-8} \text{ W} \cdot \Omega/\text{K}^2)T$$

$$K = (5.88 \times 10^7 \ \Omega^{-1}\text{m}^{-1})(2.44 \times 10^{-8} \text{ W} \cdot \Omega/\text{K}^2)(293 \text{ K}) = 422 \text{ W/K} \cdot \text{m}$$

**23.**   (a)   If we reduce the electric field by a factor of 12, then following the development of Chapter 6 for the Bohr atom, we see that the binding energy is reduced by a factor of $(12)^2$.

$$E = \frac{-13.6 \text{ eV}}{(12)^2} = -0.094 \text{ eV}$$

(b)   Again from Chapter 6, reduction of the electric field by a factor of 12 increases the orbital radius by $(12)^2$.

$$r = (12)^2 a_0 = 7.62 \text{ nm}$$

With an atomic spacing of $a = 0.235$ nm, the number of atoms encountered in a sphere of radius $r$ is

$$\frac{\frac{4}{3}\pi r^3}{a^3} = 1.4 \times 10^5 \text{ atoms}$$

24.  (a)  $N = \dfrac{662 \times 10^3 \text{ eV}}{0.72 \text{ eV/electron}} = 9.5 \times 10^5 \text{ electrons}$

(b)  $\delta N = N^{1/2} = 9.6 \times 10^2$    so    $\dfrac{\delta N}{N} = 1.04 \times 10^{-3}$

(c)  $\dfrac{\delta E}{E} = \dfrac{\delta N}{N} = 1.04 \times 10^{-3}$

$\delta E = (1.04 \times 10^{-3})(662 \text{ keV}) = 0.69 \text{ keV}$

25.  (a)  $f_{FD}(E) = \dfrac{1}{e^{(E-E_F)/kT} + 1} = \dfrac{1}{e^{0.55 \text{ eV}/0.025 \text{ eV}} + 1} = 2.79 \times 10^{-10}$

prob. $= 1 - 2.79 \times 10^{-10}$

(b)  prob. $= 2.79 \times 10^{-10}$

(c)  At $T = 393$ K, $kT = 0.0339$ eV and

$f_{FD}(E) = \dfrac{1}{e^{(E-E_F)/kT} + 1} = \dfrac{1}{e^{0.55 \text{ eV}/0.0339 \text{ eV}} + 1} = 8.84 \times 10^{-8}$

so the probabilities are $1 - 8.84 \times 10^{-8}$ and $8.84 \times 10^{-8}$.

# Chapter 12

1.     (a)    Flourine has $Z = 9$, and given $A = 19$, we have $N = A - Z = 19 - 9 = 10$. The symbol is $^{19}_{9}F_{10}$.

       (b)    Gold has $Z = 79$, so $A = Z + N = 79 + 120 = 199$. The symbol is $^{199}_{79}Au_{120}$.

       (c)    With $A = 107$ and $N = 60$, $Z = A - N = 107 - 60 = 47$. The element with $Z = 47$ is silver and the symbol is $^{107}_{47}Ag_{60}$.

2.     The atomic number of tin is $Z = 50$, and so the symbols are

$$^{114}_{50}Sn_{64} \,,\; ^{115}_{50}Sn_{65} \,,\; ^{116}_{50}Sn_{66} \,,\; ^{117}_{50}Sn_{67} \,,\; ^{118}_{50}Sn_{68} \,,\; ^{119}_{50}Sn_{69} \,,\; ^{120}_{50}Sn_{70} \,,\; ^{122}_{50}Sn_{72} \,,\; ^{124}_{50}Sn_{74}$$

3.     (a)    The radius of $^{16}O$ is

$$R = 1.2A^{1/3} = 1.2(16)^{1/3} = 3.0 \text{ fm}$$

The Coulomb repulsion energy of two charges of $8e$ whose centers are separated by 6.0 fm is

$$U = \frac{1}{4\pi\epsilon_0} \frac{q^2}{r} = \frac{e^2}{4\pi\epsilon_0} \frac{(8)^2}{6.0 \text{ fm}} = \frac{(1.440 \text{ MeV·fm})(64)}{6.0 \text{ fm}} = 15 \text{ MeV}$$

       (b)    For $^{238}U$,

$$R = 1.2A^{1/3} = 1.2(238)^{1/3} = 7.4 \text{ fm}$$

and with $Z = 92$, the repulsion energy is

$$U = \frac{e^2}{4\pi\epsilon_0} \frac{Z^2}{r} = \frac{(1.440 \text{ MeV·fm})(92)^2}{14.8 \text{ fm}} = 824 \text{ MeV}$$

4.    (a)    $R = 1.2A^{1/3} = 1.2(197)^{1/3} = 7.0$ fm

      (b)    $R = 1.2A^{1/3} = 1.2(4)^{1/3} = 1.9$ fm

      (c)    $R = 1.2A^{1/3} = 1.2(20)^{1/3} = 3.3$ fm

5.    For 60° scattering with $K = 28$ MeV, Equation 6.13 gives

$$b = \frac{zZ}{2K}\frac{e^2}{4\pi\epsilon_0}\cot\frac{\theta}{2} = \frac{2(82)}{2(28\text{ MeV})}(1.440\text{ MeV·fm})\cot 30° = 7.3\text{ fm}$$

The minimum distance between alpha particle and nucleus is found from Equation 6.21:

$$K = K\frac{b^2}{r_{min}^2} + \frac{e^2}{4\pi\epsilon_0}\frac{zZ}{r_{min}}$$

$$r_{min}^2 - \frac{e^2}{4\pi\epsilon_0}\frac{zZ}{K}r_{min} - b^2 = 0. \quad \text{or} \quad r_{min}^2 - 8.43r_{min} - 53.35 = 0$$

Solving with the quadratic formula, we find $r_{min} = 12.6$ fm or $-4.2$ fm. Rejecting the physically unacceptable negative root, we conclude

$$r_{min} = 12.6\text{ fm}$$

The nuclear radius of $^{208}$Pb is

$$R = 1.2A^{1/3} = 1.2(208)^{1/3} = 7.1\text{ fm}$$

The minimum distance is thus greater than the nuclear radius of $^{208}$Pb, and even when we include the nuclear radius of the alpha particle (1.9 fm) we might question why the Rutherford formula fails even when the projectile and target are still "outside" of each other's nuclear charge distributions. Figure 12.1 shows that the nuclear charge actually extends 1-2 fm beyond the computed mean radius, so the alpha particle charge distribution extends to 3-4 fm and the $^{208}$Pb to 8-9 fm. It is therefore not surprising that they begin to overlap at a separation of about 12-13 fm.

6.  For diffraction by a circular disk, the first minimum occurs at $\theta = \sin^{-1}\dfrac{1.22\lambda}{D}$

    For $^{12}$C at 420 MeV, $\theta = 51°$ and

    $$D = \frac{1.22\lambda}{\sin\theta} = \frac{1.22}{\sin\theta}\frac{hc}{E} = \frac{(1.22)(1240 \text{ MeV·fm})}{(\sin 51°)(420 \text{ MeV})} = 4.64 \text{ fm}$$

    $R = 2.32$ fm

    For $^{16}$O at 420 MeV, $\theta = 45°$ and

    $$D = \frac{(1.22)(1240 \text{ MeV·fm})}{(\sin 45°)(420 \text{ MeV})} = 5.09 \text{ fm} \qquad \text{and} \qquad R = 2.54 \text{ fm}$$

    For $^{16}$O at 360 MeV, $\theta = 53°$ and

    $$D = \frac{(1.22)(1240 \text{ MeV·fm})}{(\sin 53°)(360 \text{ MeV})} = 5.26 \text{ fm} \qquad \text{and} \qquad R = 2.63 \text{ fm}$$

7.  (a)  $B = [Nm_n + Zm(^1\text{H}) - m(^A X)]c^2$

    $= [126(1.008665 \text{ u}) + 82(1.007825 \text{ u}) - 207.976636 \text{ u}](931.50 \text{ MeV/u})$

    $= 1636.5$ MeV

    $B/A = (1636.5 \text{ MeV})/208 = 7.868$ MeV per nucleon

    (b)  $B = [78(1.008665 \text{ u}) + 55(1.007825 \text{ u}) - 132.905447 \text{ u}](931.50 \text{ MeV/u})$

    $= 1118.5$ MeV

    $B/A = (1118.5 \text{ MeV})/133 = 8.410$ MeV per nucleon

    (c)  $B = [50(1.008665 \text{ u}) + 40(1.007825 \text{ u}) - 89.904702 \text{ u}](931.50 \text{ MeV/u})$

    $= 783.9$ MeV

    $B/A = (783.9 \text{ MeV})/90 = 8.710$ MeV per nucleon

    (d)  $B = [32(1.008665 \text{ u}) + 27(1.007825 \text{ u}) - 58.933200 \text{ u}](931.50 \text{ MeV/u})$

    $= 517.3$ MeV

    $B/A = (517.3 \text{ MeV})/59 = 8.768$ MeV per nucleon

8.    (a)    $B = [Nm_n + Zm(^1H) - m(^AX)]c^2$

$= [2(1.008665 \text{ u}) + 2(1.007825 \text{ u}) - 4.002603 \text{ u}](931.50 \text{ MeV/u})$

$= 28.30 \text{ MeV}$

$B/A = (28.30 \text{ MeV})/4 = 7.074 \text{ MeV per nucleon}$

(b)    $B = [10(1.008665 \text{ u}) + 10(1.007825 \text{ u}) - 19.992440 \text{ u}](931.50 \text{ MeV/u})$

$= 160.6 \text{ MeV}$

$B/A = (160.6 \text{ MeV})/20 = 8.032 \text{ MeV per nucleon}$

(c)    $B = [20(1.008665 \text{ u}) + 20(1.007825 \text{ u}) - 39.962591 \text{ u}](931.50 \text{ MeV/u})$

$= 342.1 \text{ MeV}$

$B/A = (342.1 \text{ MeV})/40 = 8.551 \text{ MeV per nucleon}$

(d)    $B = [30(1.008665 \text{ u}) + 25(1.007825 \text{ u}) - 54.938049 \text{ u}](931.50 \text{ MeV/u})$

$= 482.1 \text{ MeV}$

$B/A = (482.1 \text{ MeV})/55 = 8.765 \text{ MeV per nucleon}$

9.    For $^3$He,

$B = [1(1.008665 \text{ u}) + 2(1.007825 \text{ u}) - 3.016029 \text{ u}](931.50 \text{ MeV/u})$

$= 7.718 \text{ MeV}$

For $^3$H,

$B = [2(1.008665 \text{ u}) + 1(1.007825 \text{ u}) - 3.016049 \text{ u}](931.50 \text{ MeV/u})$

$= 8.482 \text{ MeV}$

The radius of a nucleus with $A = 3$ is

$R = 1.2A^{1/3} = 1.7 \text{ fm}$

and the Coulomb repulsion energy of two protons separated by 1.7 fm is

$$U = \frac{e^2}{4\pi\epsilon_0}\frac{1}{R} = \frac{1.440 \text{ MeV·fm}}{1.7 \text{ fm}} = 0.85 \text{ MeV}$$

This is roughly equal to the difference in binding energy of 0.76 MeV, which suggests that the difference in mass between $^3$He and $^3$H arises primarily from the Coulomb interaction of the extra proton.

10. (a) Consider a nucleus $^AX$, whose total binding energy is

$$B(A) = [Nm_n + Zm(^1H) - m(^AX)]c^2$$

Removing a neutron leaves the nucleus $^{A-1}X$, whose binding energy is

$$B(A-1) = [(N-1)m_n + Zm(^1H) - m(^{A-1}X)]c^2$$

The difference in binding energy is the energy that must be supplied to separate the neutron:

$$S_n = B(A) - B(A-1) = [m_n + m(^{A-1}X) - m(^AX)]c^2$$

(b) $^{17}$O:

$$S_n = [m_n + m(^{16}O) - m(^{17}O)]c^2$$

$$= [1.008665 \text{ u} + 15.994915 \text{ u} - 16.999132 \text{ u}](931.50 \text{ MeV/u})$$

$$= 4.143 \text{ MeV}$$

$^7$Li:

$$S_n = [m_n + m(^6Li) - m(^7Li)]c^2$$

$$= [1.008665 \text{ u} + 6.015122 \text{ u} - 7.016004 \text{ u}](931.50 \text{ MeV/u})$$

$$= 7.250 \text{ MeV}$$

$^{57}$Fe:

$$S_n = [m_n + m(^{56}Fe) - m(^{57}Fe)]c^2$$

$$= [1.008665 \text{ u} + 55.934942 \text{ u} - 56.935398 \text{ u}](931.50 \text{ MeV/u})$$

$$= 7.647 \text{ MeV}$$

11.  The proton separation energy is the difference in binding energy between the nuclei $_ZX_N$ and $_{Z-1}X'_N$ :

$$S_p = \{Nm_n + Zm(^1H) - m(^AX) - [Nm_n + (Z-1)m(^1H) - m(^{A-1}X')]\}c^2$$

$$= [m(^1H) + m(^{A-1}X') - m(^AX)]c^2$$

$^4$He:

$$S_p = [m(^1H) + m(^3H) - m(^4He)]c^2$$

$$= [1.007825 \text{ u} + 3.016049 \text{ u} - 4.002603 \text{ u}](931.50 \text{ MeV/u})$$

$$= 19.814 \text{ MeV}$$

$^{12}$C:

$$S_p = [m(^1H) + m(^{11}B) - m(^{12}C)]c^2$$

$$= [1.007825 \text{ u} + 11.009306 \text{ u} - 12.000000 \text{ u}](931.50 \text{ MeV/u})$$

$$= 15.958 \text{ MeV}$$

$^{40}$Ca:

$$S_p = [m(^1H) + m(^{39}K) - m(^{40}Ca)]c^2$$

$$= [1.007825 \text{ u} + 38.963707 \text{ u} - 39.962591 \text{ u}](931.50 \text{ MeV/u})$$

$$= 8.329 \text{ MeV}$$

12.  By analogy with Equation 12.6,

$$mc^2 = \frac{\hbar c}{x} = \frac{197 \text{ MeV·fm}}{0.25 \text{ fm}} = 790 \text{ MeV}$$

13.  $$x = \frac{\hbar c}{mc^2} = \frac{197 \text{ MeV·fm}}{80 \times 10^3 \text{ MeV}} = 2.5 \times 10^{-3} \text{ fm}$$

14. $$\frac{N}{N_0} = e^{-\lambda t} = e^{-0.693(t/t_{1/2})} = (0.5)^{t/t_{1/2}}$$

(a) $t/t_{1/2} = 2$: $\quad \frac{N}{N_0} = 0.25 = \frac{1}{4}$

(b) $t/t_{1/2} = 4$: $\quad \frac{N}{N_0} = (0.5)^4 = \frac{1}{16}$

(c) $t/t_{1/2} = 10$: $\quad \frac{N}{N_0} = (0.5)^{10} = \frac{1}{1024}$

15. $\mathcal{A}_0 = 548 \text{ s}^{-1} \quad$ and $\quad \mathcal{A} = 213 \text{ s}^{-1}$ at $t = 48$ min

(a) $213 \text{ s}^{-1} = (548 \text{ s}^{-1}) e^{-(0.693)(48 \text{ min})/t_{1/2}}$

$$\frac{(0.693)(48 \text{ min})}{t_{1/2}} = -\ln\frac{213 \text{ s}^{-1}}{549 \text{ s}^{-1}} \quad \text{or} \quad t_{1/2} = 35 \text{ min}$$

(b) $\lambda = \dfrac{0.693}{t_{1/2}} = \dfrac{0.693}{35 \text{ min}} = 0.020 \text{ min}^{-1}$

(c) $\mathcal{A} = \mathcal{A}_0 e^{-\lambda t} = (548 \text{ s}^{-1}) e^{-(0.020 \text{ min}^{-1})(125 \text{ min})} = 46 \text{ s}^{-1}$

16. $t_{1/2} = 5.0 \text{ h} = 1.8 \times 10^4 \text{ s}$

$$\lambda = \frac{0.693}{t_{1/2}} = \frac{0.693}{1.8 \times 10^4 \text{ s}} = 3.9 \times 10^{-5} \text{ s}^{-1}$$

17. $$\frac{N}{N_0} = e^{-0.693(t/t_{1/2})} = e^{-0.693(50.0 \text{ y}/12.3 \text{ y})} = 0.0598$$

18.    $n = \dfrac{PV}{RT} = \dfrac{(5.0 \times 10^5 \text{ N/m}^2)(125 \times 10^{-6} \text{ m}^3)}{(8.31 \text{ J/mole·K})(300 \text{ K})} = 0.0251$ mole

$N = 0.0251$ mole$(6.022 \times 10^{23}$ molecules/mole$) = 0.151 \times 10^{23}$ molecules

$= 0.302 \times 10^{23}$ atoms          (because hydrogen is diatomic)

$\mathcal{A} = \lambda N = \dfrac{0.693N}{t_{1/2}} = \dfrac{0.693(0.302 \times 10^{23})}{(12.3 \text{ y})(3.156 \times 10^7 \text{ s/y})}$

$= 5.4 \times 10^{13} \text{ s}^{-1} = 1460$ Ci

19    (a)      $\mathcal{A}_0 = (2.00 \text{ mCi})(3.7 \times 10^{10} \text{ s}^{-1}/\text{Ci}) = 7.40 \times 10^7 \text{ s}^{-1}$

     (b)      $\mathcal{A} = \mathcal{A}_0 \, e^{-0.693t/t_{1/2}} = (7.40 \times 10^7 \text{ s}^{-1})e^{-0.693(28 \text{ d})/(8.04 \text{ d})} = 6.62 \times 10^6 \text{ s}^{-1}$

20.    (a)      $N = \dfrac{1000 \text{ g}}{39.1 \text{ g/mole}} 6.022 \times 10^{23}$ atoms/mole $= 1.54 \times 10^{25}$ atoms

Of these, 0.012% or $1.85 \times 10^{21}$ are radioactive $^{40}$K.  The activity is

$$\mathcal{A} = \lambda N = \frac{0.693}{1.3 \times 10^9 \text{ y}} 1.85 \times 10^{21} = 1.0 \times 10^{12} \text{ y}^{-1}$$

$= 3.1 \times 10^4 \text{ s}^{-1} = 0.85 \text{ μCi}$

    (b)      In a sample of $N$ atoms, $N_r$ are radioactive and $N_{nr}$ are nonradioactive:

$N = N_r + N_{nr}$

(Presently, $N_r/N = 0.012\%$.) $N_r$ changes with time:  $N_r = N_{r0}e^{-\lambda t}$

$N_{r0} = N_r e^{\lambda t} = N_r e^{0.693(4.5 \times 10^9 \text{ y}/1.3 \times 10^9 \text{ y})} = 11.0N_r$

At that time ($4.5 \times 10^9$ years ago), the total number was

$N_0 = N_{nr} + N_{r0}$

and the fraction of $^{40}K$ was

$$\frac{N_{r0}}{N_0} = \frac{N_{r0}}{N_{nr} + N_{r0}} = \frac{11N_r}{N_{nr} + 11N_r} = \frac{11N_r}{N + 10N_r}$$

$$= 11\frac{N_r/N}{1 + 10N_r/N} = \frac{11(1.2 \times 10^{-4})}{1 + 1.2 \times 10^{-3}} = 0.13\%$$

21. We assume that the radiation is emitted by the source uniformly in all directions. It is thus distributed over a sphere of radius $R = 25$ cm and area $4\pi R^2$, and the detector receives a fraction of the radiation equal to the fraction of that area it occupies (here $r$ is the radius of the detector, and s and d refer to the activities of the source and detector, respectively):

$$A_s = A_d\frac{4\pi R^2}{\pi r^2} = (1250 \text{ s}^{-1})\frac{4(25 \text{ cm})^2}{(1.5 \text{ cm})^2} = 1.39 \times 10^6 \text{ s}^{-1} = 37.5 \text{ }\mu Ci$$

22. (a) Let $t_{n+1} = t_n$. The number of decays $N_n$ between $t_{n+1}$ and $t_n$ is

$$N_n = N(t_n) - N(t_{n+1}) = N_0 e^{-\lambda t_n} - N_0 e^{-\lambda t_{n+1}}$$

$$= N_0 e^{-\lambda t_n}[1 - e^{-\lambda \Delta t}] \cong N_0 e^{-\lambda t_n}[\lambda \Delta t] \quad \text{for} \quad \Delta t \ll 1/\lambda$$

$$\tau = \frac{1}{N_0}\sum_n N_n t_n = \sum_n e^{-\lambda t_n} t_n \lambda \Delta t$$

If we let the time interval $\Delta t$ become infinitesimally small, the sum becomes an integral:

$$\tau = \lambda \int_0^\infty e^{-\lambda t} t\, dt$$

(b)    $\tau = \dfrac{1}{\lambda} \displaystyle\int_0^\infty e^{-\lambda t}(\lambda t)\, d(\lambda t) = \dfrac{1}{\lambda} \displaystyle\int_0^\infty e^{-x} x\, dx = \dfrac{1}{\lambda}\left[e^{-x}(-x - 1)\right]_0^\infty = \dfrac{1}{\lambda}$

(c)    $\tau = \dfrac{1}{\lambda} = \dfrac{t_{1/2}}{0.693} = 1.44\, t_{1/2}$     so     $\tau > t_{1/2}$

23.    (a)    $^{27}_{14}\text{Si}_{13} \rightarrow\ ^{27}_{13}\text{Al}_{14} + e^+ + \nu$

       (b)    $^{74}_{33}\text{As}_{41} \rightarrow\ ^{74}_{34}\text{Se}_{40} + e^- + \bar{\nu}$

       (c)    $^{228}_{92}\text{U}_{138} \rightarrow\ ^{4}_{2}\text{He}_2 + ^{224}_{90}\text{Th}_{134}$

       (d)    $^{93}_{42}\text{Mo}_{51} + e^- \rightarrow\ ^{93}_{41}\text{Nb}_{52} + \nu$

       (e)    $^{131}_{53}\text{I}_{78} \rightarrow\ ^{131}_{54}\text{Xe}_{77} + e^- + \bar{\nu}$

24.    $Q = K_{X'} + K_\alpha = \dfrac{p_{X'}^2}{2m_{X'}} + \dfrac{p_\alpha^2}{2m_\alpha} = \dfrac{p_\alpha^2}{2m_{X'}} + \dfrac{p_\alpha^2}{2m_\alpha}$     (with $p_{X'} = p_\alpha$)

$= \dfrac{p_\alpha^2}{2m_\alpha}\left(1 + \dfrac{m_\alpha}{m_{X'}}\right) = K_\alpha\left(1 + \dfrac{m_\alpha}{m_{X'}}\right)$

$K_\alpha = \dfrac{Q}{1 + m_\alpha/m_{X'}} = Q\left(\dfrac{m_{X'}}{m_{X'} + m_\alpha}\right)$

To a very good approximation,

$m_{X'} \cong (A - 4)\, u$     and     $m_{X'} + m_\alpha \cong (A - 4)\, u + 4\, u = A\, u$

so

$K_\alpha = Q\left(\dfrac{A - 4}{A}\right)$

25. $^{210}$Bi $\rightarrow$ $^{206}$Tl + $\alpha$

$$Q = [m(^{210}\text{Bi}) - m(^{206}\text{Tl}) - m(\alpha)]c^2$$

$$= [209.984110 \text{ u} - 205.976094 \text{ u} - 4.002603 \text{ u}](931.50 \text{ MeV/u})$$

$$= +5.04 \text{ MeV}$$

$^{203}$Hg $\rightarrow$ $^{199}$Pt + $\alpha$

$$Q = [m(^{203}\text{Hg}) - m(^{199}\text{Pt}) - m(\alpha)]c^2$$

$$= [202.972857 \text{ u} - 198.970576 \text{ u} - 4.002603 \text{ u}](931.50 \text{ MeV/u})$$

$$= -0.30 \text{ MeV}$$

$^{211}$At $\rightarrow$ $^{207}$Bi + $\alpha$

$$Q = [m(^{211}\text{At}) - m(^{207}\text{Bi}) - m(\alpha)]c^2$$

$$= [210.987490 \text{ u} - 206.978467 \text{ u} - 4.002603 \text{ u}](931.50 \text{ MeV/u})$$

$$= +5.98 \text{ MeV}$$

Alpha decay is permitted for $^{210}$Bi and $^{211}$At.

26.

$$Q = [m(^{234}\text{U}) - m(^{230}\text{Th}) - m(\alpha)]c^2$$

$$= [234.040945 \text{ u} - 230.033126 \text{ u} - 4.002603 \text{ u}](931.50 \text{ MeV/u})$$

$$= 4.859 \text{ MeV}$$

$$K_\alpha = Q\left(\frac{A - 4}{A}\right) = 4.859 \text{ MeV}\left(\frac{230}{234}\right) = 4.776 \text{ MeV}$$

27.     1.00 g of $^{239}$Pu is $\frac{1}{239}$ mole $= 2.52 \times 10^{21}$ atoms

$$\mathcal{A} = \lambda N = \frac{0.693N}{t_{1/2}} = \frac{(0.693)(2.52 \times 10^{21})}{(2.41 \times 10^4 \text{ y})(3.156 \times 10^7 \text{ s/y})} = 2.30 \times 10^9 \text{ s}^{-1}$$

The energy output per $^{239}$Pu nucleus is

$$Q = [m(^{239}\text{Pu}) - m(^{235}\text{U}) - m(^4\text{He})]c^2$$

$$= [239.052156 \text{ u} - 235.043922 \text{ u} - 4.002603 \text{ u}](931.50 \text{ MeV/u})$$

$$= 5.245 \text{ MeV} = 8.404 \times 10^{-13} \text{ J}$$

An energy of $8.404 \times 10^{-13}$ J is released in each decay, and there are $2.30 \times 10^9$ decays per second, so the power output is

$$P = (8.404 \times 10^{-13} \text{ J})(2.30 \times 10^9 \text{ s}^{-1}) = 1.93 \times 10^{-3} \text{ W}$$

28.     The mass of $^{224}$Ra in its excited state is

$$224.020202 \text{ u} + \frac{0.217 \text{ MeV}}{931.50 \text{ MeV/u}} = 224.020435 \text{ u}$$

The $Q$ value for the decay is

$$Q = [m(^{228}\text{Th}) - m(^{224}\text{Ra}) - m(^4\text{He})]c^2$$

$$= [228.028731 \text{ u} - 224.020435 \text{ u} - 4.002603 \text{ u}](931.50 \text{ MeV/u})$$

$$= 5.303 \text{ MeV}$$

$$K_\alpha = Q\left(\frac{A-4}{A}\right) = 5.303 \text{ MeV} \left(\frac{224}{228}\right) = 5.210 \text{ MeV}$$

29.    $^{232}$Th:   $R = 1.2(232)^{1/3} = 7.37$ fm

$$U_B = \frac{e^2}{4\pi\epsilon_0} \frac{z(Z-z)}{R} = \frac{(1.440 \text{ MeV·fm})(2)(88)}{7.37 \text{ fm}} = 34.37 \text{ MeV}$$

$$R' = \frac{e^2}{4\pi\epsilon_0} \frac{z(Z-z)}{K_\alpha} = \frac{(1.440 \text{ MeV·fm})(2)(88)}{4.01 \text{ MeV}} = 63.20 \text{ fm}$$

$$\frac{v}{c} = \sqrt{\frac{2K}{mc^2}} = \sqrt{\frac{2(34.01 \text{ MeV})}{3727 \text{ MeV}}} = 0.135$$

$$U_0 = \tfrac{1}{2}(U_B + K_\alpha) = 19.20 \text{ MeV} \quad \text{so} \quad U_0 - K_\alpha = 15.19 \text{ MeV}$$

$$k = \sqrt{\frac{2m}{\hbar^2}(U_0 - K_\alpha)} = \sqrt{\frac{2(3727 \text{ MeV})}{(197 \text{ MeV·fm})^2}(15.19 \text{ MeV})} = 1.71 \text{ fm}^{-1}$$

$$L = \frac{R' - R}{2} = 27.92 \text{ fm} \quad \text{so} \quad kL = 47.74$$

$$\lambda = \frac{v}{2R}e^{-2kL} = \frac{(0.135)(3.00 \times 10^8 \text{ m/s})}{2(7.37 \times 10^{-15} \text{ m})}e^{-2(47.74)} = 1.04 \times 10^{-20} \text{ s}^{-1}$$

$^{218}$Th:   $R = 1.2(218)^{1/3} = 7.22$ fm     so     $U_B = 35.10$ MeV

$$U_0 = 22.48 \text{ MeV} \quad k = 1.56 \text{ fm}^{-1}$$

$$R' = 25.73 \text{ fm} \quad L = 9.26 \text{ fm} \quad kL = 14.45$$

$$\frac{v}{c} = 0.146 \quad\quad \frac{v}{2R} = 3.03 \times 10^{21} \text{ s}^{-1}$$

$$\lambda = (3.03 \times 10^{21} \text{ s}^{-1})e^{-2(14.45)} = 9.0 \times 10^8 \text{ s}^{-1}$$

30.                $R = 1.2(226)^{1/3} = 7.31$ fm

   (a)   For alpha emission

$$U_B = \frac{e^2}{4\pi\epsilon_0}\frac{z(Z-z)}{R} = \frac{(1.440 \text{ MeV·fm})(2)(86)}{7.31 \text{ fm}} = 33.88 \text{ MeV}$$

$$R' = \frac{e^2}{4\pi\epsilon_0}\frac{z(Z-z)}{K_\alpha} = \frac{(1.440 \text{ MeV·fm})(2)(86)}{4.785 \text{ MeV}} = 51.76 \text{ fm}$$

$$\frac{v}{c} = \sqrt{\frac{2K}{mc^2}} = \sqrt{\frac{2(34.785 \text{ MeV})}{3727 \text{ MeV}}} = 0.1366$$

$$U_0 = \tfrac{1}{2}(U_B + K_\alpha) = 19.33 \text{ MeV} \qquad \text{so} \qquad U_0 - K_\alpha = 14.545 \text{ MeV}$$

$$k = \sqrt{\frac{2mc^2}{(\hbar c)^2}(U_0 - K_\alpha)} = \sqrt{\frac{2(3727 \text{ MeV})(14.545 \text{ MeV})}{(197 \text{ MeV·fm})^2}} = 1.67 \text{ fm}^{-1}$$

$$L = \frac{R' - R}{2} = 22.23 \text{ fm} \qquad \text{so} \qquad kL = 37.12$$

$$\lambda = \frac{v}{2R}e^{-2kL} = \frac{(0.1366)(3.00\times10^8 \text{ m/s})}{2(7.31\times10^{-15} \text{ m})}e^{-2(37.12)} = 1.5\times10^{-11} \text{ s}^{-1}$$

For $^{14}$C emission $Q = 28.215$ MeV and $K_C = \dfrac{A-14}{A}Q = 26.47$ MeV

$$U_B = \frac{e^2}{4\pi\epsilon_0}\frac{z(Z-z)}{R} = \frac{(1.440 \text{ MeV·fm})(6)(82)}{7.31 \text{ fm}} = 96.92 \text{ MeV}$$

$$R' = \frac{e^2}{4\pi\epsilon_0}\frac{z(Z-z)}{K_C} = \frac{(1.440 \text{ MeV·fm})(6)(82)}{26.47 \text{ MeV}} = 26.77 \text{ fm}$$

$$\frac{v}{c} = \sqrt{\frac{2K}{mc^2}} = \sqrt{\frac{2(56.47 \text{ MeV})}{(14 \text{ u})(931.5 \text{ MeV/u})}} = 0.093$$

$$U_0 = \tfrac{1}{2}(U_B + K_C) = 61.70 \text{ MeV} \quad \text{so} \quad U_0 - K_C = 35.23 \text{ MeV}$$

$$k = \sqrt{\frac{2mc^2}{(\hbar c)^2}(U_0 - K_C)} = \sqrt{\frac{2(14)(931.5 \text{ MeV})(35.23 \text{ MeV})}{(197 \text{ MeV·fm})^2}} = 4.87 \text{ fm}^{-1}$$

$$L = \frac{R' - R}{2} = 9.73 \text{ fm} \quad \text{so} \quad kL = 47.39$$

$$\lambda = \frac{v}{2R}e^{-2kL} = \frac{(0.093)(3.00 \times 10^8 \text{ m/s})}{2(7.31 \times 10^{-15} \text{ m})}e^{-2(47.39)} = 1.4 \times 10^{-20} \text{ s}^{-1}$$

(b) $$\frac{\lambda_C}{\lambda_\alpha} = \frac{1.4 \times 10^{-20} \text{ s}^{-1}}{1.5 \times 10^{-11} \text{ s}^{-1}} = 1.1 \times 10^{-9}$$

31. Negative beta decay: $^A_Z X \rightarrow \,^A_{Z+1}X' + e^- + \bar{v}$

In terms of nuclear masses $m_N$,

$$Q = [m_N(^A_Z X) - m_N(^A_{Z+1}X') - m_e]c^2$$

Neglecting the atomic binding energy of the electrons, we can convert the nuclear masses to atomic masses:

$$Q = \{[m(^A_Z X) - Zm_e] - [m(^A_{Z+1}X') - (Z+1)m_e] - m_e\}c^2$$

$$= [m(^A_Z X) - m(^A_{Z+1}X')]c^2$$

Positron beta decay: $^A_Z X \rightarrow \,^A_{Z-1}X' + e^+ + v$

$$Q = [m_N(^A_Z X) - m_N(^A_{Z-1}X') - m_e]c^2$$

$$= \{[m(^A_Z X) - Zm_e] - [m(^A_{Z-1}X') - (Z-1)m_e] - m_e\}c^2$$

$$= [m(^A_Z X) - m(^A_{Z-1}X') - 2m_e]c^2$$

Electron capture: $^A_Z X + e^- \rightarrow \, _{Z-1}^{A} X' + \nu$

$$Q = [m_N(^A_Z X) + m_e - m_N(_{Z-1}^{A} X')]c^2$$

$$= \{[m(^A_Z X) - Zm_e] + m_e - [m(_{Z-1}^{A} X') - (Z-1)m_e]\}c^2$$

$$= [m(^A_Z X) - m(_{Z-1}^{A} X')]c^2$$

32.   (a)   In the decay $n \rightarrow p + e^- + \bar{\nu}$, assume the neutrino has zero energy. Then

$$E_n = E_p + E_e = m_p c^2 + K_p + E_e$$

$$K_p + E_e = m_n c^2 - m_p c^2$$

$$= (1.0086650 \text{ u} - 1.0072765 \text{ u})(931.50 \text{ MeV/u}) = 1.293 \text{ MeV}$$

Momentum conservation gives $p_p = p_e$. The proton can be treated nonrelativistically, but the electron must be treated relativistically.

$$K_p + \sqrt{(p_e c)^2 + (m_e c^2)^2} = 1.293 \text{ MeV}$$

$$(K_p - 1.293 \text{ MeV})^2 = (p_p c)^2 + (m_e c^2)^2$$

$$K_p^2 - (2.587 \text{ MeV})K_p + 1.673 \text{ MeV}^2 = K_p(2m_p c^2) + 0.261 \text{ MeV}^2$$

$$K_p^2 - (1879.15 \text{ MeV})K_p + 1.412 \text{ MeV}^2 = 0$$

Solving using the quadratic formula gives two roots, $7.52 \times 10^{-4}$ MeV, and 1879.15 MeV. Only the smaller one is physically meaningful, so

$$K_p = 7.52 \times 10^{-4} \text{ MeV}$$

This method is tedious and allows for all sorts of errors in rounding off and significant figures. We can simplify the method if we realize that $p_p = p_e$ immediately implies $K_p \ll K_e$, since the proton is 2000 times as massive as the electron. We expect to be able to neglect $K_p$ in comparison with $K_e$ to an accuracy of about 1 part in $10^3$, so $E_e \cong 1.293$ MeV and

$$cp_e = \sqrt{E_e^2 - (m_e c^2)^2} = \sqrt{(1.293 \text{ MeV})^2 - (0.511 \text{ MeV})^2}$$

$$= 1.188 \text{ MeV}$$

Thus $cp_p = 1.118$ MeV and

$$K_p = \frac{p_p^2}{2m_p} = \frac{(cp_p)^2}{2m_p c^2} = \frac{(1.188 \text{ MeV})^2}{2(938.3 \text{ MeV})} = 7.52 \times 10^{-4} \text{ MeV}$$

(b)     For this case we assume the kinetic energy of the electron is zero, so

$$m_n c^2 = K_p + m_p c^2 + m_e c^2 + E_\nu$$

$$E_\nu = (m_n c^2 - m_p c^2 - m_e c^2) - K_p = 0.782 \text{ MeV} - K_p$$

If we again assume $K_p$ is small, we conclude

$$cp_\nu = E_\nu \cong 0.782 \text{ MeV}$$

and since $p_p = p_\nu$,

$$K_p = \frac{p_p^2}{2m_p} = \frac{(cp_p)^2}{2m_p c^2} = \frac{(0.782 \text{ MeV})^2}{2(938.3 \text{ MeV})} = 3.26 \times 10^{-4} \text{ MeV}$$

33.    $^{11}\text{Be} \rightarrow {}^{11}\text{B} + e^- + \bar{\nu}$

$$Q = [m(^{11}\text{Be}) - m(^{11}\text{B})]c^2$$

$$= [11.021658 \text{ u} - 11.009306 \text{ u}](931.50 \text{ MeV/u}) = 11.506 \text{ MeV}$$

Ignoring the small correction for the recoil kinetic energy of the $^{11}\text{B}$, we conclude that the maximum electron kinetic energy is

$$K_e = 11.506 \text{ MeV}$$

34.    $^{15}O \rightarrow {}^{15}N + e^- + \nu$

(a)    $Q = [m(^{15}O) - m(^{15}N) - 2m_e]c^2$

$= [15.003066 \text{ u} - 15.000109 \text{ u}](931.50 \text{ MeV/u}) - 2(0.511 \text{ MeV})$

$= 1.732 \text{ MeV}$

(b)    $Q = K_N + K_e + E_\nu$

The $^{15}N$ recoil kinetic energy $K_N$ can be neglected, so the electrons have their maximum energy when $E_\nu$.

$$K_e = Q = 1.732 \text{ MeV}$$

35.    $^{75}Se + e^- \rightarrow {}^{75}As + \nu$

$Q = [m(^{75}Se) - m(^{75}As)]c^2$

$= [74.922524 \text{ u} - 74.921597 \text{ u}](931.50 \text{ MeV/u}) = 0.864 \text{ MeV}$

The kinetic energy of the $^{75}As$ is negligible, so all of this energy goes into the neutrino:

$$E_\nu = 0.864 \text{ MeV}$$

36.    $^{24}Na \rightarrow {}^{24}Mg + e^- + \bar{\nu}$

$Q = [m(^{24}Na) - m(^{24}Mg)]c^2$

$= [23.990963 \text{ u} - 23.985042 \text{ u}](931.50 \text{ MeV/u}) = 5.515 \text{ MeV}$

$Q = K_e + E_\nu + K_{Mg}$

Neglecting $K_{Mg}$, we obtain

$$E_\nu = Q - K_e = 5.515 \text{ MeV} - 2.15 \text{ MeV} = 3.37 \text{ MeV}$$

37.    $^{232}_{90}\text{Th}_{142} \rightarrow \, ^{208}_{82}\text{Pb}_{126} + N_\alpha \, ^4_2\text{He}_2 + N_e \, e^- + N_e \, \bar{\nu}$

(a)    Balancing the mass numbers, we obtain

$$232 = 208 + 4N_\alpha \qquad \text{so} \qquad N_\alpha = 6$$

(b)    Balancing the electric charges, we obtain

$$90 = 82 + 2N_\alpha - N_e \qquad \text{so} \qquad N_e = 4$$

(c)    $Q = [m(^{232}\text{Th}) - m(^{208}\text{Pb}) - 6m(^4\text{He})]c^2$

$= [232.038050 \text{ u} - 207.976636 \text{ u} - 6(4.002603 \text{ u})](931.50 \text{ MeV/u})$

$= 42.659 \text{ MeV} = 68.347 \times 10^{-13} \text{ J}$

(d)    The number of atoms in the sample is

$$N = \frac{(1000 \text{ g})(6.022 \times 10^{23} \text{ atoms/mole})}{232 \text{ g/mole}} = 2.60 \times 10^{24} \text{ atoms}$$

$$\mathcal{A} = \lambda N = \frac{0.693}{(1.40 \times 10^{10} \text{ y})(3.156 \times 10^7 \text{ s/y})} 2.60 \times 10^{24}$$

$$= 4.07 \times 10^6 \text{ s}^{-1}$$

$$P = (68.347 \times 10^{-13} \text{ J})(4.07 \times 10^6 \text{ s}^{-1}) = 27.8 \text{ } \mu\text{W}$$

38.        $3.5 \text{ decays/min} = (12.4 \text{ decays/min}) e^{-\lambda t}$

$$t = \frac{\ln (12.4 \text{ min}^{-1}/3.5 \text{ min}^{-1})}{\lambda} = \frac{1.26}{0.693/5730 \text{ y}} = 1.04 \times 10^4 \text{ y}$$

39.    (a)    $\Delta E = \dfrac{\hbar}{\tau} = \dfrac{6.58 \times 10^{-16} \text{ eV·s}}{141 \times 10^{-9} \text{ s}} = 4.67 \times 10^{-9} \text{ eV}$

       (b)    $K = \dfrac{E_\gamma^2}{2mc^2} = \dfrac{(14.4 \text{ keV})^2}{2(56.935 \text{ u})(931.5 \text{ MeV/u})} = 1.95 \times 10^{-3} \text{ eV}$

       (c)    $v = c\dfrac{\Delta E}{E} = c\dfrac{4.67 \times 10^{-9} \text{ eV}}{14.4 \text{ keV}} = 3.24 \times 10^{-13} c = 0.097 \text{ mm/s}$

# Chapter 13

1.      (a)    $^{4}_{2}He_2 + {}^{14}_{7}N_7 \rightarrow {}^{17}_{8}O_9 + {}^{1}_{1}H_0$

       (b)    $^{9}_{4}Be_5 + {}^{4}_{2}He_2 \rightarrow {}^{12}_{6}C_6 + {}^{1}_{0}n_1$

       (c)    $^{27}_{13}Al_{14} + {}^{4}_{2}He_2 \rightarrow {}^{1}_{0}n_1 + {}^{30}_{15}P_{15}$

       (d)    $^{12}_{6}C_6 + {}^{2}_{1}H_1 \rightarrow {}^{13}_{7}N_6 + {}^{1}_{0}n_1$

2.    Assuming the highest energy protons lead to the ground state of the product nucleus, the energies of the excited states are

      16.2 MeV – 6.7 MeV = 9.5 MeV

      16.2 MeV – 8.9 MeV = 7.3 MeV

      16.2 MeV – 11.6 MeV = 4.6 MeV

      16.2 MeV – 14.8 MeV = 1.4 MeV

      ————————— $E = 9.5$ MeV

      ————————— $E = 7.3$ MeV

      ————————— $E = 4.6$ MeV

      ————————— $E = 1.4$ MeV

      ————————— $E = 0$

3.    From Equation 13.6, the fraction of the maximum activity $f = \mathcal{A}(t)/R$ is

$$f = 1 - e^{-\lambda t} = 1 - e^{-0.693t/t_{1/2}} = 1 - \left(\frac{1}{2}\right)^{t/t_{1/2}}$$

      (a)    at $t = t_{1/2}$    $f = 1 - \left(\frac{1}{2}\right)^1 = \frac{1}{2}$

      (b)    at $t = 2t_{1/2}$    $f = 1 - \left(\frac{1}{2}\right)^2 = \frac{3}{4}$

      (c)    at $t = 4t_{1/2}$    $f = 1 - \left(\frac{1}{2}\right)^4 = \frac{15}{16}$

4.    The target is a foil of copper of thickness 2.5 μm and a diameter 0.50 cm.  The mass of the target is

$$(8.96 \text{ g/cm}^3)(2.5 \times 10^{-4} \text{ cm})\pi(0.25 \text{ cm})^2 = 4.40 \times 10^{-4} \text{ g}$$

$$N = (6.022 \times 10^{23} \text{ atoms/mole})\frac{(4.40 \times 10^{-4} \text{ g})}{63 \text{ g/mole}} = 4.20 \times 10^{18} \text{ atoms}$$

$$I_0 = \frac{7.5 \times 10^{-6} \text{ A}}{2 \times 1.6 \times 10^{-19} \text{ C/particle}} = 2.34 \times 10^{13} \text{ particles/s}$$

$$R = \frac{I_0 \sigma N}{S} = \frac{(2.34 \times 10^{13} \text{ s}^{-1})(1.25 \times 10^{-24} \text{ cm}^2)(4.20 \times 10^{18})}{\pi(0.25 \text{ cm})^2}$$

$$= 6.26 \times 10^8 \text{ neutrons/s}$$

5.    $$I_0 = \frac{20 \times 10^{-6} \text{ A}}{1.6 \times 10^{-19} \text{ C/proton}} = 12.5 \times 10^{13} \text{ protons/s}$$

Let the target thickness be $t$.  Then

$$\frac{N}{S} = \frac{(N_A\rho/M)V}{S} = \frac{N_A\rho t}{M}$$

$$= \frac{(6.022 \times 10^{23} \text{ atoms/mole})(10.5 \text{ g/cm}^3)(4.5 \times 10^{-4} \text{ cm})}{107 \text{ grams/mole}}$$

$$= 2.65 \times 10^{19} \text{ atoms/cm}^2$$

Because 3 neutrons are produced in each reaction, the reaction rate is $R = (8.5 \times 10^6 \text{ s}^{-1})/3 = 2.83 \times 10^6 \text{ s}^{-1}$.

$$\sigma = \frac{R/I_0}{N/S} = \frac{(2.83 \times 10^6 \text{ s}^{-1})/(12.5 \times 10^{13} \text{ s}^{-1})}{2.65 \times 10^{19} \text{ cm}^{-2}}$$

$$= 8.6 \times 10^{-28} \text{ cm}^2 = 8.6 \times 10^{-4} \text{ b}$$

6.  $$\frac{dN}{dt} = \frac{d}{dt}\left[\frac{R}{\lambda}(1 - e^{-\lambda t})\right] = Re^{-\lambda t}$$

$$R - \lambda N = R - R(1 - e^{-\lambda t}) = Re^{-\lambda t} = \frac{dN}{dt}$$

7.  $$R = \phi\sigma\frac{m}{M}N_A$$

$$= \left(2.5 \times 10^{13}\ \frac{n}{cm^2 \cdot s}\right)\left(0.53 \times 10^{-24}\ \frac{cm^2}{atom}\right)$$

$$\times \left(\frac{1.0 \times 10^{-6}\ g}{23.0\ g/mole}\right)\left(6.022 \times 10^{23}\ \frac{atoms}{mole}\right)$$

$$= 3.47 \times 10^5\ s^{-1}$$

$$\mathcal{A} = R(1 - e^{-\lambda t}) = (3.47 \times 10^5\ s^{-1})(1 - e^{-0.693(4\ h/15\ h)})$$

$$= 5.85 \times 10^4\ s^{-1} = 1.58\ \mu Ci$$

8.  Titanium:

$$R = \mathcal{A}(1 - e^{-\lambda t})^{-1} = \frac{105\ s^{-1}}{1 - e^{-0.693(2.5\ min/5.8\ min)}} = 407\ s^{-1}$$

$$N = \frac{R}{\phi\sigma} = \frac{407\ s^{-1}}{(3.0 \times 10^{12}\ n/cm^2/s)(0.14 \times 10^{-24}\ cm^2)}$$

$$= 9.68 \times 10^{14}\ \text{atoms of } {}^{50}Ti$$

Titanium is 5.25% ${}^{50}Ti$, so the total number of titanium atoms is

$$N = \frac{9.68 \times 10^{14}\ atoms}{0.0525} = 1.84 \times 10^{16}\ atoms = N_A\frac{m}{M}$$

$$m = \frac{NM}{N_A} = \frac{(1.84 \times 10^{16}\ atoms)(47.9\ g/mole)}{6.022 \times 10^{23}\ atoms/mole} = 1.47\ \mu g$$

Cobalt:

$$R = \mathcal{A}(1 - e^{-\lambda t})^{-1} = \frac{12 \text{ s}^{-1}}{1 - e^{-0.693(2.5 \text{ min})/[(5.27 \text{ y})(5.26 \times 10^5 \text{ min/y})]}}$$

$$= 1.92 \times 10^7 \text{ s}^{-1}$$

$$N = \frac{R}{\phi \sigma} = \frac{1.92 \times 10^7 \text{ s}^{-1}}{(3.0 \times 10^{12} \text{ n/cm}^2/\text{s})(19 \times 10^{-24} \text{ cm}^2)} = 3.36 \times 10^{17} \text{ atoms}$$

$$m = \frac{NM}{N_A} = \frac{(3.36 \times 10^{17} \text{ atoms})(58.9 \text{ g/mole})}{6.022 \times 10^{23} \text{ atoms/mole}} = 33 \text{ } \mu\text{g}$$

9. The total number of copper atoms in the target is

$$\frac{2.0 \times 10^{-3} \text{ g}}{63.5 \text{ g/mole}}(6.022 \times 10^{23} \text{ atoms/mole}) = 1.90 \times 10^{19} \text{ atoms}$$

For $^{63}\text{Cu} + \text{n} \rightarrow {}^{64}\text{Cu}$, $N(^{63}\text{Cu}) = 0.69(1.90 \times 10^{19}) = 1.31 \times 10^{19}$ atoms.

$$R = \mathcal{A}(1 - e^{-\lambda t})^{-1} = \frac{(72 \times 10^{-6} \text{ Ci})(3.7 \times 10^{10} \text{ s}^{-1}/\text{Ci})}{1 - e^{-0.693(10 \text{ min}/12.7 \times 60 \text{ min})}} = 2.94 \times 10^8 \text{ s}^{-1}$$

From Equation 13.2,

$$\sigma = \frac{RM}{\phi m N_A} = \frac{R}{\phi N} = \frac{2.94 \times 10^8 \text{ s}^{-1}}{(5.0 \times 10^{12} \text{ n/cm}^2/\text{s})(1.31 \times 10^{19})}$$

$$= 4.49 \times 10^{-24} \text{ cm}^2 = 4.49 \text{ b}$$

For $^{65}\text{Cu} + \text{n} \rightarrow {}^{66}\text{Cu}$, $N(^{65}\text{Cu}) = 0.31(1.90 \times 10^{19}) = 0.589 \times 10^{19}$ atoms.

$$R = \mathcal{A}(1 - e^{-\lambda t})^{-1} = \frac{(1.30 \times 10^{-3} \text{ Ci})(3.7 \times 10^{10} \text{ s}^{-1}/\text{Ci})}{1 - e^{-0.693(10 \text{ min}/5.1 \text{ min})}} = 6.47 \times 10^7 \text{ s}^{-1}$$

$$\sigma = \frac{R}{\phi N} = \frac{6.47 \times 10^7 \text{ s}^{-1}}{(5.0 \times 10^{12} \text{ n/cm}^2/\text{s})(0.589 \times 10^{19})}$$

$$= 2.20 \times 10^{-24} \text{ cm}^2 = 2.20 \text{ b}$$

10.  (a)  The number of atoms in the target is

$$N = \frac{m}{M} N_A = \frac{\rho A\, dx}{M} N_A = nA\, dx$$

where $n = \rho N_A/M$ is the number of target nuclei per unit volume.  The rate at which reactions occur in the target is

$$R = \phi\sigma \frac{m}{M} N_A = \phi\sigma nA\, dx = I\sigma n\, dx$$

where the neutron beam intensity $I$ (neutrons/s) is $\phi A$.  The beam therefore loses intensity $dI$, where

$$dI = -I\sigma n\, dx$$

(b)  The total absorption after passing through a thickness $x$ is

$$\int_{I_0}^{I} \frac{dI}{I} = -\int_{0}^{x} \sigma n\, dx$$

$$\ln I - \ln I_0 = -\sigma n x \qquad \text{or} \qquad I = I_0 e^{-\sigma n x}$$

11.  $$\tfrac{1}{2} m_x (v_x - v)^2 + \tfrac{1}{2} m_X(-v)^2 + m_x c^2 + m_X c^2 = m_y c^2 + m_Y c^2$$

Substituting $v = v_x m_x/(m_x + m_X)$, we obtain

$$\tfrac{1}{2} m_x \left( v_x - \frac{v_x m_x}{m_x + m_X} \right)^2 + \tfrac{1}{2} m_X \left( - \frac{v_x m_x}{m_x + m_X} \right)^2$$

$$= (m_y + m_Y - m_x - m_X)c^2 = -Q$$

$$\tfrac{1}{2} m_x v_x^2 \left[ \frac{m_X^2}{(m_x + m_X)^2} + \frac{m_x m_X}{(m_x + m_X)^2} \right] = -Q$$

$$K_{th} \left[ \frac{m_X}{m_x + m_X} \right] = -Q \qquad \text{or} \qquad K_{th} = -Q\left[ 1 + \frac{m_x}{m_X} \right]$$

12.     $n = \dfrac{\rho N_A}{M} = \dfrac{(8.95 \text{ g/cm}^3)(6.022 \times 10^{23} \text{ atoms/mole})}{63.5 \text{ g/mole}} = 8.49 \times 10^{22} \text{ atoms/cm}^3$

           $n\sigma = (8.49 \times 10^{22} \text{ atoms/cm}^3)(5.0 \times 10^{-24} \text{ cm}^2) = 0.424 \text{ cm}^{-1}$

(a)     $x = 1.0 \text{ mm} = 0.10 \text{ cm}: \quad \dfrac{I}{I_0} = e^{-n\sigma x} = e^{-(0.424 \text{ cm}^{-1})(0.10 \text{ cm})} = 0.958$

      so 4.2 % is lost.

(b)     $x = 1.0 \text{ cm}: \quad \dfrac{I}{I_0} = e^{-n\sigma x} = e^{-(0.424 \text{ cm}^{-1})(1.0 \text{ cm})} = 0.654$

      so 34.6 % is lost.

(c)     $x = 1.0 \text{ m} = 100 \text{ cm}: \quad \dfrac{I}{I_0} = e^{-n\sigma x} = e^{-(0.424 \text{ cm}^{-1})(100 \text{ cm})} = 3.85 \times 10^{-19}$

      so the beam is virtually completely absorbed.

13.    (a)     $\text{p} + {}^{55}\text{Mn} \rightarrow {}^{54}\text{Fe} + 2\text{n}$

           $Q = [m({}^{1}\text{H}) + m({}^{55}\text{Mn}) - m({}^{54}\text{Fe}) - 2m(\text{n})]c^2$

             $= (1.007825 \text{ u} + 54.938049 \text{ u} - 53.939615 \text{ u}$

                $- 2 \times 1.008665 \text{ u})(931.50 \text{ MeV/u}) = -10.313 \text{ MeV}$

   (b)     ${}^{3}\text{He} + {}^{40}\text{Ar} \rightarrow {}^{41}\text{K} + {}^{2}\text{H}$

           $Q = [m({}^{3}\text{He}) + m({}^{40}\text{Ar}) - m({}^{41}\text{K}) - m({}^{2}\text{H})]c^2$

             $= (3.016029 \text{ u} + 39.962383 \text{ u} - 40.961826 \text{ u}$

                $- 2.014102 \text{ u})(931.50 \text{ MeV/u}) = 2.314 \text{ MeV}$

14.    (a)     ${}^{6}\text{Li} + \text{n} \rightarrow {}^{3}\text{H} + {}^{4}\text{He}$

           $Q = [m({}^{6}\text{Li}) + m(\text{n}) - m({}^{3}\text{H}) - m({}^{4}\text{He})]c^2$

             $= (6.015122 \text{ u} + 1.008665 \text{ u} - 3.016049 \text{ u}$

                $- 4.002603 \text{ u})(931.50 \text{ MeV/u}) = 4.783 \text{ MeV}$

(b)     $p + {}^2H \rightarrow 2p + n$

$$Q = [m({}^1H) + m({}^2H) - 2m({}^1H) - m(n)]c^2$$
$$= (2.014102 \text{ u} - 1.007825 \text{ u} - 1.008665 \text{ u})(931.50 \text{ MeV/u})$$
$$= -2.224 \text{ MeV}$$

(c)     ${}^7Li + {}^2H \rightarrow {}^8Be + n$

$$Q = [m({}^7Li) + m({}^2H) - m({}^8Be) - m(n)]c^2$$
$$= (7.016004 \text{ u} + 2.014102 \text{ u} - 8.005305 \text{ u}$$
$$- 1.008665 \text{ u})(931.50 \text{ MeV/u}) = 15.031 \text{ MeV}$$

15.    ${}^2H + {}^3He \rightarrow p + {}^4He$

$$Q = [m({}^2H) + m({}^3He) - m({}^1H) - m({}^4He)]c^2$$
$$= (2.014102 \text{ u} + 3.016029 \text{ u} - 1.007825 \text{ u} - 4.002603 \text{ u})(931.50 \text{ MeV/u})$$
$$= 18.353 \text{ MeV}$$

Let $y = p$, $Y = {}^4He$, $x = {}^2H$

$$Q = K_y + K_Y - K_x$$
$$K_y + K_Y = Q + K_x = 18.353 \text{ MeV} + 5.00 \text{ MeV}$$
$$\frac{p_y^2}{2m_y} + \frac{p_Y^2}{2m_Y} = 23.353 \text{ MeV}$$
$$p_x = \sqrt{2m_x K_x} = \frac{1}{c}\sqrt{2m_x c^2 K_x}$$
$$= \frac{1}{c}\sqrt{2(2.014102 \text{ u})(931.50 \text{ MeV/u})(5.000 \text{ MeV})} = 137.0 \text{ MeV}/c$$

Momentum conservation gives

$$p_y = p_x - p_Y = 137 \text{ MeV}/c - p_Y$$
$$\frac{(137.0 \text{ MeV}/c - p_Y)^2}{2m_y} + \frac{p_Y^2}{2m_Y} = 23.353 \text{ MeV}$$

$$c^2 p_Y^2 \left[ \frac{1}{2m_y c^2} + \frac{1}{2m_Y c^2} \right] - \frac{137.0 \text{ MeV}}{m_y c^2} c p_Y$$

$$+ \frac{(137.0 \text{ MeV})^2}{2m_y c^2} - 23.353 \text{ MeV} = 0$$

Solving for $cp_Y$ with the quadratic formula, we find

$$cp_Y = 288.4 \text{ MeV}, \; -69.5 \text{ MeV}$$

The first solution corresponds to the $^4$He moving in the same direction as the original $^2$H, while the protons move in the opposite direction ($cp_y = 137.0 \text{ MeV} - cp_Y = -151.4 \text{ MeV}$). The kinetic energies are

$$K_Y = \frac{(cp_Y)^2}{2m_Y c^2} = \frac{(288.4 \text{ MeV})^2}{2(4.002603 \text{ u})(931.50 \text{ MeV/u})} = 11.152 \text{ MeV}$$

$$K_y = 23.353 \text{ MeV} - 11.152 \text{ MeV} = 12.201 \text{ MeV}$$

The second solution gives $^4$He moving opposite to the original direction of the $^2$H, with kinetic energy

$$K_Y = \frac{(69.5 \text{ MeV})^2}{2(4.002603 \text{ u})(931.50 \text{ MeV/u})} = 0.647 \text{ MeV}$$

$$K_y = 23.353 \text{ MeV} - 0.647 \text{ MeV} = 22.706 \text{ MeV}$$

16.  (a)  $\text{p} + \,^4\text{He} \rightarrow \,^2\text{H} + \,^3\text{He}$

$$Q = [m(^1\text{H}) + m(^4\text{He}) - m(^2\text{H}) - m(^3\text{He})]c^2$$

$$= (1.007825 \text{ u} + 4.002603 \text{ u} - 2.014102 \text{ u}$$

$$- 3.016029 \text{ u})(931.50 \text{ MeV/u}) = -18.353 \text{ MeV}$$

(b)  For protons incident on $^4$He, $x = \,^1$H and $X = \,^4$He:

$$K_{\text{th}} = -Q\left[1 + \frac{m_x}{m_X}\right] = 18.353 \text{ MeV}\left[1 + \frac{1.007825 \text{ u}}{4.002603 \text{ u}}\right] = 22.974 \text{ MeV}$$

(c)     For $^4$He incident on protons, $x = {}^4$He and $X = {}^1$H:

$$K_{th} = -Q\left[1 + \frac{m_x}{m_X}\right] = 18.353 \text{ MeV}\left[1 + \frac{4.002603 \text{ u}}{1.007825 \text{ u}}\right] = 91.242 \text{ MeV}$$

17.     $^4_2\text{He}_2 + {}^7_3\text{Li}_4 \rightarrow {}^{11}_5\text{B}_6 + \gamma$

$$Q = [m(^4\text{He}) + m(^7\text{Li}) - m(^{11}\text{B})]c^2$$
$$= (4.002603 \text{ u} + 7.016004 \text{ u} - 11.009306 \text{ u})(931.50 \text{ MeV/u})$$
$$= 8.664 \text{ MeV}$$

If we can neglect the energies of the incident particles,

$$Q = K_B + E_\gamma \qquad \text{and} \qquad p_B = p_\gamma$$

$$K_B + E_\gamma = \frac{p_B^2}{2m_B} + E_\gamma = \frac{p_\gamma^2}{2m_B} + E_\gamma = \frac{E_\gamma^2}{2m_B c^2} + E_\gamma$$

$$\frac{E_\gamma^2}{2m_B c^2} + E_\gamma - Q = 0$$

$$E_\gamma = \left[-1 \pm \sqrt{1 + 4Q/2m_B c^2}\right]m_B c^2 = 8.660 \text{ MeV}$$

The kinetic energy of the boron is only 0.004 MeV, but it is not negligible at the precision of this calculation.

18.     $\gamma + {}^7\text{Li} \rightarrow {}^3\text{H} + {}^4\text{He}$

$$Q = [m(^7\text{Li}) - m(^3\text{H}) - m(^4\text{He})]c^2$$
$$= (7.016004 \text{ u} - 3.016049 \text{ u} - 4.002603 \text{ u})(931.50 \text{ MeV/u})$$
$$= -2.4666 \text{ MeV} = K_H + K_{He} - E_\gamma$$

if we assume the $^7$Li is at rest. Momentum conservation gives

$$p_\gamma = p_H + p_{He}$$

If we supply only the minimum gamma-ray energy, the $^3$H and $^4$He will move together, as in a reaction at threshold. With $v_H = v_{He} = v$, we have

$$p_\gamma = m_H v + m_{He} v = v(m_H + m_{He})$$

$$v = \frac{p_\gamma}{(m_H + m_{He})}$$

$$Q = -E_\gamma + K_H + K_{He} = -E_\gamma + \left(\frac{1}{2}m_H + \frac{1}{2}m_{He}\right)v^2$$

$$= -E_\gamma + \frac{1}{2}(m_H + m_{He})\frac{p_\gamma^2}{(m_H + m_{He})^2} = -E_\gamma + \frac{E_\gamma^2}{2(m_H + m_{He})c^2}$$

$$\frac{E_\gamma^2}{2(m_H + m_{He})c^2} - E_\gamma - Q = 0$$

$$E_\gamma = \left[1 \pm \sqrt{1 + 4Q/2(m_H + m_{He})c^2}\right](m_H + m_{He})c^2 = 2.4671 \text{ MeV}$$

The additional energy for the momenta of the $^3$H and $^4$He must be supplied by the gamma ray, but this energy is small, only 0.0005 MeV above the $Q$ value.

19.    $^{113}$Cd + n → $^{114}$Cd + γ

$$Q = [m(^{113}\text{Cd}) + m(\text{n}) - m(^{114}\text{Cd})]c^2$$

$$= (112.904401 \text{ u} + 1.008665 \text{ u} - 113.903359 \text{ u})(931.50 \text{ MeV/u})$$

$$= 9.042 \text{ MeV}$$

$$Q = K_{Cd} + E_\gamma - K_n$$

where $K_{Cd}$ is the energy given to the $^{114}$Cd. The neutron kinetic energy is negligible. Thus

$$K_{Cd} + E_\gamma = 9.042 \text{ MeV}$$

The momentum of the Cd and the photon must be equal:

$$p_{Cd} = p_\gamma$$

and the kinetic energy of the heavy Cd will certainly be negligible in comparison with $E_\gamma$. We therefore conclude

$$E_\gamma = 9.042 \text{ MeV}$$

We can check our assumptions by computing the kinetic energy $K_{Cd}$ when the momentum $p_{Cd}$ is equal to 9.042 MeV/c. The result, $4 \times 10^{-4}$ MeV, is indeed negligible within the accuracy of this problem.

20.        $$\frac{\Delta K}{K} = \frac{4m/M}{(1 + m/M)^2} \quad \text{with } m = 1 \text{ u (neutron)}$$

(a)   $M = 1$ u (hydrogen):   $\dfrac{\Delta K}{K} = \dfrac{4}{(2)^2} = 1$   (all kinetic energy is lost)

$M = 2$ u (deuteron):   $\dfrac{\Delta K}{K} = \dfrac{4(1/2)}{(1 + 1/2)^2} = 0.89$

$M = 12$ u (carbon):   $\dfrac{\Delta K}{K} = \dfrac{4(1/12)}{(1 + 1/12)^2} = 0.28$

(b)   After one scattering, the new kinetic energy is

$$K' = K - \Delta K = K - K\frac{4m/M}{(1 + m/M)^2} = K\left(\frac{1 - m/M}{1 + m/M}\right)^2$$

After $n$ scatterings, the kinetic energy is

$$K' = K\left(\frac{1 - m/M}{1 + m/M}\right)^{2n}$$

$$0.025 \text{ eV} = 2.0 \text{ MeV}\left(\frac{1 - 1/12}{1 + 1/12}\right)^{2n}$$

$$n = \frac{\log\left[(0.025 \text{ eV})/2 \times 10^6 \text{ eV}\right]}{2 \log(11/13)} = 54.5 \quad \text{or} \quad 55 \text{ scatterings}$$

21.    (a)    $\Delta E = [m(^{235}\text{U}) + m(\text{n}) - m(^{236}\text{U})]c^2$

$= (235.043922 \text{ u} + 1.008665 \text{ u} - 236.045561 \text{ u})(931.50 \text{ MeV/u})$

$= 6.545 \text{ MeV}$

(b)    $\Delta E = [m(^{238}\text{U}) + m(\text{n}) - m(^{239}\text{U})]c^2$

$= (238.050784 \text{ u} + 1.008665 \text{ u} - 239.054289 \text{ u})(931.50 \text{ MeV/u})$

$= 4.807 \text{ MeV}$

(c)    If $^{235}\text{U}$ + n gives enough energy of excitiation to make the $^{236}\text{U}$ fission easily, then $^{238}\text{U}$ + n needs about 1.7 MeV of additional energy to reach the same state of excitation and therefore to have about the same probability to fission. This additional energy must come from the incident neutrons, so $^{238}\text{U}$ can be fissioned readily only by "fast" neutrons with 1-2 MeV of kinetic energy.

(d)    $\Delta E = [m(^{239}\text{Pu}) + m(\text{n}) - m(^{240}\text{Pu})]c^2$

$= (239.052156 \text{ u} + 1.008665 \text{ u} - 240.053807 \text{ u})(931.50 \text{ MeV/u})$

$= 6.534 \text{ MeV}$

Since $^{239}\text{Pu}$ + n has about the same relative excitation as $^{235}\text{U}$ + n, we expect that it will fission about as easily, and therefore only slow neutrons are needed.

22.    The number of $^{235}\text{U}$ atoms in 1000 g of U (= 30 g of $^{235}\text{U}$) is

$$\frac{(30 \text{ g})(6.022 \times 10^{23} \text{ atoms/mole})}{235 \text{ g/mole}} = 5.9 \times 10^{22} \text{ atoms}$$

If each fission releases about 200 MeV, the total energy released is

$$E = (200 \text{ MeV/atom})(5.9 \times 10^{22} \text{ atoms}) = 1.2 \times 10^{31} \text{ eV} = 1.9 \times 10^{12} \text{ J}$$

23.    $Q = [m(^{235}\text{U}) + m(\text{n}) - m(^{93}\text{Rb}) - m(^{141}\text{Cs}) - 2m(\text{n})]c^2$

$= (235.043922 \text{ u} - 92.92195 \text{ u} - 140.92005 \text{ u} - 1.008665 \text{ u})(931.50 \text{ MeV/u})$

$= 180.02 \text{ MeV}$

24. We must first find the Coulomb barrier that keeps the helium nuclei from coming together; to find the potential energy of two helium nuclei that just touch at their surfaces, we need the nuclear radius,

$$R = 1.2A^{1/3} = 1.2(4)^{1/3} = 1.9 \text{ fm}$$

When the charges of $+2e$ are separated by $2R$, the potential energy is

$$U = \frac{1}{4\pi\epsilon_0} \frac{(2e)^2}{2(1.9 \text{ fm})} = \frac{2(1.440 \text{ MeV·fm})}{1.9 \text{ fm}} = 1.5 \text{ MeV}$$

We could overcome this barrier if each helium had a kinetic enegy of 0.75 MeV. The corresponding temperature would be

$$\frac{3}{2}kT = 0.75 \text{ MeV}$$

$$T = \frac{0.75 \text{ MeV}}{1.5(8.6 \times 10^{-5} \text{ eV/K})} = 5.8 \times 10^9 \text{ K}$$

25. (a) $^{12}\text{C} + {}^1\text{H} \rightarrow {}^{13}\text{N} + \gamma$

$$Q = [m(^{12}\text{C}) + m(^1\text{H}) - m(^{13}\text{N})]c^2$$

$$= (12.000000 \text{ u} + 1.007825 \text{ u} - 13.005739 \text{ u})(931.50 \text{ MeV/u})$$

$$= 1.943 \text{ MeV}$$

$^{13}\text{N} \rightarrow {}^{13}\text{C} + e^+ + \nu$

$$Q = [m(^{13}\text{N}) - m(^{13}\text{C}) - 2m_e]c^2$$

$$= (13.005739 \text{ u} - 13.003355 \text{ u} - 2 \times 0.0005486 \text{ u})(931.50 \text{ MeV/u})$$

$$= 1.199 \text{ MeV}$$

$^{13}\text{C} + {}^1\text{H} \rightarrow {}^{14}\text{N} + \gamma$

$$Q = [m(^{13}\text{C}) + m(^1\text{H}) - m(^{14}\text{N})]c^2$$

$$= (13.003355 \text{ u} + 1.007825 \text{ u} - 14.003074 \text{ u})(931.50 \text{ MeV/u})$$

$$= 7.551 \text{ MeV}$$

$$^{14}\text{N} + {}^1\text{H} \rightarrow {}^{15}\text{O} + \gamma$$

$$Q = [m(^{14}\text{N}) + m(^1\text{H}) - m(^{15}\text{O})]c^2$$

$$= (14.003074 \text{ u} + 1.007825 \text{ u} - 15.003066 \text{ u})(931.50 \text{ MeV/u})$$

$$= 7.296 \text{ MeV}$$

$$^{15}\text{O} \rightarrow {}^{15}\text{N} + e^+ + \nu$$

$$Q = [m(^{15}\text{O}) - m(^{15}\text{N}) - 2m_e]c^2$$

$$= (15.003066 \text{ u} - 15.000109 \text{ u} - 2 \times 0.0005486 \text{ u})(931.50 \text{ MeV/u})$$

$$= 1.732 \text{ MeV}$$

$$^{15}\text{N} + {}^1\text{H} \rightarrow {}^{12}\text{C} + {}^4\text{He}$$

$$Q = [m(^{15}\text{N}) + m(^1\text{H}) - m(^{12}\text{C}) - m(^4\text{He})]c^2$$

$$= (15.000109 \text{ u} + 1.007825 \text{ u} - 12.000000 \text{ u}$$

$$- 4.002603 \text{ u})(931.50 \text{ MeV/u}) = 4.966 \text{ MeV}$$

(b)     When the 6 reactions or decays are added, four electrons must be added to each side of the equations, as in the proton-proton cycle. (Two electrons are necessary to balance each of the two positron decays in the carbon cycle.) The net $Q$ value is the sum of the $Q$ values for the 6 processes plus $4m_e c^2$, which gives 26.7 MeV.

26.     $^2\text{H} + {}^3\text{H} \rightarrow {}^4\text{He} + \text{n}$

$$Q = [m(^2\text{H}) + m(^3\text{H}) - m(^4\text{He}) - m(\text{n})]c^2$$

$$= (2.014102 \text{ u} + 3.016049 \text{ u} - 4.002603 \text{ u} - 1.008665 \text{ u})(931.50 \text{ MeV/u})$$

$$= 17.590 \text{ MeV}$$

27. $^2\text{H} + {}^3\text{H} \rightarrow {}^4\text{He} + \text{n}$    with $Q = 17.6$ MeV

$Q = K_{\text{He}} + K_{\text{n}}$    neglecting the initial kinetic energies of $^2\text{H}$ and $^3\text{H}$

With $p_{\text{He}} = p_{\text{n}}$,

$$Q = \frac{p_{\text{He}}^2}{2m_{\text{He}}} + \frac{p_{\text{n}}^2}{2m_{\text{n}}} = \frac{p_{\text{n}}^2}{2m_{\text{He}}} + \frac{p_{\text{n}}^2}{2m_{\text{n}}} = K_{\text{n}}\left(1 + \frac{m_{\text{n}}}{m_{\text{He}}}\right)$$

$$K_{\text{n}} = \frac{Q}{1 + m_{\text{n}}/m_{\text{He}}} = \frac{17.6 \text{ MeV}}{1.25} = 14.1 \text{ MeV}$$

28. (a) The number of molecules of water is

$$N = \frac{6.022 \times 10^{23} \text{ mole}^{-1}}{18 \text{ g/mole}}(100 \text{ cm}^3)(1 \text{ g/cm}^3) = 3.3 \times 10^{24}$$

The number of $D_2O$ molecules is 0.015 percent of this, or $5.0 \times 10^{20}$. Each molecule includes two deuterons, but each fusion reaction takes two deuterons, so that consuming all the $D_2O$ would result in $5.0 \times 10^{20}$ fusion reactions, each of which releases 4.0 MeV. The total energy release is

$$E = (5.0 \times 10^{20} \text{ reactions})(4.0 \text{ MeV/reaction})$$
$$= 2.0 \times 10^{21} \text{ MeV} = 3.2 \times 10^8 \text{ J}$$

(b) If only 2/3 of the deuterium participated in the first reaction, the energy released would be 2/3 of that found in part (a), or $2.1 \times 10^{21}$ J. Each reaction produces a single $^3\text{H}$, so the number of $^3\text{H}$ produced is $1/3 \times 5.0 \times 10^{20}$, which then react with the remaining $1/3 \times 5.0 \times 10^{20}$ deuterons. Each of these reactions releases 17.6 MeV, for a total energy of

$$E = \tfrac{1}{3}(5.0 \times 10^{20} \text{ reactions})(17.6 \text{ MeV/reaction})$$
$$= 2.9 \times 10^{21} \text{ MeV} = 4.7 \times 10^8 \text{ J}$$

The total energy released in the entire process is

$$E = 2.1 \times 10^8 \text{ J} + 4.7 \times 10^8 \text{ J} = 6.8 \times 10^8 \text{ J}$$

We obtain more than twice the energy in this second process.

29.    $3\,^4\text{He} \rightarrow\ ^{12}\text{C}$

$$Q = [3m(^4\text{He}) - m(^{12}\text{C})]c^2$$

$$= (3 \times 4.002603\ \text{u} - 12.000000\ \text{u})(931.50\ \text{MeV/u}) = 7.274\ \text{MeV}$$

This energy is about 0.6 MeV per reacting nucleon, far smaller than the 6.7 MeV per reacting nucleon released in the fusion of 4 protons to form $^4$He.

30.    (a)    $n\tau \geq 10^{20}\ \text{s·m}^{-3}$    for    $\tau = 0.60\ \text{s}$

$$n \geq \frac{10^{20}\ \text{s·m}^{-3}}{\tau} = \frac{10^{20}\ \text{s·m}^{-3}}{0.60\ \text{s}} = 1.67 \times 10^{20}\ \text{m}^{-3}$$

(b)    For $n = 1.67 \times 10^{20}\ \text{m}^{-3}$, Figure 13.17 indicates $T > 1.5 \times 10^8$ K.

31.    Let the alpha particle move with velocity $v$ before the collision. After the collision, the alpha particle moves (in the reverse direction) with velocity $v'$ and kinetic energy $K'$, and the atom moves with recoil velocity $v_R$ and kinetic energy $K_R$. We assume the kinetic energies to be nonrelativistic.

Conservation of energy:

$$K = K' + K_R \qquad \text{or} \qquad \tfrac{1}{2}mv^2 = \tfrac{1}{2}mv'^2 + \tfrac{1}{2}Mv_R^2 \tag{1}$$

Conservation of momentum:

$$mv = Mv_R - mv' \qquad \text{or} \qquad v_R = \frac{m}{M}(v + v') \tag{2}$$

Combining (1) and (2) to eliminate $v_R$, we obtain

$$v - v' = \frac{m}{M}(v + v') \qquad \text{or} \qquad v' = v\left(\frac{1 - m/M}{1 + m/M}\right)$$

$$\Delta K = \tfrac{1}{2}mv^2 - \tfrac{1}{2}mv'^2 = K\left(1 - \frac{v'^2}{v^2}\right)$$

$$= K\left[1 - \left(\frac{1 - m/M}{1 + m/M}\right)^2\right] = K\left[\frac{4m/M}{(1 + m/M)^2}\right]$$

32.  (a)  $^{63}$Cu:  $\Delta K = (2.50\ \text{MeV})\left[\dfrac{4(4/63)}{(1 + 4/63)^2}\right] = 0.561\ \text{MeV}$

$^{107}$Ag:  $\Delta K = (2.50\ \text{MeV})\left[\dfrac{4(4/107)}{(1 + 4/107)^2}\right] = 0.347\ \text{MeV}$

$^{197}$Au:  $\Delta K = (2.50\ \text{MeV})\left[\dfrac{4(4/197)}{(1 + 4/197)^2}\right] = 0.195\ \text{MeV}$

(b)  $^{65}$Cu:  $\Delta K = (2.50\ \text{MeV})\left[\dfrac{4(4/65)}{(1 + 4/65)^2}\right] = 0.546\ \text{MeV}$

$^{109}$Ag:  $\Delta K = (2.50\ \text{MeV})\left[\dfrac{4(4/109)}{(1 + 4/109)^2}\right] = 0.342\ \text{MeV}$

The energy differences are 0.015 MeV for Cu and 0.005 MeV for Ag.

33.  $^{238}$Pu $\rightarrow$ $^{234}$U + $\alpha$

(a)  $Q = [m(^{238}\text{Pu}) - m(^{234}\text{U}) - m(\alpha)]c^2$

$= (238.049553\ \text{u} - 234.040945\ \text{u} - 4.002603\ \text{u})(931.50\ \text{MeV/u})$

$= 5.594\ \text{MeV}$

(b)         $1.0 \text{ g} = \dfrac{1}{238} \text{ mole} = \dfrac{1}{238} (6.02 \times 10^{23}) \text{ atoms} = 2.53 \times 10^{21} \text{ atoms}$

$\mathcal{A} = \lambda N = \dfrac{0.693}{(88 \text{ y})(3.16 \times 10^7 \text{ s/y})} 2.53 \times 10^{21} = 6.30 \times 10^{11} \text{ s}^{-1}$

$P = \mathcal{A}Q = (6.30 \times 10^{11} \text{ decays/s})(5.594 \text{ MeV/decay})(1.60 \times 10^{-13} \text{ J/MeV})$

$= 0.56 \text{ W}$

# Chapter 14

1.     (a)     Strong, because of the lifetime ($10^{-24}$ s).

        (b)     Electromagnetic, because of the photons.

        (c)     Weak, because of the leptons.

        (d)     Weak, because of the lifetime ($10^{-10}$ s).

        (e)     Strong, because of the lifetime ($10^{-21}$ s).

        (f)     Weak, because of the lifetime ($10^{-10}$ s).

2.     (a)     Lepton number ($L_e = 0 \rightarrow L_e = -1$).

        (b)     Energy ($m_\Lambda c^2 < m_p c^2 + m_K c^2$).

        (c)     Strangeness ($S = -3 \rightarrow S = -1$; only $\Delta S = 1$ is allowed).

        (d)     Baryon number ($B = 1 \rightarrow B = 0$).

        (e)     Strangeness ($S = -1 \rightarrow S = 0$; only $\Delta S = 0$ for electromagnetic decays).

        (f)     Energy ($m_\Omega c^2 < m_\Xi c^2 + m_K c^2$).

        (g)     Energy ($m_\Xi c^2 < m_\Sigma c^2 + m_\pi c^2$).

        (h)     Electron and muon lepton numbers ($L_e = 0 \rightarrow L_e = 1$; $L_\mu = 1 \rightarrow L_\mu = 0$).

3.     (a)     Electron lepton number ($L_e = +1 \rightarrow L_e = -1$).

        (b)     Strangeness ($S = 0 \rightarrow S = -1$).

        (c)     Baryon number ($B = 2 \rightarrow B = 3$).

        (d)     Strangeness ($S = 0 \rightarrow S = -2$).

        (e)     Baryon number ($B = 1 \rightarrow B = 2$).

4.     $K^+ \rightarrow e^+ + \nu_e$,    $K^+ \rightarrow \pi^0 + \mu^+ + \nu_\mu$,    $K^+ \rightarrow \pi^+ + \pi^0$,

      $K^+ \rightarrow \pi^+ + \pi^- + \pi^+$,    $K^+ \rightarrow \pi^+ + \pi^0 + \pi^0$

5.  (a)   $K^- \rightarrow \pi^0 + e^+ + \nu_e$          (c)   $\eta \rightarrow \pi^+ + \pi^- + \pi^0$

    (b)   $K^0 \rightarrow \pi^0 + \pi^0 + \pi^0$

6.  (a)   $\overline{\Lambda}^0 \rightarrow \overline{p} + \pi^+$          (c)   $\overline{K}^0 \rightarrow \pi^+ + \pi^-$

    (b)   $\overline{\Omega}^- \rightarrow \overline{\Lambda}^0 + K^+$          (d)   $\overline{n} \rightarrow \overline{p} + e^+ + \nu_e$

7.  (a)   $p_{1x} = p_1 \cos 30° = 457 \text{ MeV/}c$          $p_{1y} = p_1 \sin 30° = 264 \text{ MeV/}c$

    $p_{2x} = p_2 \cos 7° = 2150 \text{ MeV/}c$          $p_{2y} = -p_2 \sin 7° = -264 \text{ MeV/}c$

    $p_x = p_{1x} + p_{2x} = 2607 \text{ MeV/}c$          $p_y = p_{1y} + p_{2y} = 0$

    $E_1 = \sqrt{c^2 p_1^2 + m_\pi^2 c^4} = \sqrt{(528 \text{ MeV})^2 + (140 \text{ MeV})^2} = 546 \text{ MeV}$

    $E_2 = \sqrt{c^2 p_2^2 + m_\pi^2 c^4} = \sqrt{(2166 \text{ MeV})^2 + (140 \text{ MeV})^2} = 2171 \text{ MeV}$

    $mc^2 = \sqrt{(E_1 + E_2)^2 - c^2 p^2}$

    $\qquad = \sqrt{(546 \text{ MeV} + 2171 \text{ MeV})^2 - (2607 \text{ MeV})^2} = 764 \text{ MeV}$

    (b)   $p_{1x} = p_1 \cos 20° = 606 \text{ MeV/}c$          $p_{1y} = p_1 \sin 20° = 221 \text{ MeV/}c$

    $p_{2x} = p_2 \cos 3° = 4217 \text{ MeV/}c$          $p_{2y} = -p_2 \sin 3° = -221 \text{ MeV/}c$

    $p_x = p_{1x} + p_{2x} = 4823 \text{ MeV/}c$          $p_y = p_{1y} + p_{2y} = 0$

    $E_1 = \sqrt{c^2 p_1^2 + m_\pi^2 c^4} = \sqrt{(645 \text{ MeV})^2 + (140 \text{ MeV})^2} = 660 \text{ MeV}$

    $E_2 = \sqrt{c^2 p_2^2 + m_\pi^2 c^4} = \sqrt{(4223 \text{ MeV})^2 + (140 \text{ MeV})^2} = 4225 \text{ MeV}$

    $mc^2 = \sqrt{(E_1 + E_2)^2 - c^2 p^2}$

    $\qquad = \sqrt{(660 \text{ MeV} + 4225 \text{ MeV})^2 - (4823 \text{ MeV})^2} = 775 \text{ MeV}$

(c)  $p_{1x} = p_1 \cos 45° = 84$ MeV/c  $\qquad p_{1y} = p_1 \sin 45° = 84$ MeV/c

$p_{2x} = p_2 \cos 5° = 958$ MeV/c  $\qquad p_{2y} = -p_2 \sin 5° = -84$ MeV/c

$p_x = p_{1x} + p_{2x} = 1042$ MeV/c  $\qquad p_y = p_{1y} + p_{2y} = 0$

$E_1 = \sqrt{c^2 p_1^2 + m_\pi^2 c^4} = \sqrt{(119 \text{ MeV})^2 + (140 \text{ MeV})^2} = 183$ MeV

$E_2 = \sqrt{c^2 p_2^2 + m_\pi^2 c^4} = \sqrt{(962 \text{ MeV})^2 + (140 \text{ MeV})^2} = 972$ MeV

$mc^2 = \sqrt{(E_1 + E_2)^2 - c^2 p^2}$

$= \sqrt{(183 \text{ MeV} + 972 \text{ MeV})^2 - (1042 \text{ MeV})^2} = 498$ MeV

8.  $\qquad Q = 358.2$ MeV $= K_\pi + K_e + E_\nu$

With $K_\pi = 0$,

$Q = K_e + E_\nu = \sqrt{(p_e c)^2 + (m_e c^2)^2} - m_e c^2 + p_\nu c$

Momentum conservation gives $p_e = p_\nu = p$, so

$Q + m_e c^2 - pc = \sqrt{p^2 c^2 + m_e^2 c^4}$

$Q^2 + (m_e c^2)^2 + (pc)^2 + 2Q m_e c^2 - 2Qpc - 2m_e pc^3 = p^2 c^2 + m_e^2 c^4$

$cp = \dfrac{Q^2 + 2Q m_e c^2}{2Q + 2m_e c^2} = 179.4$ MeV

$E_e = \sqrt{(pc)^2 + (m_e c^2)^2} = \sqrt{(179.4 \text{ MeV})^2 + (0.511 \text{ MeV})^2} = 179.4$ MeV

9.  In the laboratory, $t_{1/2} = d/v$ with $d = 2.0$ m. For the $\Lambda^0$ particle, $\tau_0 = 2.6 \times 10^{-10}$ s.

$\tau = \dfrac{\tau_0}{\sqrt{1 - v^2/c^2}} = \dfrac{t_{1/2}}{0.693} = \dfrac{d}{0.693v}$

$$\frac{v}{c} = \frac{1}{\sqrt{1 + (0.693c\tau_0/d)^2}} = 0.999635$$

$$E = \frac{mc^2}{\sqrt{1 - v^2/c^2}} = \frac{1116 \text{ MeV}}{\sqrt{1 - (0.999635)^2}} = 41.3 \text{ GeV}$$

$$K = E - mc^2 = 40.2 \text{ GeV}$$

10.   For $\Sigma^-$,   $\tau_0 = 1.5 \times 10^{-10}$ s        (proper lifetime)

$$E = K + mc^2 = 3642 \text{ MeV} + 1197 \text{ MeV} = 4839 \text{ MeV} = \frac{mc^2}{\sqrt{1 - v^2/c^2}}$$

$$\frac{v}{c} = \sqrt{1 - \left(\frac{mc^2}{E}\right)^2} = \sqrt{1 - \left(\frac{1197 \text{ MeV}}{4839 \text{ MeV}}\right)^2} = 0.9689$$

$$\tau = \frac{\tau_0}{\sqrt{1 - v^2/c^2}} = \frac{1.5 \times 10^{-10} \text{ s}}{0.247} = 6.07 \times 10^{-10} \text{ s}$$

$$D = v\tau = (0.9689)(3.00 \times 10^8 \text{ m/s})(6.07 \times 10^{-10} \text{ s}) = 0.18 \text{ m}$$

11.   (a)   From Table 14.5, the lifetime for the $\eta$ meson is $\Delta t = 8.0 \times 10^{-19}$ s.

$$\Delta E = \frac{\hbar}{\Delta t} = \frac{6.58 \times 10^{-16} \text{ eV·s}}{8.0 \times 10^{-19} \text{ s}} = 820 \text{ eV}$$

(b)   $$\Delta E = \frac{\hbar}{\Delta t} = \frac{6.58 \times 10^{-16} \text{ eV·s}}{2.2 \times 10^{-21} \text{ s}} = 0.30 \text{ MeV}$$

(c)   $$\Delta E = \frac{\hbar}{\Delta t} = \frac{6.58 \times 10^{-16} \text{ eV·s}}{7.4 \times 10^{-20} \text{ s}} = 8.9 \text{ keV}$$

(d)   $$\Delta E = \frac{\hbar}{\Delta t} = \frac{6.58 \times 10^{-16} \text{ eV·s}}{6 \times 10^{-24} \text{ s}} = 110 \text{ MeV}$$

12.    (a)    $\Omega^- \rightarrow \Lambda^0 + K^-$

Momentum conservation:  $p_\Lambda = p_K = p$

Energy conservation:  $E_\Lambda + E_K = E_\Omega$

$$\sqrt{(pc)^2 + (m_\Lambda c^2)^2} + \sqrt{(pc)^2 + (m_K c^2)^2} = m_\Omega c^2$$

$$(pc)^2 + (m_\Lambda c^2)^2 = (m_\Omega c^2)^2 + (pc)^2 + (m_K c^2)^2 - 2m_\Omega c^2 \sqrt{(pc)^2 + (m_K c^2)^2}$$

$$E_K = \sqrt{(pc)^2 + (m_K c^2)^2} = \frac{(m_\Omega c^2)^2 + (m_K c^2)^2 - (m_\Lambda c^2)^2}{2m_\Omega c^2}$$

$$= \frac{(1672 \text{ MeV})^2 + (494 \text{ MeV})^2 - (1116 \text{ MeV})^2}{2(1672 \text{ MeV})} = 537 \text{ MeV}$$

$$K_K = E_K - m_K c^2 = 537 \text{ MeV} - 494 \text{ MeV} = 43 \text{ MeV}$$

$$E_\Lambda = E_\Omega - E_K = 1672 \text{ MeV} - 537 \text{ MeV} = 1135 \text{ MeV}$$

$$K_\Lambda = E_\Lambda - m_\Lambda c^2 = 1135 \text{ MeV} - 1116 \text{ MeV} = 19 \text{ MeV}$$

(b)    $\pi^+ \rightarrow \mu^+ + \nu_\mu$

Momentum conservation:  $p_\mu = p_\nu = p$

Energy conservation:  $E_\mu + E_\nu = E_\pi = m_\pi c^2$

$$\sqrt{(pc)^2 + (m_\mu c^2)^2} + pc = m_\pi c^2$$

$$(pc)^2 + (m_\mu c^2)^2 = (m_\pi c^2 - pc)^2 = (m_\pi c^2)^2 - 2m_\pi pc^3 + (pc)^2$$

$$E_\nu = pc = \frac{(m_\pi c^2)^2 - (m_\mu c^2)^2}{2m_\pi c^2} = \frac{(140 \text{ MeV})^2 - (105.7 \text{ MeV})^2}{2(140 \text{ MeV})} = 30.1 \text{ MeV}$$

$$E_\mu = E_\pi - E_\nu = 140 \text{ MeV} - 30 \text{ MeV} = 110 \text{ MeV}$$

$$K_\mu = E_\mu - m_\mu c^2 = 110 \text{ MeV} - 106 \text{ MeV} = 4 \text{ MeV}$$

(c)      $K^0 \rightarrow \pi^+ + \pi^-$

By momentum conservation, the two pi mesons have equal momenta and therefore equal energies; thus

$$E_K = E_\pi + E_\pi = 2E_\pi$$

$$E_\pi = \tfrac{1}{2}E_K = \tfrac{1}{2}(498 \text{ MeV}) = 249 \text{ MeV}$$

$$K_\pi = E_\pi - m_\pi c^2 = 249 \text{ MeV} - 140 \text{ MeV} = 109 \text{ MeV}$$

13.   (a)   $Q = m_\pi c^2 - m_\mu c^2 = 140 \text{ MeV} - 105.7 \text{ MeV} = 34 \text{ MeV}$

(b)   $Q = m_\pi c^2 = 135 \text{ MeV}$

(c)   $Q = m_K c^2 - 2m_\pi c^2 = 498 \text{ MeV} - 2 \times 140 \text{ MeV} = 218 \text{ MeV}$

(d)   $Q = m_\Sigma c^2 - m_p c^2 - m_\pi c^2$
$= 1189 \text{ MeV} - 938 \text{ MeV} - 135 \text{ MeV} = 116 \text{ MeV}$

(e)   $Q = m_\Sigma c^2 - m_\Lambda c^2 = 1192 \text{ MeV} - 1116 \text{ MeV} = 76 \text{ MeV}$

14.   (a)   $\Omega^- \rightarrow \Xi^- + \pi^0$    or    $\Xi^0 + \pi^-$

(b)   $\Lambda^0 \rightarrow n + \pi^0$    or    $p + e^- + \overline{\nu}_e$

(c)   $\Sigma^+ \rightarrow \Lambda^0 + e^+ + \nu_e$    or    $n + \pi^+$

15.   (a)   $p + p \rightarrow p + \Lambda^0 + K^+$          (d)   $K^- + n \rightarrow \Lambda^0 + \pi^-$

(b)   $p + \overline{p} \rightarrow n + \overline{n}$          (e)   $\overline{\nu}_\mu + p \rightarrow n + \mu^+$

(c)   $\pi^- + p \rightarrow \Xi^0 + K^0 + K^0$          (f)   $K^- + p \rightarrow K^+ + \Xi^-$

16. (a) By momentum conservation, $p_M = p_1$ (b) $E_1 + E_2 = E_M$

(c) With $p_M = p_1 = p$,

$$\sqrt{(pc)^2 + (m_1c^2)^2} + m_2c^2 = \sqrt{(pc)^2 + (Mc^2)^2}$$

$$(pc)^2 + (m_1c^2)^2 + 2m_2c^2\sqrt{(pc)^2 + (m_1c^2)^2} + (m_2c^2)^2 = (pc)^2 + (Mc^2)^2$$

$$\sqrt{(pc)^2 + (m_1c^2)^2} = \frac{(Mc^2)^2 - (m_1c^2)^2 - (m_2c^2)^2}{2m_2c^2}$$

$$K_{th} = \sqrt{(pc)^2 + (m_1c^2)^2} - m_1c^2 = \frac{(Mc^2)^2 - (m_1c^2)^2 - (m_2c^2)^2}{2m_2c^2} - m_1c^2$$

$$= \frac{(Mc^2 + m_1c^2 + m_2c^2)(Mc^2 - m_1c^2 - m_2c^2)}{2m_2c^2}$$

With $Q = m_1c^2 + m_2c^2 - Mc^2$, this becomes

$$K_{th} = -Q\frac{M + m_1 + m_2}{2m_2}$$

17. In the non-relativistic limit, all kinetic energies are very small compared with rest energies, and so the $Q$-value is small compared with the rest energies.

$$Q = [m_1 + m_2 - (m_3 + m_4 + m_5 + ...)]c^2 \cong 0$$

$$m_1 + m_2 \cong m_3 + m_4 + m_5 + ...$$

$$K_{th} = -Q\frac{m_1 + m_2 + m_3 + m_4 + m_5 + ...}{2m_2}$$

$$\cong -Q\left[\frac{m_1 + m_2 + (m_1 + m_2)}{2m_2}\right] = -Q\left[1 + \frac{m_1}{m_2}\right]$$

18.    (a)    $K^- + p \to \Lambda^0 + \pi^0$

$Q = m_K c^2 + m_p c^2 - m_\Lambda c^2 - m_\pi c^2$

$= 494 \text{ MeV} + 938 \text{ MeV} - 1116 \text{ MeV} - 135 \text{ MeV} = 181 \text{ MeV}$

(b)    $\pi^+ + p \to \Sigma^+ + K^+$

$Q = m_\pi c^2 + m_p c^2 - m_\Sigma c^2 - m_K c^2$

$= 140 \text{ MeV} + 938 \text{ MeV} - 1189 \text{ MeV} - 494 \text{ MeV} = -605 \text{ MeV}$

(c)    $K^- + p \to \Omega^- + K^+ + K^0$

$Q = m_{K^-} c^2 + m_p c^2 - m_\Omega c^2 - m_{K^+} c^2 - m_{K^0} c^2$

$= 938 \text{ MeV} - 1672 \text{ MeV} - 498 \text{ MeV} = -1232 \text{ MeV}$

(d)    $p + p \to p + \pi^+ + \Lambda^0 + K^0$

$Q = 2m_p c^2 - m_p c^2 - m_\pi c^2 - m_\Lambda c^2 - m_K c^2$

$= 938 \text{ MeV} - 140 \text{ MeV} - 1116 \text{ MeV} - 498 \text{ MeV} = -816 \text{ MeV}$

(e)    $\gamma + n \to \pi^- + p$

$Q = m_n c^2 - m_\pi c^2 - m_p c^2$

$= 940 \text{ MeV} - 140 \text{ MeV} - 938 \text{ MeV} = -138 \text{ MeV}$

19.    (a)    $p + p \to n + \Sigma^+ + K^0 + \pi^+$

$Q = 2m_p c^2 - m_n c^2 - m_\Sigma c^2 - m_K c^2 - m_\pi c^2$

$= 2(938 \text{ MeV}) - 940 \text{ MeV} - 1189 \text{ MeV} - 498 \text{ MeV} - 140 \text{ MeV}$

$= -891 \text{ MeV}$

$$K_{th} = -Q \left[ \frac{2m_p + m_n + m_\Sigma + m_K + m_\pi}{2m_p} \right]$$

$$= 891 \text{ MeV}\left[\frac{2(938 \text{ MeV}) + 940 \text{ MeV} + 1189 \text{ MeV} + 498 \text{ MeV} + 140 \text{ MeV}}{2(938 \text{ MeV})}\right]$$

$$= 2205 \text{ MeV}$$

(b)  $\pi^- + \text{p} \rightarrow \Sigma^0 + \text{K}^0$

$Q = m_\pi c^2 + m_\text{p} c^2 - m_\Sigma c^2 - m_\text{K} c^2$

$\quad = 140 \text{ MeV} + 938 \text{ MeV} - 1192 \text{ MeV} - 498 \text{ MeV} = -612 \text{ MeV}$

$$K_\text{th} = -Q\left[\frac{m_\pi + m_\text{p} + m_\Sigma + m_\text{K}}{2m_\text{p}}\right]$$

$$= 612 \text{ MeV}\left[\frac{140 \text{ MeV} + 938 \text{ MeV} + 1192 \text{ MeV} + 498 \text{ MeV}}{2(938 \text{ MeV})}\right]$$

$$= 903 \text{ MeV}$$

(c)  $\text{p} + \text{n} \rightarrow \text{p} + \Sigma^- + \text{K}^+$

$Q = m_\text{p} c^2 + m_\text{n} c^2 - m_\text{p} c^2 - m_\Sigma c^2 - m_\text{K} c^2$

$\quad = 940 \text{ MeV} - 1197 \text{ MeV} - 494 \text{ MeV} = -751 \text{ MeV}$

$$K_\text{th} = -Q\left[\frac{m_\text{p} + m_\text{n} + m_\text{p} + m_\Sigma + m_\text{K}}{2m_\text{n}}\right]$$

$$= 751 \text{ MeV}\left[\frac{2(938 \text{ MeV}) + 940 \text{ MeV} + 1197 \text{ MeV} + 494 \text{ MeV}}{2(940 \text{ MeV})}\right]$$

$$= 1800 \text{ MeV}$$

(d)  $\pi^+ + \text{p} \rightarrow \text{p} + \text{p} + \bar{\text{n}}$

$Q = m_\pi c^2 + m_\text{p} c^2 - 2m_\text{p} c^2 - m_\text{n} c^2$

$\quad = 140 \text{ MeV} - 938 \text{ MeV} - 940 \text{ MeV} = -1738 \text{ MeV}$

$$K_{\text{th}} = -Q\left[\frac{m_\pi + 3m_p + m_n}{2m_p}\right]$$

$$= 1738 \text{ MeV}\left[\frac{140 \text{ MeV} + 3(938 \text{ MeV}) + 940 \text{ MeV}}{2(938 \text{ MeV})}\right] = 3608 \text{ MeV}$$

20.  Let $\theta$ be the angles that the two pi mesons make with the original direction of the K meson, and let $p_+$, $E_+$ and $p_-$, $E_-$ represent the momentum and energy of $\pi^+$ and $\pi^-$. Conservation of momentum gives

$$p_K = p_+ \cos\theta + p_- \cos\theta \qquad \text{(forward direction)}$$

$$0 = p_+ \sin\theta - p_- \sin\theta \qquad \text{(transverse direction)}$$

Thus $p_+ = p_- = p_\pi$ and therefore $E_+ = E_- = E_\pi$.

The total energy of the K meson is $E_K = K_K + m_K c^2 = 276 \text{ MeV} + 498 \text{ MeV} = 774 \text{ MeV}$. Conservation of energy gives:

$$E_K = E_+ + E_- = 2E_\pi \quad \text{so} \quad E_\pi = \tfrac{1}{2}E_K = \tfrac{1}{2}(774 \text{ MeV}) = 387 \text{ MeV}$$

$$cp_K = \sqrt{E_K^2 - (m_K c^2)^2} = \sqrt{(774 \text{ MeV})^2 - (498 \text{ MeV})^2} = 592.5 \text{ MeV}$$

$$cp_\pi = \sqrt{E_\pi^2 - (m_\pi c^2)^2} = \sqrt{(387 \text{ MeV})^2 - (140 \text{ MeV})^2} = 360.8 \text{ MeV}$$

$$2p_\pi \cos\theta = p_K$$

$$\theta = \cos^{-1}\frac{p_K}{2p_\pi} = \cos^{-1}\frac{592.5 \text{ MeV}/c}{2(360.8 \text{ MeV}/c)} = \cos^{-1}0.821 = 34.9°$$

21. $E_\Sigma = K_\Sigma + m_\Sigma c^2 = 250 \text{ MeV} + 1197 \text{ MeV} = 1447 \text{ MeV}$

$cp_\Sigma = \sqrt{E_\Sigma^2 - (m_\Sigma c^2)^2} = \sqrt{(1447 \text{ MeV})^2 - (1197 \text{ MeV})^2} = 813 \text{ MeV}$

Let the neutron move at an angle $\theta$ with the original direction of the $\Sigma^-$.
Conservation of energy:

$E_\Sigma = E_\pi + E_n$

Conservation of momentum:

$p_\Sigma = p_n \cos\theta$                 (forward direction)

$0 = p_n \sin\theta - p_\pi$            (transverse direction)

Thus

$p_n^2 = p_\pi^2 + p_\Sigma^2$

$E_\Sigma = \sqrt{(cp_\pi)^2 + (m_\pi c^2)^2} + \sqrt{(cp_n)^2 + (m_n c^2)^2}$

$(cp_\pi)^2 + (m_\pi c^2)^2 = E_\Sigma^2 - 2E_\Sigma \sqrt{(cp_n)^2 + (m_n c^2)^2} + (cp_n)^2 + (m_n c^2)^2$

$E_n = \sqrt{(cp_n)^2 + (m_n c^2)^2} = \dfrac{(m_n c^2)^2 + E_\Sigma^2 - (m_\pi c^2)^2 + (cp_n)^2 - (cp_\pi)^2}{2E_\Sigma}$

$\qquad = \dfrac{(940 \text{ MeV})^2 + (1447 \text{ MeV})^2 - (140 \text{ MeV})^2 + (813 \text{ MeV})^2}{2(1447 \text{ MeV})}$

$\qquad = 1250 \text{ MeV}$

$K_n = E_n - m_n c^2 = 1250 \text{ MeV} - 940 \text{ MeV} = 310 \text{ MeV}$

$E_\pi = E_\Sigma - E_n = 1447 \text{ MeV} - 1250 \text{ MeV} = 197 \text{ MeV}$

$K_\pi = E_\pi - m_\pi c^2 = 197 \text{ MeV} - 140 \text{ MeV} = 57 \text{ MeV}$

$cp_n = \sqrt{E_n^2 - (m_n c^2)^2} = \sqrt{(1250 \text{ MeV})^2 - (940 \text{ MeV})^2} = 824 \text{ MeV}$

$\theta = \cos^{-1}\dfrac{p_\Sigma}{p_n} = \cos^{-1}\dfrac{813 \text{ MeV}/c}{824 \text{ MeV}/c} = \cos^{-1} 0.987 = 9.4°$

22.  (a)           $K^- + p \rightarrow \Lambda^0 + \pi^0$

                   $su + uud \rightarrow usd + u\bar{u}$

Here the quarks are merely rearranged, with the incoming $K^-$ exchanging its s quark for a u quark, becoming a $\pi^0$ and turning the p into a $\Lambda^0$.

(b)           $\pi^+ + p \rightarrow \Sigma^+ + K^+$

              $u\bar{d} + uud \rightarrow uus + u\bar{s}$

Cancelling the 3 u quarks from each side of the reaction, we find the net process to be

$$\bar{d} + d \rightarrow s + \bar{s}$$

that is, annihilation of d and $\bar{d}$, followed by pair production of s and $\bar{s}$.

(c)           $K^- + p \rightarrow \Omega^- + K^+ + K^0$

              $s\bar{u} + uud \rightarrow sss + u\bar{s} + d\bar{s}$

              $\bar{u} + u \rightarrow s + \bar{s} + s + \bar{s}$

The fundamental processes are annihilation of u and $\bar{u}$, followed by double pair production of s and $\bar{s}$.

(d)           $p + p \rightarrow p + \pi^+ + \Lambda^0 + K^0$

              $uud + uud \rightarrow uud + u\bar{d} + usd + d\bar{s}$

              $energy \rightarrow d + \bar{d} + s + \bar{s}$

The incident proton energy creates two quark-antiquark pairs.

(e)           $\gamma + n \rightarrow \pi^- + p$

                   $udd \rightarrow d\bar{u} + uud$

              $energy \rightarrow u + \bar{u}$

The incident photon energy produces a $u + \bar{u}$ pair.

23.  (a)     $$\Omega^- \rightarrow \Lambda^0 + K^-$$

$$sss \rightarrow usd + \overline{u}s$$

The basic decay is

$$s \rightarrow d + u + \overline{u}$$

which can be accomplished by $s \rightarrow u + W^-$ followed by $W^- \rightarrow d + \overline{u}$.

(b)     $$n \rightarrow p + e^- + \nu_e$$

$$udd \rightarrow uud + e^- + \nu_e$$

$$d \rightarrow u + e^- + \nu_e$$

This is "beta decay" of the d quark: $d \rightarrow u + W^-$ and $W^- \rightarrow e^- + \nu_e$.

(c)     $$\pi^0 \rightarrow \gamma + \gamma$$

$$u\overline{u} \rightarrow energy$$

Here the u and $\overline{u}$ annihilate and give their energy to the photons.

(d)     $$K^0 \rightarrow \pi^+ + \pi^-$$

$$d\overline{s} \rightarrow u\overline{d} + d\overline{u}$$

$$\overline{s} \rightarrow \overline{d} + u + \overline{u}$$

This process is similar to that of part (a): $\overline{s} \rightarrow \overline{u} + W^+$ and $W^+ \rightarrow \overline{d} + u$.

(e)     $$\Delta^{*++} \rightarrow p + \pi^+$$

$$uuu \rightarrow uud + u\overline{d}$$

$$energy \rightarrow d + \overline{d}$$

This is a pair creation process.

(f)     $$\Sigma^- \rightarrow n + \pi^-$$

$$dds \rightarrow udd + d\overline{u}$$

$$s \rightarrow d + u + \overline{u}$$

Here again: $s \rightarrow u + W^-$ and $W^- \rightarrow d + \overline{u}$.

24.     $D^0$      $c\overline{u}$          $D^+$      $c\overline{d}$          $D_s^+$      $c\overline{s}$

        $\overline{D_0}$      $u\overline{c}$          $D^-$      $d\overline{c}$          $D_s^-$      $s\overline{c}$

25.   (a)   Weak interaction

      (b)          $D_s^+ \rightarrow \phi + \pi^+$                          $D_s^+ \rightarrow \mu^+ + \nu_\mu$

             $C = +1 \rightarrow 0 + 0$                      $C = +1 \rightarrow 0 + 0$

             $S = +1 \rightarrow 0 + 0$                      $S = +1 \rightarrow 0 + 0$

                   $D_s^+ \rightarrow K^+ + \overline{K^0}$

             $C = +1 \rightarrow 0 + 0$

             $S = +1 \rightarrow +1 + (-1)$

      (c)   $D_s^+ \rightarrow \phi + \pi^+$                          $D_s^+ \rightarrow \mu^+ + \nu_\mu$

            $c\overline{s} \rightarrow s\overline{s} + u\overline{d}$                          $c\overline{s} \rightarrow W^+ \rightarrow \mu^+ + \nu_\mu$

            $c \rightarrow s + W^+$  and  $W^+ \rightarrow u + \overline{d}$

            $D_s^+ \rightarrow K^+ + \overline{K^0}$

            $c\overline{s} \rightarrow u\overline{s} + s\overline{d}$

            $c \rightarrow s + W^+$  and  $W^+ \rightarrow u + \overline{d}$

      (d)   The weak interaction cannot change $S$ by 2 units.

# Chapter 15

1.
$$v = R\omega = (6.96 \times 10^8 \text{ m}) \frac{2\pi}{(26 \text{ d})(86,400 \text{ s/d})} = 1950 \text{ m/s}$$

$$\frac{v}{c} = \frac{1950 \text{ m/s}}{3.00 \times 10^8 \text{ m/s}} = 6.49 \times 10^{-6}$$

$$\Delta\lambda \cong \frac{v}{c}\lambda = 6.49 \times 10^{-6}\lambda$$

This is about 3 times larger than the general relativistic shift.

2. At the surface of the Earth, the gravitational potential is

$$V = \frac{-GM}{R} = \frac{-(6.67 \times 10^{-11} \text{ N·m}^2/\text{kg}^2)(5.98 \times 10^{24} \text{ kg})}{6.37 \times 10^6 \text{ m}}$$

$$= -6.26 \times 10^7 \text{ J/kg}$$

For a typical star, such as the Sun,

$$V = \frac{-GM}{R} = \frac{-(6.67 \times 10^{-11} \text{ N·m}^2/\text{kg}^2)(1.99 \times 10^{30} \text{ kg})}{6.96 \times 10^8 \text{ m}}$$

$$= -1.91 \times 10^{11} \text{ J/kg}$$

3.
$$dt' = \frac{dt - (u/c^2)\,dx}{\sqrt{1 - u^2/c^2}} \quad \text{and} \quad dx' = \frac{dx - u\,dt}{\sqrt{1 - u^2/c^2}}$$

$$(ds')^2 = (c\,dt')^2 - (dx')^2 = \left[\frac{c\,dt - (u/c)\,dx}{\sqrt{1 - u^2/c^2}}\right]^2 - \left[\frac{dx - u\,dt}{\sqrt{1 - u^2/c^2}}\right]^2$$

$$= \frac{c^2(dt)^2 - 2u(dx)(dt) + (u^2/c^2)(dx)^2 - (dx)^2 + 2u(dx)(dt) - u^2(dt)^2}{1 - u^2/c^2}$$

$$= \frac{c^2(1 - u^2/c^2)(dt)^2 - (1 - u^2/c^2)(dx)^2}{1 - u^2/c^2} = c^2(dt)^2 - (dx)^2$$

4.  $$\Delta \nu = \nu \frac{gH}{c^2} = \frac{(10^9 \text{ Hz})(9.8 \text{ m/s}^2)(150 \times 10^3 \text{ m})}{9 \times 10^{16} \text{ m}^2/\text{s}^2} = 1.6 \times 10^{-2} \text{ Hz}$$

5.  $$\Delta E = h\Delta \nu = h(2.5 \times 10^{-15} \nu) = 2.5 \times 10^{-15} E$$

$$\Delta t = \frac{\hbar}{\Delta E} = \frac{6.58 \times 10^{-16} \text{ eV·s}}{(2.5 \times 10^{-15})(14.4 \times 10^3 \text{ eV})} = 1.8 \times 10^{-5} \text{ s}$$

6.  The deflection according to general relativity is twice the value given by Equation 15.9:

$$\theta = \frac{4GM}{c^2R} = \frac{4(6.67 \times 10^{-11} \text{ N·m}^2/\text{kg}^2)(2.0 \times 10^{30} \text{ kg})}{(9 \times 10^{16} \text{ m}^2/\text{s}^2)(7.0 \times 10^6 \text{ m})} = 8.5 \times 10^{-4} \text{ rad}$$

Let $2x$ be the separation between the two images of the star.  Then

$$\frac{x}{2} = (20 \text{ light-years}) \tan \frac{\theta}{2} \cong (20 \text{ light-years}) \frac{\theta}{2}$$

But also

$$x = (80 \text{ light-years}) \tan \frac{\alpha}{2} \cong (80 \text{ light-years}) \frac{\alpha}{2}$$

Thus

$$\alpha = \frac{20 \text{ light-years}}{40 \text{ light-years}} \theta = \tfrac{1}{2}\theta = 4.2 \times 10^{-4} \text{ rad}$$

7.
$$F_{\text{Coulomb}} = \frac{e^2}{4\pi\epsilon_0} \frac{zZ}{r^2} \qquad \text{and} \qquad F_{\text{grav}} = \frac{GmM}{r^2}$$

so we can change expressions based on the Coulomb force to those based on the gravitational force by replacing $zZe^2/4\pi\epsilon_0$ with $GmM$.

$$b = \frac{zZ}{2(\frac{1}{2}mv^2)} \frac{e^2}{4\pi\epsilon_0} \cot\frac{1}{2}\theta \qquad \rightarrow \qquad b = \frac{GmM}{mv^2} \cot\frac{1}{2}\theta$$

For a photon that grazes the Sun, $b = R$ and $v = c$, so

$$R = \frac{GM}{c^2} \cot\frac{1}{2}\theta$$

$$\frac{\theta}{2} \cong \tan\frac{\theta}{2} = \frac{GM}{Rc^2} \qquad \text{or} \qquad \theta \cong \frac{2GM}{Rc^2}$$

8.  (a)  From Equation 12.36 for electron capture

$$Q = [m(^7\text{Be}) - m(^7\text{Li})]c^2$$

$$= (7.016929 \text{ u} - 7.016004 \text{ u})(931.50 \text{ MeV/u}) = 0.862 \text{ MeV}$$

$$= E_v + K_R - K_e - K_{\text{Be}}$$

where $K_R$ is the recoil kinetic energy of the Li. Assuming the initial kinetic energies of Be and $e^-$ are small, and estimating the recoil energy

$$K_R = \frac{(E_v)^2}{2Mc^2} \cong \frac{Q^2}{2Mc^2} = 7 \times 10^{-5} \text{ MeV}$$

we conclude

$$E_v = 0.862 \text{ MeV}$$

(b)  $$Q = [m(^{37}\text{Cl}) - m(^{37}\text{Ar})]c^2$$

$$= (36.965903 \text{ u} - 36.966776 \text{ u})(931.50 \text{ MeV/u}) = -0.813 \text{ MeV}$$

9.      $\nu_e + {}^{71}\text{Ga} \rightarrow {}^{71}\text{Ge} + e^-$

$$Q = [m_i - m_f]c^2 = [m_N({}^{71}\text{Ga}) - m_N({}^{71}\text{Ge}) - m_e]c^2$$

using nuclear masses $m_N$. Converting to atomic masses, we obtain

$$Q = [m_N({}^{71}\text{Ga}) + 32m_e - m_N({}^{71}\text{Ge}) - 32m_e - m_e]c^2$$

$$= [m({}^{71}\text{Ga}) - m({}^{71}\text{Ge})]c^2$$

$$= (70.924707 \text{ u} - 70.924954 \text{ u})(931.50 \text{ MeV/u}) = -0.230 \text{ MeV}$$

10.     (a)     ${}^4\text{He} + {}^4\text{He} \rightarrow {}^8\text{Be}$

$$Q = [2m({}^4\text{He}) - m({}^8\text{Be})]c^2$$

$$= (2 \times 4.002603 \text{ u} - 8.005305 \text{ u})(931.50 \text{ MeV/u}) = -0.092 \text{ MeV}$$

(b)     $\frac{1}{2}e^{-\Delta E/kT} = \frac{1}{2}e^{-0.092 \text{ MeV}/0.00862 \text{ MeV}} = 1.12 \times 10^{-5}$

11.     ${}^{63}\text{Cu} + n \rightarrow {}^{64}\text{Cu}$                        ${}^{69}\text{Ga} + n \rightarrow {}^{70}\text{Ga}$

${}^{64}\text{Cu} \rightarrow {}^{64}\text{Zn} + e^- + \overline{\nu}_e$   $(t_{1/2} = 13 \text{ h})$          ${}^{70}\text{Ga} \rightarrow {}^{70}\text{Ge} + e^- + \overline{\nu}_e$   $(t_{1/2} = 21 \text{ m})$

${}^{64}\text{Zn} + n \rightarrow {}^{65}\text{Zn}$                        ${}^{70}\text{Ge} + n \rightarrow {}^{71}\text{Ge}$

${}^{65}\text{Zn} \rightarrow {}^{65}\text{Cu} + e^+ + \nu_e$   $(t_{1/2} = 244 \text{ d})$          ${}^{71}\text{Ge} + e^- \rightarrow {}^{71}\text{Ga} + \overline{\nu}_e$   $(t_{1/2} = 11 \text{ d})$

${}^{65}\text{Cu} + n \rightarrow {}^{66}\text{Cu}$                        ${}^{71}\text{Ga} + n \rightarrow {}^{72}\text{Ga}$

${}^{66}\text{Cu} \rightarrow {}^{66}\text{Zn} + e^- + \overline{\nu}_e$   $(t_{1/2} = 5 \text{ m})$          ${}^{72}\text{Ga} \rightarrow {}^{72}\text{Ge} + e^- + \overline{\nu}_e$   $(t_{1/2} = 14 \text{ m})$

${}^{66}\text{Zn} + n \rightarrow {}^{67}\text{Zn}$                        ${}^{72}\text{Ge} + n \rightarrow {}^{73}\text{Ge}$

${}^{67}\text{Zn} + n \rightarrow {}^{68}\text{Zn}$                        ${}^{73}\text{Ge} + n \rightarrow {}^{74}\text{Ge}$

${}^{68}\text{Zn} + n \rightarrow {}^{69}\text{Zn}$                        ${}^{74}\text{Ge} + n \rightarrow {}^{75}\text{Ge}$

${}^{69}\text{Zn} \rightarrow {}^{69}\text{Ga} + e^- + \overline{\nu}_e$   $(t_{1/2} = 56 \text{ m})$          ${}^{75}\text{Ge} \rightarrow {}^{75}\text{As} + e^- + \overline{\nu}_e$   $(t_{1/2} = 83 \text{ m})$

12.

$^{81}\text{Br} + \text{n} \rightarrow {}^{82}\text{Br}$

$^{82}\text{Br} \rightarrow {}^{82}\text{Kr} + \text{e}^- + \overline{\nu}_e \quad (t_{1/2} = 35 \text{ h})$

$^{82}\text{Kr} + \text{n} \rightarrow {}^{83}\text{Kr}$

$^{83}\text{Kr} + \text{n} \rightarrow {}^{84}\text{Kr}$

$^{84}\text{Kr} + \text{n} \rightarrow {}^{85}\text{Kr}$

$^{85}\text{Kr} + \text{n} \rightarrow {}^{86}\text{Kr}$

$^{86}\text{Kr} + \text{n} \rightarrow {}^{87}\text{Kr}$

$^{87}\text{Kr} \rightarrow {}^{87}\text{Rb} + \text{e}^- + \overline{\nu}_e \quad (t_{1/2} = 76 \text{ m})$

$^{87}\text{Rb} + \text{n} \rightarrow {}^{88}\text{Rb}$

$^{88}\text{Rb} \rightarrow {}^{88}\text{Sr} + \text{e}^- + \overline{\nu}_e \quad (t_{1/2} = 18 \text{ m})$

$^{88}\text{Sr} + \text{n} \rightarrow {}^{89}\text{Sr}$

$^{89}\text{Sr} \rightarrow {}^{89}\text{Y} + \text{e}^- + \overline{\nu}_e \quad (t_{1/2} = 50 \text{ d})$

$^{89}\text{Y} + \text{n} \rightarrow {}^{90}\text{Y}$

$^{90}\text{Y} \rightarrow {}^{90}\text{Zr} + \text{e}^- + \overline{\nu}_e \quad (t_{1/2} = 64 \text{ h})$

$^{90}\text{Zr} + \text{n} \rightarrow {}^{91}\text{Zr}$

$^{91}\text{Zr} + \text{n} \rightarrow {}^{92}\text{Zr}$

$^{92}\text{Zr} + \text{n} \rightarrow {}^{93}\text{Zr}$

$^{93}\text{Zr} + \text{n} \rightarrow {}^{94}\text{Zr}$

$^{94}\text{Zr} + \text{n} \rightarrow {}^{95}\text{Zr}$

$^{95}\text{Zr} \rightarrow {}^{95}\text{Nb} + \text{e}^- + \overline{\nu}_e \quad (t_{1/2} = 64 \text{ d})$

$^{95}\text{Nb} \rightarrow {}^{95}\text{Mo} + \text{e}^- + \overline{\nu}_e \quad (t_{1/2} = 35 \text{ h})$

13. (a) Only the mass $m$ inside the sphere of radius $r$ attracts $dm$.

$$m = \tfrac{4}{3}\pi r^3 \rho$$

(b) $$dU = -\frac{Gm\,dm}{r} = -\tfrac{4}{3}\pi G\rho r^2\,dm$$

(c) The volume element $dV$ in spherical coordinates is $r^2\,dr\,\sin\theta\,d\theta\,d\phi$.

$$dm = \rho\,dV = \rho r^2\,dr\,\sin\theta\,d\theta\,d\phi$$

(d) $$U = \int dU = -\tfrac{4}{3}\pi G\rho^2 \int_0^R r^4\,dr \int_0^\pi \sin\theta\,d\theta \int_0^{2\pi} d\phi = -\tfrac{4}{3}\pi G\rho^2 \frac{R^5}{5}(2)(2\pi)$$

$$= -\tfrac{4}{3}\pi G\left(\frac{M}{4\pi R^3/3}\right)^2 \frac{R^5}{5}(4\pi) = -\frac{3}{5}\frac{GM^2}{R}$$

14.    With $N_e \cong N/2$ and $M \cong Nm_n$,

$$E = \frac{3}{5}\frac{N}{2}\frac{\hbar^2}{2m_e}\left(\frac{3\pi^2 N}{2V}\right)^{2/3} - \frac{3}{5}\frac{Gm_n^2 N^2}{R}$$

$$= \frac{3}{5}\frac{\hbar^2}{4m_e}\left(\frac{3\pi^2}{8\pi/3}\right)^{2/3}\frac{N^{5/3}}{R^2} - \frac{3}{5}\frac{Gm_n^2 N^2}{R}$$

$$\frac{dE}{dR} = \frac{3}{5}\frac{\hbar^2}{4m_e}\left(\frac{9\pi}{8}\right)^{2/3}N^{5/3}(-2R^{-3}) - \frac{3}{5}Gm_n^2 N^2(-R^{-2}) = 0$$

$$R = \frac{\dfrac{6}{5}\dfrac{\hbar^2}{4m_e}\left(\dfrac{9\pi}{8}\right)^{2/3}N^{5/3}}{\dfrac{3}{5}Gm_n^2 N^2} = \frac{3^{4/3}\pi^{2/3}}{8}\frac{\hbar^2}{Gm_e m_n^2}N^{-1/3}$$

15.    With $M = Nm_n$, then $M_\odot = N_\odot m_n$ and

$$N_\odot = \frac{M_\odot}{m_n} = \frac{1.99 \times 10^{30}\ \text{kg}}{1.675 \times 10^{-27}\ \text{kg}} = 1.188 \times 10^{57}$$

$$R = \frac{3^{4/3}\pi^{2/3}}{8}\frac{\hbar^2}{Gm_e m_n^2}N_\odot^{-1/3}\left(\frac{M}{M_\odot}\right)^{-1/3}$$

$$= \frac{3^{4/3}\pi^{2/3}(1.055 \times 10^{-34}\ \text{J·s})^2(1.188 \times 10^{57})^{-1/3}(M/M_\odot)^{-1/3}}{8(6.673 \times 10^{-11}\ \text{N·m}^2/\text{kg}^2)(9.11 \times 10^{-31}\ \text{kg})(1.675 \times 10^{-27}\ \text{kg})^2}$$

$$= (7145\ \text{km})\left(\frac{M}{M_\odot}\right)^{-1/3}$$

16. (a) $E_{\text{F}} = 0.194$ MeV

$$p = \sqrt{2mE_{\text{F}}} = \frac{1}{c}\sqrt{2mc^2E_{\text{F}}}$$

$$= \frac{1}{c}\sqrt{2(0.511 \text{ MeV})(0.194 \text{ MeV})} = 0.445 \text{ MeV}/c$$

$$\lambda = \frac{hc}{pc} = \frac{1240 \text{ MeV·fm}}{0.445 \text{ MeV}} = 2.78 \times 10^{-12} \text{ m}$$

(b) Let $N$ = number of iron atoms

$$N = \frac{M}{m_{\text{atom}}} = \frac{1.99 \times 10^{30} \text{ kg}}{(56 \text{ u})(1.66 \times 10^{-27} \text{ kg/u})} = 2.14 \times 10^{55} \text{ atoms}$$

From Problem 15, $R = 7145$ km when $M = M_{\odot}$.

$$U = \frac{4}{3}\pi R^3 = \frac{4}{3}\pi(7145 \text{ km})^3 = 1.50 \times 10^{21} \text{ m}^3$$

With $2.14 \times 10^{55}$ atoms in a volume of $1.50 \times 10^{21}$ m$^3$ there is about one atom per $7.01 \times 10^{-35}$ m$^3$, and the average spacing is about $(7.01 \times 10^{-35} \text{ m}^3)^{1/3} = 4.12 \times 10^{-12}$ m. This is of the same order as the de Broglie wavelength, and thus the electrons should be easily scattered by the lattice of atoms.

17. Let $N_e = fN$

$$E = \frac{3}{5}fN\frac{\hbar^2}{2m_e}\left(\frac{3\pi^2 fN}{V}\right)^{2/3} - \frac{3}{5}\frac{Gm_n^2N^2}{R}$$

$$\frac{dE}{dR} = \frac{3}{5}(fN)^{5/3}\frac{\hbar^2}{2m_e}\left(\frac{9\pi}{4}\right)^{2/3}(-2R^{-3}) - \frac{3}{5}Gm_n^2N^2(-R^{-2}) = 0$$

$$R = \frac{\dfrac{6}{5}\dfrac{\hbar^2}{2m_e}\left(\dfrac{9\pi}{4}\right)^{2/3}(fN)^{5/3}}{\dfrac{3}{5}Gm_n^2 N^2} = \frac{3^{4/3}\pi^{2/3}}{4^{2/3}}\frac{\hbar^2}{Gm_e m_n^2}f^{5/3}N^{-1/3}$$

Thus $R \propto f^{5/3}$, and so $R \propto N_e^{5/3}$.

18.  The rotational inertia of a uniform sphere is $I = \frac{2}{5}mR^2$.

The angular momentum $L = I\omega$ is conserved in the collapse, so $I_1\omega_1 = I_2\omega_2$.

$$\omega_2 = \omega_1 \frac{I_1}{I_2} = \omega_1\left(\frac{R_1}{R_2}\right)^2 = (1 \text{ revolution/year})\left(\frac{7 \times 10^5 \text{ km}}{11 \text{ km}}\right)^2$$

$$= 4.0 \times 10^9 \text{ revolutions/year} = 128 \text{ revolutions/s}$$

19.  (a)  $Gm_n^2 = (6.6726 \times 10^{-11} \text{ N·m}^2/\text{kg}^2)(1.6750 \times 10^{-27} \text{ kg})^2$

$$= 1.8721 \times 10^{-64} \text{ J·m}$$

(b)  $\dfrac{\hbar^2}{m_n} = \dfrac{\hbar^2 c^2}{m_n c^2} = \dfrac{(1239.842 \text{ MeV·fm}/2\pi)^2}{939.5656 \text{ MeV}} = 4.144249 \times 10^{-29} \text{ MeV·m}^2$

(c)  $\dfrac{\hbar^2}{Gm_n^3} = \dfrac{\hbar^2/m_n}{Gm_n^2} = \dfrac{(4.144249 \times 10^{-29} \text{ MeV·m}^2)(1.6022 \times 10^{-13} \text{ J/MeV})}{1.8721 \times 10^{-64} \text{ J·m}}$

$$= 3.5468 \times 10^{22} \text{ m}$$

(d)  $\dfrac{G^2 m_n^5}{\hbar^2} = \dfrac{(Gm_n^2)^2}{\hbar^2/m_n} = \dfrac{(1.8721 \times 10^{-64} \text{ J·m})^2}{(4.144249 \times 10^{-29} \text{ MeV·m}^2)(1.6022 \times 10^{-13} \text{ J/MeV})}$

$$= 3.2944 \times 10^{-74} \text{ MeV}$$

20. $$R = \frac{3^{4/3}\pi^{2/3}}{2^{4/3}} \frac{\hbar^2}{Gm_n^3} N^{-1/3} = \frac{3^{4/3}\pi^{2/3}}{2^{4/3}} \frac{\hbar^2}{Gm_n^3} N_\odot^{-1/3} \left(\frac{M}{M_\odot}\right)^{-1/3}$$

$$= \frac{3^{4/3}\pi^{2/3}}{2^{4/3}} \frac{3.5468 \times 10^{22} \text{ m}}{(1.188 \times 10^{57})^{1/3}} \left(\frac{M}{M_\odot}\right)^{-1/3} = (12.34 \text{ km}) \left(\frac{M}{M_\odot}\right)^{-1/3}$$

$$E_F = \frac{\hbar^2}{2m_n} (3\pi^2)^{2/3} \frac{N^{2/3}}{V^{2/3}} = \frac{\hbar^2}{2m_n} \frac{(3\pi^2)^{2/3}}{(4\pi/3)^{2/3}} \frac{N^{2/3}}{R^2}$$

$$= \frac{\hbar^2}{2m_n} \left(\frac{9\pi}{4}\right)^{2/3} N^{2/3} (12.34 \text{ km})^{-2} \left(\frac{M}{M_\odot}\right)^{2/3}$$

$$= \frac{1}{2}(4.1442 \times 10^{-29} \text{ MeV·m}^2) \left(\frac{9\pi}{4}\right)^{2/3} (12.34 \text{ km})^{-2} N_\odot^{2/3} \left(\frac{M}{M_\odot}\right)^{4/3}$$

$$= (56.27 \text{ MeV}) \left(\frac{M}{M_\odot}\right)^{4/3}$$

21. (a) $E_F = (56.27 \text{ MeV}) (2)^{4/3} = 140 \text{ MeV}$

(b) $E_m = \frac{3}{5}E_F = 85 \text{ MeV}$

(c) $E = NE_m = 2N_\odot E_m$

$N_\odot = 1.188 \times 10^{57}$

$E = 2(1.188 \times 10^{57})(85 \text{ MeV}) = 2.0 \times 10^{59} \text{ MeV}$

(d) $R = (12.34 \text{ km}) \left(\frac{M}{M_\odot}\right)^{-1/3} = 9.79 \text{ km}$

$$U = -\frac{3}{5}\frac{GM^2}{R} = -\frac{3}{5}\frac{(6.67 \times 10^{-11} \text{ N·m}^2/\text{kg}^2)(2 \times 1.99 \times 10^{30} \text{ kg})^2}{9.79 \text{ km}}$$

$$= -4.0 \times 10^{59} \text{ MeV}$$

(e)     Half of the original energy ended with the neutrons.  The remainder was lost to radiation or is stored as rotational kinetic energy.

22.    $E_F = (56.27 \text{ MeV})\left(\frac{M}{M_\odot}\right)^{4/3} = (56.27 \text{ MeV})(1.5)^{4/3} = 97 \text{ MeV}$

23.    $E_F = (56.27 \text{ MeV})\left(\frac{M}{M_\odot}\right)^{4/3} = (56.27 \text{ MeV})(1.80)^{4/3} = 123 \text{ MeV}$

$$p = \sqrt{2mE_F} = \frac{1}{c}\sqrt{2mc^2E_F} = \frac{1}{c}\sqrt{2(939 \text{ MeV})(123 \text{ MeV})} = 48.1 \text{ MeV}/c$$

$$\lambda = \frac{hc}{pc} = \frac{1240 \text{ MeV·fm}}{48.1 \text{ MeV}} = 2.58 \text{ fm}$$

$$R = (12.34 \text{ km})\left(\frac{M}{M_\odot}\right)^{-1/3} = (12.34 \text{ km})(1.80)^{-1/3} = 10.14 \text{ km}$$

$$N = N_\odot\frac{M}{M_\odot} = (1.188 \times 10^{57})(1.80) = 2.14 \times 10^{57}$$

There are $2.14 \times 10^{57}$ neutrons in a volume of $(4/3)\pi R^3$, or $4.90 \times 10^{44}$ neutrons/m$^3$.  The average spacing is therefore about , or $(4.90 \times 10^{44})^{-1/3}$, or $1.27 \times 10^{-15}$ m = 1.27 fm.  Since this is of the same order as the de Broglie wavelength, there will be considerable scattering.

24.  (a)  $R = (12.34 \text{ km}) \left( \dfrac{M}{M_\odot} \right)^{-1/3} = (12.34 \text{ km})(2.00)^{-1/3} = 9.79 \text{ km}$

(b)  $I = \dfrac{2}{5} MR^2 = \dfrac{2}{5}(3.98 \times 10^{30} \text{ kg})(9.79 \times 10^3 \text{ m})^2 = 1.53 \times 10^{38} \text{ kg·m}^2$

$L = I\omega = (1.53 \times 10^{38} \text{ kg·m}^2)(2\pi \text{ rad/s}) = 9.60 \times 10^{38} \text{ kg·m}^2\text{/s}$

(c)  $K = \dfrac{1}{2} I\omega^2 = \dfrac{1}{2}(1.53 \times 10^{38} \text{ kg·m}^2)(2\pi \text{ rad/s})^2 = 3.01 \times 10^{39} \text{ J}$

(d)  With $K = \dfrac{1}{2} I\omega^2$, $\Delta K = I\omega \, \Delta \omega$

$$\dfrac{\Delta K}{K} = 2\dfrac{\Delta \omega}{\omega} = 2(10^{-9}/\text{day})$$

$$\Delta K = (2 \times 10^{-9}/\text{day}) K = (2 \times 10^{-9}/\text{day})(3.01 \times 10^{39} \text{ J})$$

$$= 6.02 \times 10^{30} \text{ J/day}$$

(e)  $P = (6.02 \times 10^{30} \text{ J/day})(1 \text{ day}/86{,}400 \text{ s}) = 6.98 \times 10^{25} \text{ W}$

25.  (a)  The distance from Earth is $R = 10^4$ light-years $= 9.46 \times 10^{19}$ m.  The radiation flux is $P/4\pi R^2$, or

$$\dfrac{6.98 \times 10^{25} \text{ W}}{4\pi (9.46 \times 10^{19} \text{ m})^2} = 6.21 \times 10^{-15} \text{ W/m}^2$$

Thus a 1 m$^2$ antenna receives $6.21 \times 10^{-15}$ W.

# Chapter 16

1.     (a)    $d = 1.0 \times 10^6$ light-years $= 0.307$ Mpc

$$v = Hd = \frac{75 \text{ km/s}}{\text{Mpc}}(0.307 \text{ Mpc}) = 23.0 \text{ km/s} = 7.67 \times 10^{-5}c$$

$$\lambda' = \lambda\sqrt{\frac{1 + v/c}{1 - v/c}} = (590.0 \text{ nm})\sqrt{\frac{1 + 7.67 \times 10^{-5}}{1 - 7.67 \times 10^{-5}}} = 590.0 \text{ nm}$$

     (b)    $d = 1.0 \times 10^8$ light-years $= 30.7$ Mpc

$$v = Hd = \frac{75 \text{ km/s}}{\text{Mpc}}(30.7 \text{ Mpc}) = 2.30 \times 10^3 \text{ km/s} = 7.67 \times 10^{-3}c$$

$$\lambda' = \lambda\sqrt{\frac{1 + v/c}{1 - v/c}} = (590.0 \text{ nm})\sqrt{\frac{1 + 7.67 \times 10^{-3}}{1 - 7.67 \times 10^{-3}}} = 594.5 \text{ nm}$$

     (c)    $d = 1.0 \times 10^{10}$ light-years $= 3.07 \times 10^3$ Mpc

$$v = Hd = \frac{75 \text{ km/s}}{\text{Mpc}}(3.07 \times 10^3 \text{ Mpc}) = 2.30 \times 10^5 \text{ km/s} = 0.767c$$

$$\lambda' = \lambda\sqrt{\frac{1 + v/c}{1 - v/c}} = (590.0 \text{ nm})\sqrt{\frac{1 + 0.767}{1 - 0.767}} = 1625 \text{ nm}$$

2.     $$\lambda_{max} = \frac{2.898 \times 10^{-3} \text{ m·K}}{T} = \frac{2.898 \times 10^{-3} \text{ m·K}}{2.7 \text{ K}} = 1.1 \text{ mm}$$

3. (a)
$$u(E) = \frac{8\pi E^3}{(hc)^3} \frac{1}{e^{E/kT} - 1}$$

$$\frac{du}{dE} = \frac{24\pi E^2}{(hc)^3} \frac{1}{e^{E/kT} - 1} - \frac{8\pi E^3}{(hc)^3} \frac{e^{E/kT}(1/kT)}{(e^{E/kT} - 1)^2} = 0$$

$$3 = \frac{E}{kT} \frac{e^{E/kT}}{e^{E/kT} - 1} \qquad \text{or} \qquad e^{-x} = 1 - \frac{x}{3} \qquad \text{with} \quad x = E/kT$$

This equation must be solved numerically. It is apparent that $x \approx 3$; solving, we obtain

$$x = 2.821$$

$$E_{max} = 2.821\,kT = (2.431 \times 10^{-4} \text{ eV/K})\,T$$

(b) $E_{max} = (2.431 \times 10^{-4} \text{ eV/K})(2.7 \text{ K}) = 6.56 \times 10^{-4} \text{ eV}$

4.
$$U = \frac{\sigma}{c/4} T^4 = \frac{5.67 \times 10^{-8} \text{ W/m}^2 \cdot \text{K}^4}{0.25\,(3.00 \times 10^8 \text{ m/s})} T^4$$

$$= \frac{7.56 \times 10^{-16} \text{ J/m}^3 \cdot \text{K}^4}{1.602 \times 10^{-19} \text{ J/eV}} T^4 = (4.73 \times 10^3 \text{ eV/m}^3)\,T^4$$

$$N = \frac{8\pi}{(hc)^3} (kT)^3 \int_0^\infty \frac{x^2\,dx}{e^x - 1}$$

$$= \frac{8\pi(8.617 \times 10^{-5} \text{ eV/K})^3 T^3}{(1240 \text{ eV·nm})^3} (2.404) = (2.03 \times 10^7 \text{ m}^{-3})\,T^3$$

$$E_m = \frac{U}{N} = \frac{(4.73 \times 10^3 \text{ eV/m}^3)\,T^4}{(2.03 \times 10^7 \text{ m}^{-3})\,T^3} = (2.33 \times 10^{-4} \text{ eV})\,T$$

In all of these expressions, $T$ is measured in units of K.

5.    (a)    At $T = 2.7$ K, $kT = 2.33 \times 10^{-4}$ eV.

$$\frac{E_0}{kT} = \frac{2 \text{ eV}}{2.33 \times 10^{-4} \text{ eV}} = 8.60 \times 10^3$$

$$N_{>2 \text{ eV}} = \frac{8\pi}{(hc)^3} (kT)^3 \, e^{-E_0/kT} \left[ \left( \frac{E_0}{kT} \right)^2 + 2 \frac{E_0}{kT} + 2 \right]$$

$$= \frac{8\pi (2.33 \times 10^{-4} \text{ eV})^3}{(1240 \text{ eV·nm})^3} e^{-8.60 \times 10^3} [(8.60 \times 10^3)^2 + 2(8.60 \times 10^3) + 2]$$

$$= 1.4 \times 10^{-3746} \text{ nm}^{-3} = 1.4 \times 10^{-3719} \text{ m}^{-3}$$

For $E_0 = 3$ eV, $E_0/kT = 1.29 \times 10^4$

$$N_{>3 \text{ eV}} = \frac{8\pi (2.33 \times 10^{-4} \text{ eV})^3}{(1240 \text{ eV·nm})^3} e^{-1.29 \times 10^4} [(1.29 \times 10^4)^2 + 2(1.29 \times 10^4) + 2]$$

$$= 1.1 \times 10^{-5586} \text{ m}^{-3}$$

The number density of photons between 2 eV and 3 eV is thus

$$N_{>2 \text{ eV}} - N_{>3 \text{ eV}} = 1.4 \times 10^{-3719} \text{ m}^{-3}$$

This is far too small to be observed.

(b)    We will try to find the temperature at which $N_{>2 \text{ eV}} \sim 100 \text{ cm}^{-3} = 10^{-19} \text{ nm}^{-3}$. Letting $x = E_0/kT$, we obtain

$$N_{>E_0} = \frac{8\pi}{(hc)^3} \left( \frac{E_0}{x} \right)^3 e^{-x} [x^2 + 2x + 2]$$

$$1.0 \times 10^{-19} \text{ nm}^{-3} = \frac{8\pi (2 \text{ eV})^3}{(1240 \text{ eV·nm})^3} x^{-3} e^{-x} [x^2 + 2x + 2]$$

$$1.0 \times 10^{-12} = e^{-x} [x^{-1} + 2x^{-2} + 2x^{-3}] \qquad \text{or} \qquad x = 24$$

$$kT = \frac{E_0}{x} = \frac{2 \text{ eV}}{24} = 0.08 \text{ eV}$$

$$T = \frac{0.08 \text{ eV}}{8.617 \times 10^{-5} \text{ eV/K}} = 1000 \text{ K}$$

$$t = \left( \frac{1.5 \times 10^{10} \text{ s}^{1/2} \cdot \text{K}}{1000 \text{ K}} \right)^2 = \frac{2.25 \times 10^{14} \text{ s}}{3.156 \times 10^7 \text{ s/y}} = 7 \times 10^6 \text{ y}$$

6.  The rotational energies are $E_L = \dfrac{L(L+1)\hbar^2}{2mR^2}$, with $E_0 = 0$.

$$E_1 = \frac{\hbar^2}{mR^2} = 4.70 \times 10^{-4} \text{ eV}$$

$$E_2 = \frac{6\hbar^2}{2mR^2} = 3E_1 = 14.1 \times 10^{-4} \text{ eV}$$

$$E_3 = \frac{12\hbar^2}{2mR^2} = 6E_1 = 28.2 \times 10^{-4} \text{ eV}$$

At $T = 2.7 \text{ K}$, $kT = 2.33 \times 10^{-4} \text{ eV}$.

$$\frac{p(E_i)}{p(E_j)} = \frac{2L_i + 1}{2L_j + 1} e^{-(E_i - E_j)/kT}$$

$$\frac{p(E_1)}{p(E_0)} = \frac{2 \times 1 + 1}{2 \times 0 + 1} e^{-4.70 \times 10^{-4} \text{ eV}/2.33 \times 10^{-4} \text{ eV}} = 0.399$$

$$\frac{p(E_2)}{p(E_0)} = \frac{2 \times 2 + 1}{2 \times 0 + 1} e^{-14.1 \times 10^{-4} \text{ eV}/2.33 \times 10^{-4} \text{ eV}} = 0.0118$$

$$\frac{p(E_3)}{p(E_0)} = \frac{2 \times 3 + 1}{2 \times 0 + 1} e^{-28.2 \times 10^{-4} \text{ eV}/2.33 \times 10^{-4} \text{ eV}} = 3.88 \times 10^{-5}$$

7.
$$\left(\frac{dR}{dt}\right)^2 = \frac{8\pi}{3}G\rho R^2 - kc^2$$

$$2\frac{dR}{dt}\frac{d^2R}{dt^2} = \frac{8\pi}{3}G\frac{d\rho}{dt}R^2 + \frac{8\pi}{3}G\rho\left(2R\frac{dR}{dt}\right)$$

With $\rho_m = CR^{-3}$, $\quad \dfrac{d\rho_m}{dt} = -3CR^{-4}\dfrac{dR}{dt} = -3\dfrac{\rho_m}{R}\dfrac{dR}{dt}$

$$2\frac{dR}{dt}\frac{d^2R}{dt^2} = \frac{8\pi}{3}G\left(-3\rho_m R\frac{dR}{dt} + 2\rho_m R\frac{dR}{dt}\right) = -\frac{8\pi}{3}G\rho_m R\frac{dR}{dt}$$

$$q = -\frac{R\,d^2R/dt^2}{(dR/dt)^2} = \frac{(4\pi/3)G\rho_m R^2}{(dR/dt)^2} = \frac{4\pi G\rho_m}{3H^2}$$

8.  With $R = At^n$, $\quad \dfrac{dR}{dt} = nAt^{n-1}$ $\quad$ and $\quad \dfrac{d^2R}{dt^2} = n(n-1)At^{n-2}$

$$q = -\frac{R\,d^2R/dt^2}{(dR/dt)^2} = -\frac{(At^n)[n(n-1)At^{n-2}]}{n^2A^2t^{2n-2}} = -\frac{n-1}{n} = n^{-1} - 1$$

For a matter-dominated universe, $n = 2/3$ and $q = 1/2$.

For a radiation-dominated universe, $n = 1/2$ and $q = 1$.

9.
$$t = \sqrt{\frac{3}{32\pi G\rho_r}} = \sqrt{\frac{3c^2}{32\pi GU(T)}}$$

With $U(T) = (4.73 \times 10^3 \text{ eV/m}^3\cdot\text{K}^4)T^3 = (7.56 \times 10^{-16} \text{ J/m}^3\cdot\text{K}^4)T^4$, we obtain

$$t = \sqrt{\frac{3(9 \times 10^{16} \text{ m}^2/\text{s}^2)}{32\pi(6.673 \times 10^{-11} \text{ N·m}^2/\text{kg}^2)(7.56 \times 10^{-16} \text{ J/m}^3\text{·K}^4)T^4}}$$

$$= \frac{1}{T^2}(2.31 \times 10^{20} \text{ s·K}^2)$$

$$T = \left(\frac{2.31 \times 10^{20} \text{ s·K}^2}{t}\right)^{1/2} = \frac{1.5 \times 10^{10} \text{ s}^{1/2}\text{·K}}{t^{1/2}}$$

10. (a) $T = \dfrac{mc^2}{k} = \dfrac{940 \text{ MeV}}{8.617 \times 10^{-5} \text{ eV/K}} = 1.09 \times 10^{13} \text{ K}$

$$t = \left(\frac{1.5 \times 10^{10} \text{ s}^{1/2}\text{·K}}{T}\right)^2 = \left(\frac{1.5 \times 10^{10} \text{ s}^{1/2}\text{·K}}{1.09 \times 10^{13} \text{ K}}\right)^2 = 1.9 \times 10^{-6} \text{ s}$$

(b) $T = \dfrac{mc^2}{k} = \dfrac{140 \text{ MeV}}{8.617 \times 10^{-5} \text{ eV/K}} = 1.62 \times 10^{12} \text{ K}$

$$t = \left(\frac{1.5 \times 10^{10} \text{ s}^{1/2}\text{·K}}{T}\right)^2 = \left(\frac{1.5 \times 10^{10} \text{ s}^{1/2}\text{·K}}{1.62 \times 10^{12} \text{ K}}\right)^2 = 8.6 \times 10^{-5} \text{ s}$$

11. (a) $T = \dfrac{mc^2}{k} = \dfrac{500 \text{ MeV}}{8.617 \times 10^{-5} \text{ eV/K}} = 5.8 \times 10^{12} \text{ K}$

(b) $t = \left(\dfrac{1.5 \times 10^{10} \text{ s}^{1/2}\text{·K}}{T}\right)^2 = \left(\dfrac{1.5 \times 10^{10} \text{ s}^{1/2}\text{·K}}{5.8 \times 10^{12} \text{ K}}\right)^2 = 6.7 \times 10^{-6} \text{ s}$

12. $$N_{E>E_0} = \int_{E_0}^{\infty} n(E)\,dE = \frac{8\pi}{(hc)^3} \int_{E_0}^{\infty} E^2 e^{-E/kT}\,dE$$

Let $x = E/kT$.

$$N_{E>E_0} = \frac{8\pi}{(hc)^3}(kT)^3 \int_{E_0/kT}^{\infty} x^2 e^{-x}\,dx = \frac{8\pi}{(hc)^3}(kT)^3 \left[-x^2 e^{-x} - 2xe^{-x} - 2e^{-x}\right]_{E_0/kT}^{\infty}$$

$$= \frac{8\pi}{(hc)^3}(kT)^3 e^{-E_0/kT}\left[\left(\frac{E_0}{kT}\right)^2 + 2\left(\frac{E_0}{kT}\right) + 2\right]$$

Using Equation 16.11, we obtain

$$f = \frac{N_{E>E_0}}{N} = \frac{\dfrac{8\pi}{(hc)^3}(kT)^3 e^{-E_0/kT}\left[\left(\dfrac{E_0}{kT}\right)^2 + 2\dfrac{E_0}{kT} + 2\right]}{\dfrac{8\pi}{(hc)^3}(kT)^3 (2.404)}$$

$$= 0.42\,e^{-E_0/kT}\left[\left(\frac{E_0}{kT}\right)^2 + 2\left(\frac{E_0}{kT}\right) + 2\right]$$

13. (a) $$t = \left(\frac{1.5 \times 10^{10} \text{ s}^{1/2} \cdot \text{K}}{5000 \text{ K}}\right)^2 = 9 \times 10^{12} \text{ s} = 3 \times 10^5 \text{ y}$$

This occurs during the era of nucleosynthesis.

(b) $$E_m = (2.33 \times 10^{-4} \text{ eV/K})\,T = 1.17 \text{ eV}$$

(c) The nucleon rest energy is 940 MeV, so the relative energy densities are

$$\frac{10^9\,(1.17 \text{ eV})}{940 \times 10^6 \text{ eV}} = 1.24$$

14.     (a)     Assume that $\rho_r = \rho_m$ occurred after antimatter annihilates, and take $10^9$ photons/nucleon. If $E_m$ is the average photon energy, then

$$10^9 E_m = m_{nucleon}c^2$$

$$10^9 [(2.33 \times 10^{-4} \text{ eV/K})T] = 940 \times 10^6 \text{ eV} \quad \text{or} \quad T = 4000 \text{ K}$$

    (b)     $t = \left( \dfrac{1.5 \times 10^{10} \text{ s}^{1/2} \cdot \text{K}}{4000 \text{ K}} \right)^2 = 1.4 \times 10^{13} \text{ s}$

15.     $N_\nu = N_{photon} = 4.0 \times 10^8 \text{ m}^{-3}$

$$\rho_\nu = (4.0 \times 10^8 \text{ m}^{-3})m_\nu = \rho_{cr} = 1 \times 10^{-26} \text{ kg/m}^3$$

$$m_\nu = 0.25 \times 10^{-34} \text{ kg}$$

$$m_\nu c^2 = (0.25 \times 10^{-34} \text{ kg})(9 \times 10^{16} \text{ m}^2/\text{s}^2) = 2.25 \times 10^{-18} \text{ J} = 14 \text{ eV}$$

16.     (a)     $f = \dfrac{1}{6} \times 10^{-8} = 0.42 e^{-E_0/kT} \left[ \left( \dfrac{E_0}{kT} \right)^2 + 2\left( \dfrac{E_0}{kT} \right) + 2 \right]$    gives    $\dfrac{E_0}{kT} = 25$

$$T = \frac{E_0}{25k} = \frac{2.22 \text{ MeV}}{25(8.617 \times 10^{-5} \text{ eV/K})} = 1.0 \times 10^9 \text{ K}$$

    (b)     $t = \left( \dfrac{1.5 \times 10^{10} \text{ s}^{1/2} \cdot \text{K}}{T} \right)^2 = \left( \dfrac{1.5 \times 10^{10} \text{ s}^{1/2} \cdot \text{K}}{1.0 \times 10^9 \text{ K}} \right)^2 = 225 \text{ s}$

    (c)     $f = 10^{-8} = 0.42 e^{-E_0/kT} \left[ \left( \dfrac{E_0}{kT} \right)^2 + 2\left( \dfrac{E_0}{kT} \right) + 2 \right]$    gives    $\dfrac{E_0}{kT} = 24$

$$T = \frac{E_0}{24k} = \frac{13.6 \text{ eV}}{24(8.617 \times 10^{-5} \text{ eV/K})} = 6600 \text{ K}$$

$$t = \left( \frac{1.5 \times 10^{10} \text{ s}^{1/2} \cdot \text{K}}{6600 \text{ K}} \right)^2 = 5.2 \times 10^{12} \text{ s} = 1.6 \times 10^5 \text{ y}$$

These times are not very different from those computed using $10^{-8}$ for the matter-antimatter imbalance.

17.  (a)  $t \propto h^i c^j G^k$

$[t] = [h]^i [c]^j [G]^k$      where [ ] indicates dimensions

$\text{s} = (\text{J}\cdot\text{s})^i (\text{m}\cdot\text{s}^{-1})^j (\text{N}\cdot\text{m}^2\cdot\text{kg}^{-2})^k = (\text{kg}\cdot\text{m}^2\cdot\text{s}^{-1})^i (\text{m}\cdot\text{s}^{-1})^j (\text{m}^3\cdot\text{s}^{-2}\cdot\text{kg}^{-1})^k$

$\qquad = (\text{kg})^{i-k} (\text{m})^{2i+j+3k} (\text{s})^{-i-j-2k}$

Equating powers of dimensions on both sides of the equation, we obtain

$i - k = 0, \qquad 2i + j + 3k = 0, \qquad \text{and} \qquad -i - j - 2k = 1$

or

$i = 1/2, \quad j = -5/2, \quad k = 1/2$

(b)  $t = \sqrt{\frac{hG}{c^5}} = \frac{(6.6 \times 10^{-34} \text{ J}\cdot\text{s})(6.67 \times 10^{-11} \text{ N}\cdot\text{m}^2/\text{kg}^2)}{(3.0 \times 10^8 \text{ m/s})^5} = 1.3 \times 10^{-43} \text{ s}$

18.  $H = 50 \frac{\text{km/s}}{\text{Mpc}} \frac{1 \text{ Mpc}}{3.26 \times 10^6 \text{ light-year}} \frac{1 \text{ light-year}}{9.46 \times 10^{12} \text{ km}} = 1.62 \times 10^{-18} \text{ s}^{-1}$

$$\rho_{cr} = \frac{3qH^2}{4\pi G} = \frac{3(1/2)(1.62 \times 10^{-18} \text{ s}^{-1})^2}{4\pi(6.67 \times 10^{-11} \text{ N·m}^2/\text{kg}^2)} = 4.7 \times 10^{-27} \text{ kg/m}^3$$

$$= 4.7 \times 10^{-30} \text{ g/cm}^3 \qquad \text{for} \quad H = 50 \, \frac{\text{km/s}}{\text{Mpc}}$$

When $H = 100$ (km/s)/Mpc, $\rho_{cr}$ will be 4 times as large, since $\rho_{cr} \propto H^2$.

$$\rho_{cr} = 1.9 \times 10^{-29} \text{ g/cm}^3 \qquad \text{for} \quad H = 100 \, \frac{\text{km/s}}{\text{Mpc}}$$

19. 
$$\left(\frac{dR}{dt}\right)^2 = \frac{8\pi}{3}G\rho R^2 - kc^2 = 2qH^2R^2 - kc^2 = 2q\left(\frac{dR}{dt}\right)^2 - kc^2$$

$$\left(\frac{dR}{dt}\right)^2(1 - 2q) = -kc^2$$

20. 
$$\rho = \left(3 \times 10^{-28} \, \frac{\text{kg}}{\text{m}^3}\right)\left(\frac{1 \text{ H atom}}{1.7 \times 10^{-27} \text{ kg}}\right) = 0.18 \text{ H atom/m}^3$$

21. 
$$\rho = \left(3 \times 10^{-28} \, \frac{\text{kg}}{\text{m}^3}\right)\left(\frac{1 \text{ star}}{6 \times 10^{30} \text{ kg}}\right)\left(\frac{9.46 \times 10^{15} \text{ m}}{1 \text{ light-year}}\right)^3$$

$$= 4.2 \times 10^{-11} \text{ stars/light-year}^3 = 1 \text{ star}/2.36 \times 10^{10} \text{ light-year}^3$$

average spacing $\sim [2.36 \times 10^{10} \text{ light-year}^3]^{1/3} = 2.9 \times 10^3 \text{ light-year}$